Production Forecasting, Planning, and Control

3RD EDITION

Production Forecasting,
Planning, and Control

E. H. MAC NIECE

Technical Consultant
Permacel Division
Johnson & Johnson

John Wiley & Sons, Inc., New York · London

To American industry
for the opportunity to be
a part of it and
to learn its lessons,
and
to New York University and
Rutgers University
for the
privilege of teaching young men
who will contribute in
industry's service of
human needs.

Preface

In the preface of the first edition of this book I said: "As a student, I was both impressed and puzzled by the methods and achievements of American industry. I was impressed because both were so generally successful, but puzzled because there seemed to be no general reasons for success." Many things apparently had been done, and were still being done, by rule of thumb and by unscientific methods. Production executives were too busy producing dramatic effects by feel and hunch to bother about determining and explaining causes.

My perplexity was fully justified in the early 1920's. Today, however, it is generally acknowledged that the most successful companies are those in which principles of scientific management are fully understood and consistently applied. Modern executives want to discuss principles, causes, and effects. Moreover, they are alert to learn new concepts, principles, and techniques. They know that the success of their enterprises depends upon the use of every scientific advantage that can be brought into their operations.

In sharp contrast to yesterday's forceful executive who got things done by whatever means seemed right at the moment, today's progressive executive understands and applies the principles of production engineering. He takes time to discuss subjects such as operations research, mathematical programming, decision theory, and many other newly developed scientific techniques. He knows where they can best be applied to his problems. If he has not grasped fully the details of these advanced methods or has not the time to apply them personally, he seeks consultative assistance and has them applied by experts.

While improving his scientific and technical knowledge, the modern executive has developed an understanding of the human factors of industrial operation. He has learned his responsibilities to

American workmen, and he knows that the proper motivation will mean advancement to them, to him, to his company, and to human welfare. Most of this executive enlightenment comes from excellent basic training supplemented by graduate work in our universities, or from seminars conducted by our management and professional societies.

Today's accelerated advances in science are paced by changes in the social and political climate in which business must be done. Both demand that the methods of scientific production be applied throughout our increasingly complex industrial plant. Modern executives understand this demand and, in the main, meet it. The youth who was puzzled by rule-of-thumb success in the 1920's now, after four decades, is both impressed and reassured by the way in which progressive executives keep production technology abreast of almost explosive advances in science.

Progressive executives do this; happily, they are many, and their number is growing. But there still are companies whose managers need to learn principles and apply the methods of modern production engineering. Our system of competitive enterprise demands that they do so and allows a rapidly dwindling chance for survival to companies that do not meet this demand.

The revision of this book has brought many pleasant rewards. I have visited many new factories and examined the methods used in them. Everyone has been generous with discussion and criticism. I have consulted with many old friends and made many new ones in my search for new material. To all the men and women in Europe and America who have helped me with this task, I wish to acknowledge my sincere gratitude.

E. H. Mac Niece

New Market, N. J.
November, 1960

Contents

1
Purpose and Scope

This book is primarily intended as a textbook for a one-semester course in production forecasting, planning, and control. It may also be used by executives who wish to modernize their stock of information about a field in which great progress has been made during recent years.

During these years, forecasting, planning, and control have taken an increasingly important place in American industry, with effects that are far-reaching in both social and economic realms. Their great achievements, however, will come in the future—a future which, if external conditions permit, will be one of increasing material wealth and advancing human welfare. It is of vital importance, therefore, for executives in industry, whose efforts are directed toward the improvement of their own companies and the maintenance of our system of competitive enterprise, to re-examine some of the factors that make it better serve the interests of all segments of our social structure.

It is equally important for those students who will be the industrial executives of tomorrow to understand the methods, plans, and techniques that enable industry to operate effectively. They must also understand the concepts supporting these methods and techniques, since business management has become the trustee for many interests. The thought and action of executives, therefore, should seek to eliminate or minimize industrial and social dislocations that arouse popular resentment and invite governmental planning. However well intended it may be, total planning by government leads to total control, with destruction of individual freedom and a costly bureaucracy that soon becomes a burden upon the national economy. That our federal government itself recognizes the limitations of state control and operation of industry has been shown by the eagerness with which it has turned back railroads, aluminum, and other industries to a healthy system of

1

free competition as soon as emergencies have ceased to exist. With individual and corporate freedom go the responsibilities for intelligent forecasting, planning, and control of industrial production.

This book describes the basic principles of production forecasting, planning, and control. It also explains how these principles are applied. Since forecasting, planning, and control extend into many departments of industrial organizations, their relations with these departments are explained. A complete discussion of each associated department, however, is not within the limits of this text.

Techniques and principles of other factors such as automation, electronic data processing, specialization, standardization, simplification, and financial planning are so intimately associated with and interdependent upon production forecasting, planning, and control that it would be a serious omission if they were not discussed. Other books explain these subjects in excellent detail. In this book only the relationship to and the application of these subjects in the practice of production engineering will be discussed.

Some specific examples of effective applications are used to illustrate basic principles. It must be emphasized, however, that no single system of forecasting, planning, and control is suited to all industrial enterprises, no matter how well it may meet the needs of this or that special company. The reader is advised, therefore, to focus his attention upon basic principles. Once he understands them and sees how they can be applied, he will be ready to make the application that will meet his own and his company's needs.

Technically, production forecasting, planning, and control are engineering activities. This book, however, supplements discussions written from the engineering viewpoint with treatments of economic and social implications. This approach is necessary because the long-range success of production forecasting, planning, and control depends upon correlation with economics and human welfare, both of the individual and of the nation.

Summaries at the end of chapters present essential points in capsule form. They are followed by questions to check comprehension. These are not intended as any real challenge to the reader's ingenuity, but they will enable him to determine whether or not he has grasped the meaning of the subject matter. Problems that follow these questions are intended to develop the reader's ability to cope with situations that arise in the practice of production engineering.

Discussion cases follow the problems. They represent situations that are not unusual in the actual industrial scene. All names are fictitious and are introduced only for the sake of convenience in discussion. Each case is concluded by inviting *you* to discuss it. *You* can be the reader who may wish to make an independent critical study of each case, or *you* can be a discussion group of students and practice skills in group problem solving.

Since the purpose of each case is to develop objective thought and provide experience in analyzing and solving industrial problems, the presentation is kept close to reality. As in the workaday world, cases mix pertinent facts with other information of little significance, and let personalities intrude into what should be engineering problems. As in real life, too, facts sometimes are missing, and statements of them stop "in the air." The reader thus is allowed to make his decisions from facts that are available, bridging gaps and eliminating personalities or other extraneous matter as he proceeds to his goal.

In analyzing each case, the reader should begin by listing the things that are wrong with each situation. Then, after each item so listed, he should note down the reason why it is wrong. In doing this, he must take care not to confuse *effects* with *causes*. As an example, a case may state that employees were laid off for two weeks and then required to work overtime when they returned from the layoff. These are only effects. The cause may be faulty forecasting or planning, or poor inventory control. Whatever it is, it must be found before the reader takes the third step, which is to list the actions to be taken to correct each fault.

To further test the reader's ability to apply the basic principles he has learned, a problem involving the complete forecasting, planning, and control of a business is included in Chapter Twenty-Four. The reader is urged to accept this interesting challenge and solve the problem before referring to the solution, which forms Chapter Twenty-Five.

War leads to explosive progress in logistics and production engineering. National security, especially during protracted cold war, also forces both the Armed Services and industry to hasten innovations and improvements in production engineering as well as in science and technology. Since these innovations can be applied to civilian production they not only increase our productivity and security but also bring benefits for our economic welfare. Production forecasting, planning, and control for the defense of our nation are therefore vitally important subjects for discussion.

2

Good Production Management
Serves Many Interests

American industry likes to proclaim that its factories, its machines, its products are the results of scientific research. Seldom, however, does it make this claim for the methods and disciplines practiced by management. For aught public declarations reveal, management might still do its work by rule of thumb and the percepts of time-honored custom.

This is not true, of course, and it has not been true for decades. The record of American industry is one of growth and progress at an ever-increasing rate. Somewhere in the course of that progress the demands upon management outgrew old-time rules of thumb, even when they were based upon intimate knowledge and applied with almost infallible judgment. The speed, volume, and complexity resulting from applied science demanded that management itself apply scientific methods. The demand was felt everywhere, from the treasurer's sanctum to the advertising office, from the table at which directors made decision to the production line. Results, of course, were manifold, but this book is concerned with only three. They are the closely related trio of forecasting, planning, and control.

Forecasting, as we shall deal with it, is the phase of production management that projects the past and the present into the future as a means of predicting it. Since the purpose is practical and commercial, predications take the form of estimates known as sales forecasts. These forecasts are used in various ways, but their first purpose is to tell how much a company may hope to sell during a given period. This prognosis is based on several factors: past experience as revealed by records; an appraisal of consumer demand; the economic value [1] of

---

[1] Economic value is not the same as price. It is a factor secured by balancing price against intrinsic worth, utility, demand, and other elements that may be left

products to be sold in comparison with the value and appeal of those offered by competitors. Broad company policies as well as sales and advertising programs also are considered in formulating forecasts.

Planning is the determinative phase of production management; it "figures out" what is to be done. In this book it has three subdivisions: manufacturing planning, factory planning, and production planning.

Manufacturing planning deals with the processing and fabrication of products. It establishes the methods to be used and from them determines the equipment and the time required to perform the various operations. Manufacturing planning also determines the material required per unit of production and estimates costs at various levels of activity. Production can be restudied and replanned if these estimates suggest that costs will not permit a profit.

Factory planning includes the study of new industrial buildings, as well as that involved in additions to, or modifications of, structures already built. It also includes plans for utilities or services needed in such buildings. Since good industrial practice first requires the planning of equipment and machinery arrangement and then designs the structure to house it, plant layout is included in factory planning rather than in manufacturing planning. This also holds true when old buildings are remodeled, though construction changes are generally kept at the minimum.

Production planning translates sales forecasts into master production schedules, takes off material, personnel, and equipment requirements, and prepares detailed area or department schedules. It also determines the maintaining of raw materials and finished goods at proper levels. Finally, it prepares alternative plans of action as a means of meeting emergencies.

Control is often said to include the whole field of planning and control. In this book, however, it is considered as the regulative phase of production management, a phase that balances production and inventories apart from the determinative phase of planning. Production control supervises the execution of production schedules so that work flows through the manufacturing departments on time and without interruptions. Control also maintains raw-material inventories at levels that neither tie up excessive amounts of working capital nor lead to shortages that interrupt production. At the same time, finished goods inventories are regulated so that they neither become excessive nor

to books on consumer economics. Obviously, however, the economic value of a diamond ring represents a different balance from that of a turret lathe or a toothbrush. To overlook such differences in making sales forecasts would be a serious omission.

fall so low that they fail to meet demands and so cause back orders to accumulate.

We have said that forecasting, planning and control are phases of production management. As such, they are dynamic factors that help industry in its effort to supply human needs. Yet they have only begun to exert their full influence in some fields, as we may see from the following review of their present and potential benefits:

A. BENEFITS TO CONSUMERS

1. Increased Productivity. The term *productivity* should not be confused with *efficiency,* for they are not synonymous. A man with a hoe may work at high efficiency, doing 90 to 95 per cent of the work he is able to do. In spite of this, he may cultivate only a quarter-acre per day, and so have a low productivity. The modern farmer with a small tractor may do only 80 per cent of what he might do and yet cultivate 4 acres per day. Thus, he achieves a 1,500 per cent increase in productivity, even though his efficiency is 10 to 15 per cent below that of the hand worker.

Our emphasis is on planning and use of arrangements that make us more productive without forcing ourselves beyond our limitations in physical effort. With 6 per cent [1] of the world's population, the United States produced almost one-half [2] the world's manufactured goods in 1948. In spite of this, the needs of a large part of our population are not adequately met. This means that industry must become more productive, that it must reduce prices and increase sales volume so that manufactured goods can and will reach more and more consumers. We shall see that forecasting, planning, and control of production can help achieve this double objective.

2. Better Values. The continued development of better quality in terms of a product's intended use, at continually lowered prices in terms of real dollars, is not an accident. It is the result of intelligently developed product specifications, integrated with a well-planned system of controlled production. It also rests upon forecasts that call for items of a given quality and price, designed to meet the accurately known desires of consumers.

---

[1] United Nations, *World Economic Report,* 1948, Columbia University Press.
[2] United Nations, *Economic Survey of Europe,* 1948, Columbia University Press.

3. Deliveries at Proper Times. In the days of custom production by hand, the consumer had to place an order and then wait while the article was manufactured. Today we walk into stores or salesrooms and get anything from a pair of shoes to an automobile. Only when we ourselves make special demands does the dealer or storekeeper keep us waiting.

The availability of goods that customers want *when they want them* is the result of forecasting, planning, and control on a vast and highly complex scale. An automobile, for example, is a product of iron and coal mines, steel mills, hardware suppliers, makers of electrical equipment, cotton and rubber plantations, textile mills, and many other enterprises. All these must be balanced and synchronized before the factory can make an automobile and send it to a dealer for delivery to the customer. Even when the delivery is made, the customer would not be able to use the automobile unless the petroleum industry's forecasting, planning, and control had been related to the whole scheme and gasoline was available at the right time.

The benefits to the consumer have been listed first because without customers any other benefits would be of only academic interest. Industry must first serve its customers.

B. BENEFITS TO PRODUCERS [1]

1. Adequate Wages. Only companies that make money can afford to pay good wages. Unfortunately, many employers waste their resources on excessive inventories, lose income because they cannot fill orders, or allow profits to vanish through rework and spoilage. Though forecasting, planning, and control are not cure-alls, they can do much to remedy these conditions and make good wages possible. Indeed, many companies make wage increases essential parts of their plans.

2. Uninterrupted Employment. In the early days of American industry there was little or no planning as it is practiced today. When orders became heavy, the owner of the business generally visited neighbors who had files, carving tools, or saws and knew how to use

[1] Producers are all the people whose work contributes to the production of goods and services. In this sense they are not the owners, as are the millions of people who have invested their money in industry. Many people in the ranks of labor and management, however, are both owners and producers.

them. These friends were prevailed upon to leave their farm work for a while until the backlog of orders was reduced to normal. Since materials were simple and abundant, no long-range procurement program was required.

As industry became mechanized, industrialists gave thought to the material aspects of planning. They built factories and bought machines; they laid in stocks of materials or sought reliable suppliers. But they still filled their plants with labor on a day-to-day basis. When orders poured in they hired new people with little or no training and at the lowest going wages. When business lagged, they laid off or dismissed employees.

Today, in many companies, all this is changed. Industry projects its sales forecasts as far as possible into the future; plans for the completion of buildings are made one, two, and three years in advance. Complex machinery is often ordered months and sometimes even years before it will be used. Sources of raw materials are found and placed under contract well in advance of production. Supplies of labor are appraised or developed, and employees are trained so they can go to work as soon as buildings and machines are ready.

Such planning is essentially selfish, since it provides the supply of skilled workers needed to keep factories going. Modern industry, however, does not stop with this. It knows that few present-day workers can go back to farms if factory employment ceases. As a result, plans are laid to maintain steady employment, without layoffs or terminations. Many companies, confronted by increased business, pay overtime to old employees rather than add new ones before the increase is assured. Other companies carry large inventories of finished goods or increase their sales efforts as a means of maintaining uninterrupted employment.

3. Job Security. Too little is known of the magnificent plans for steady work and job security that have been made and put into effect by many large companies. One example is provided by the Standard Oil Company (New Jersey). Its efforts were summarized in the following words by Frank W. Pierce, a director, when he spoke before the Society for the Advancement of Management on December 2, 1947:

> I am now happy to report that we have reached a point today where 90 per cent of our employees (wage as well as salaried) have been continuously employed since the day they were hired. We regard this as heartening progress toward the goal of the steady job. I may add that the average

domestic employee of the company and its affiliates has been employed in the family for about 17 years.

This is big business at its best. Behind it is masterful forecasting, planning, and control, coupled with sincere interest in the security of employees.

4. Improved Working Conditions. Factories once were dark, inconvenient structures, excessively hot in summer but cold and drafty during other seasons. Jobs were dirty and needlessly hard, and there were few facilities for comfort or cleanliness. Analysis showed that such conditions were wasteful. Darkness and discomfort kept people from doing good work; inconvenience wasted time and caused accidents; dirt damaged materials and lowered worker morale. Modern planning therefore produced well-lighted, heated, and ventilated factories with cafeterias, locker rooms, and adequate toilet facilities. At the same time, jobs were restudied to make them cleaner, easier, and less subject to accident than they once were. The result was improvement in working conditions—improvement which, though substantial, has not come to an end.

5. Increased Satisfaction. No one likes to work amid confusion, recrimination, and an atmosphere of futility. Employees need to know that their work will not be disrupted again and again to meet emergencies or halted because materials are not available. Even the person who cares little about waste and spoilage can take no satisfaction in an output that must be sold for scrap.

Forecasting, planning, and control forestall these conditions and make for a smoothly running, effective organization. In such an organization, work is done to a purpose, and the natural craftsman can take pride in the company that employs him. Moreover, since good organizational planning generally goes with good production planning, avenues to promotion are defined and are kept open. Few incentives to satisfaction surpass promotion that is promptly and properly granted once it has been earned.

C. BENEFITS TO INVESTORS

We often think of investors as people who, in their own names, own stock in a company. Actually, however, every participant in a pension plan is an investor, and so is the man or woman who owns an insurance policy. For neither pension nor insurance payments could be made if money were not safely invested in business enterprises yielding adequate returns. How can forecasting, planning, and control help secure these two benefits?

1. Security. Modern business is both highly complex and highly competitive. Any company that neglects both the safeguards and the guidance for expansion that are provided by forecasting and planning is likely to get into difficulties. On the other hand, companies that utilize forecasting, planning, and control are likely to grow and become stronger with the passing years.

2. Adequacy of Return. The most secure company is not always the one that makes the most money *during a short period.* In the long pull, however, a company that uses the most advanced methods is the one that will earn enough profit to pay taxes and still compensate the investor for the use of his capital.

D. BENEFITS TO SUPPLIERS

1. Cooperation. All companies, no matter how large or how small, depend upon other companies as sources of raw materials and services. These other companies, in turn, depend upon the organizations that buy their materials and services. There is a growing recognition of the fact that each member of this team is responsible to the others and that each company must do its part if quality is to be maintained and production is to flow smoothly. An example of this awareness is provided by the Personal Products Corporation of Milltown, New Jersey, which has prepared a booklet called *Principles of Good Source Relations,* which lists twenty responsibilities of this company to its suppliers and ten responsibilities of suppliers to it. Of especial importance to suppliers is the statement that it is the duty of the Corporation "to plan our procurement scheduling sufficiently in advance so that our suppliers will know our future requirements. Any major changes in those requirements shall be made with sufficient notice to assure ample time to make adjustments. Unforeseen emergencies shall be interpreted and satisfactory action mutually decided."

The essence of these thirty declarations is found in the statement that both the Personal Products Corporation and its suppliers intend "to look upon our association as a long-term working partnership and always be governed by *what is best for our partnership.*" Fair and enlightened relationships between suppliers and manufacturers must always be governed, of course, by satisfaction of the ultimate consumer's desires and needs.

E. BENEFITS TO THE COMMUNITY

1. Stability. Communities fortunate enough to have industrial companies that effectively forecast, plan, and control their activity are generally progressive and happy. With stable employment, many families own their homes and are able to pay taxes promptly. As a result, schools and streets are good, and public works are adequately financed. Executives responsible for the industrial planning in their companies generally are members of the planning commissions or hold public office. This makes for good management in community affairs.

The merchants of such communities are progressive because they are not harassed by fears that periodic layoffs will destroy purchasing power and plunge consumers into debt. The banks are healthy. There are few business failures, because companies are not heavily indebted for working capital to carry excess inventories.

In short, the entire community runs on a sound business basis. It is therefore one in which people can live with pride and can plan their future with assurance limited only by economic and political factors that lie beyond local control.

F. BENEFITS TO THE NATION

1. Security. In times of war, our nation depends upon industry for production. If population were the deciding factor in production (as it is where production methods have not been modernized), the United States would be at a great disadvantage in today's largely hostile world. What we lack in population can be offset by our ability to plan and control our production. Next to enthusiasm, our greatest resource is skill in getting things done.

2. Prosperity. No nation can prosper if its industrial companies fail to make adequate profits. A large part of the taxes that pay the costs of government comes from industrial profits. Most of the remainder comes from taxes on incomes. Industrial forecasting, planning, and control enable industries to operate safely and profitably. Thus they safeguard the first source of taxes and at the same time insure the second against shrinkage through unemployment.

The need for the foregoing benefits to consumers, producers, investors, communities, and the nation cannot be denied. More effective methods of production forecasting, planning, and control can make important contributions to the securing of more of these benefits. It should be understood that such effective methods are far from being fully applied in American industry. That they are used to the extent of making our total accomplishment outstanding is creditable. Any comforting thoughts from this knowledge should not dull the efforts of managers and let them become satisfied with any mediocre methods that get by but dilute our total national effectiveness.

Much remains to be done to strengthen our competitive enterprise system by the study and implementation of arrangements for intelligent production forecasting, planning, and control. Specific patterns of excellent practices have been set in many widely spread areas of diversified industrial activity. These patterns can and must be reduced to general practices. They must then be studied for application to all segments of our great productive industrial system to make it even stronger and more bountiful to those who wish to be progressive, happy, and free.

A first consideration by all industrial companies should be the study and recognition of the need for effective treatment of forecasting, planning, and control of production. Each company should then list its primary beliefs and objectives. Improved techniques can follow and can be held within the confines of a basic framework of policy. Some leading industrial companies have carefully studied and listed their broad management policies and objectives. A statement of them constitutes their "Articles of Faith." Figure 1 shows the Johnson & Johnson credo. An examination of it reveals that the foregoing reasons for effective forecasting, planning, and control of industrial production bear a striking similarity to the basic objectives of a company that has seriously studied its responsibilities.

A recognition of the growing and important need for better treatment of production forecasting, planning, and control is essential. This recognition leads to the clarification of broad management objectives and the establishment of policies. Once set, these policies provide the pathways to the accomplishment of the objectives.

Our Credo

WE BELIEVE THAT OUR FIRST RESPONSIBILITY IS TO OUR CUSTOMERS.
OUR PRODUCTS MUST ALWAYS BE GOOD, AND
WE MUST STRIVE TO MAKE THEM BETTER AT LOWER COSTS.
OUR ORDERS MUST BE PROMPTLY AND ACCURATELY FILLED.
OUR DEALERS MUST MAKE A FAIR PROFIT.

OUR SECOND RESPONSIBILITY IS TO THOSE WHO WORK WITH US —
THE MEN AND WOMEN IN OUR FACTORIES AND OFFICES.
THEY MUST HAVE A SENSE OF SECURITY IN THEIR JOBS.
WAGES MUST BE FAIR AND ADEQUATE,
MANAGEMENT JUST, HOURS SHORT, AND WORKING CONDITIONS CLEAN AND ORDERLY.
WORKERS SHOULD HAVE AN ORGANIZED SYSTEM FOR SUGGESTIONS AND COMPLAINTS.
FOREMEN AND DEPARTMENT HEADS MUST BE QUALIFIED AND FAIR MINDED.
THERE MUST BE OPPORTUNITY FOR ADVANCEMENT — FOR THOSE QUALIFIED
AND EACH PERSON MUST BE CONSIDERED AN INDIVIDUAL
STANDING ON HIS OWN DIGNITY AND MERIT.

OUR THIRD RESPONSIBILITY IS TO OUR MANAGEMENT.
OUR EXECUTIVES MUST BE PERSONS OF TALENT, EDUCATION, EXPERIENCE AND ABILITY.
THEY MUST BE PERSONS OF COMMON SENSE AND FULL UNDERSTANDING.

OUR FOURTH RESPONSIBILITY IS TO THE COMMUNITIES IN WHICH WE LIVE.
WE MUST BE A GOOD CITIZEN — SUPPORT GOOD WORKS AND CHARITY,
AND BEAR OUR FAIR SHARE OF TAXES.
WE MUST MAINTAIN IN GOOD ORDER THE PROPERTY WE ARE PRIVILEGED TO USE.
WE MUST PARTICIPATE IN PROMOTION OF CIVIC IMPROVEMENT,
HEALTH, EDUCATION AND GOOD GOVERNMENT,
AND ACQUAINT THE COMMUNITY WITH OUR ACTIVITIES.

OUR FIFTH AND LAST RESPONSIBILITY IS TO OUR STOCKHOLDERS.
BUSINESS MUST MAKE A SOUND PROFIT.
RESERVES MUST BE CREATED, RESEARCH MUST BE CARRIED ON,
ADVENTUROUS PROGRAMS DEVELOPED, AND MISTAKES MADE AND PAID FOR.
BAD TIMES MUST BE PROVIDED FOR, HIGH TAXES PAID, NEW MACHINES PURCHASED,
NEW FACTORIES BUILT, NEW PRODUCTS LAUNCHED, AND NEW SALES PLANS DEVELOPED.
WE MUST EXPERIMENT WITH NEW IDEAS.
WHEN THESE THINGS HAVE BEEN DONE THE STOCKHOLDER SHOULD RECEIVE A FAIR RETURN.
WE ARE DETERMINED WITH THE HELP OF GOD'S GRACE
TO FULFILL THESE OBLIGATIONS TO THE BEST OF OUR ABILITY.

Johnson & Johnson

Fig. 1. The basic beliefs of one company. (Courtesy of Johnson & Johnson.)

SUMMARY

Production forecasting, planning, and control have done much for economic and social progress. They may, however, do much more for the six essential segments of our society.

The consumer benefits from improved industrial productivity, increased value in the goods he purchases, and delivery of goods when and as he needs them.

Benefits for the producer include adequate wages, stable employment, job security, improved working conditions, and increased personal satisfaction in his work.

Investors benefit by increased security for their investments and by assurance of adequate returns.

Suppliers and the companies that buy their materials and services benefit from enlightened cooperation, effective intercommunication, and mutual trust.

Community benefits include economic and social stability as well as pride and satisfaction among citizens.

The nation will achieve prosperity and security as its industries prosper and render effective service. Forecasting, planning, and control are vital means of securing these benefits.

Much remains to be done in improving these industrial techniques and further extending these benefits. A first step toward this end is the listing, by each company, of its basic beliefs. From them the need for effective forecasting, planning, and control of production will be recognized. Policies can then be determined, and standard procedures established, which will guide the way to the accomplishment of the broad management objectives.

QUESTIONS TO CHECK COMPREHENSION

1. What has forced industry to use more scientific management methods?

2. What are the terms most commonly used to describe the estimative, determinative, and regulative phases of production management?

3. Who are the beneficiaries of good production forecasting, planning, and control?

4. Can well forecasted, planned, and controlled production actually contribute to better values?   Give reasons for your answer.

5. What is the difference between productivity and efficiency?

6. Why is it important to have goods delivered when they are needed?

7. Can adequate wages result from effective planning?

8. Do improved working conditions pay off, or are they merely paternalistic expenses?

9. How can good production and organizational planning contribute to employee satisfaction?

10. Why does industrial management plan for stability and security of employment?

11. A company has earned a surplus of $100,000 over dividend requirements and other charges.   It has notoriously poor toilets and washroom facilities.   Should it install modern and adequate facilities or earmark the money for plant expansion in the hope that business will also expand?

12. During World War II a mother worked for two companies.   One had inadequate planning and much confusion.   The other was a well-planned, smoothly functioning organization, but it was breaking into a highly competitive field and therefore paid 5 per cent lower wages.   Her son must start to work.   Which company will he choose?

13. What do investors look for in industrial companies before they invest their money in them?

14. Is the recognition of responsibilities between suppliers and the companies that use their materials and services an important factor in production management?

15. When it is known that certain material will not be needed at some future date, should the supplier be notified of the fact?

16. In what way is the effectiveness of industrial forecasting, planning, and control reflected in the community?

17. What important resource does the United States have that some other nations lack?

18. Are effective methods of production forecasting, planning, and control fully applied throughout all industry in the United States?

19. How can a company obtain a better perspective of its responsibilities and thereby recognize the essential need for more scientific treatment of production forecasting, planning, and control?

20. If you were the chief executive of a company, would you first try to develop all the rules for running the business and then translate these into basic policy, or would you try to establish basic policy first?

PROBLEM

1. Select a company that you consider to be ideal in its service to all segments of society and give examples of its benefits to consumers, producers, investors, suppliers, the community or communities in which it operates, and to the nation. Support your arguments with facts from your own knowledge as well as others secured from newspapers, booklets, and other publications.

DISCUSSION CASE

The Martin Company employed 100 people. Its capital stock was owned by some 200 citizens in the community in which it operated. Some of the employees were stockholders. About 50 people in the community were its customers. Its assessment was about 2 per cent of the local taxes. In times of war it had been an important subcontractor of war material.

This company had never considered its basic responsibilities to shareholders, employees, customers, the community, and the nation. It had never studied its basic beliefs other than to state that it was in business to make and sell as much product as possible. Scientific organization of production forecasting, planning, and control had never been used. Through the years excessive inventories of certain raw materials and finished goods had accumulated. The company held unfilled customers' orders for which there was no raw material, and it had insufficient cash with which to run the business.

Five plans of action were possible. The business could be allowed to continue until income from accounts receivable was exhausted, and the company could then go into bankruptcy. Stockholders could be asked for more money. Customers could be asked for advances. Employees could be laid off until income from accounts receivable was sufficient to purchase some of the raw materials needed to fill orders. Some of the slow-moving excess raw materials and finished goods could be sold at a sacrifice.

A decision was made to follow one of these plans. This resulted in the least dislocation to all concerned. Before the plan was put into effect, however, the management of the company held a meeting to examine its basic beliefs and responsibilities and to reorganize its management techniques so that a similar crisis would not occur. Assume that you have been asked to participate in this meeting. List the causes for the accumulated difficulties and suggest what should be done either to continue the business or to liquidate it.

3
Types of Production

The principles underlying forecasting, planning, and control of production never vary, nor do their ultimate objectives. In spite of this, methods, organization, and operations differ from company to company. They also differ with the two basic types of production, even when both are used by a single corporation. These types are manufacture or production to stock, and job-order production.

Type of Operation	Production to Order	Production to Stock
Project	Special material-handling systems Special solvent-recovery systems	
Job lot	Lots of special machined parts on definite orders	Job lots of clothing made in one season for sale in another
	Lots of packaging material for a special merchandise promotion	Lots of various sizes and styles of footwear
Batch	Batches of special paint on definite order	Batches of standard stock paint
	Batches of rare chemicals on definite order	Batches of dyestuffs made for stock
Progressive or continuous	Manufacture of tin cans Corrugated shipping cases	Manufacture of newsprint Manufacture of heavy chemicals Manufacture of gasoline Food packing (cereals)

Goods are made either to fill definite customer's orders or they are made to stock. They are also produced by four general types of operation: project, job lot, batch, and continuous. Many combinations of goods are produced either to stock or to order by these types of operation. The preceding table lists some examples of articles generally made by the four types of operation in production to stock and production to order, except in the case of project operation, which is always on a production-to-order basis.

Both job-order and stock production may be used within a single company and even under one roof. The Western Electric Company, for example, produces telephone sets to stock, but its private branch exchange production is on a job-order basis. Other companies normally manufacture to stock but are periodically required to supply the same items with special treatment and packing to meet specific government contracts.

Some companies simplify their treatment of job-order and stock production mixtures by code designation of their products:

"A" products are those carried in stock.

"B" products are those produced only on customer's orders, but for which raw materials are carried in stock.

"C" products are those produced only on customer's orders, and for which no raw materials are carried in stock.

"D" products are those that have been produced experimentally. They may be offered to customers only on the basis of a cooperative development program.

This type of codification is helpful to production planners. Planning methods for stock production based upon sales forecasts are used for type "A" products. Job-order planning methods are used for type "B" products and raw materials are maintained within prescribed limits and reorder points. Full job-order planning methods with raw materials ordered specifically for each customer order are used for type "C" products.

Some customers award term contracts for commodities in the "B" and "C" categories. These contracts enable manufacturers to plan production in advance and to avoid uneconomical lot sizes. The customer generally agrees that he will accept a specified quantity of a certain product during a year, six months, or some other period. He generally also specifies the estimated quantity he will need monthly and the minimum quantity he will order at one time.

Under such a contract the supplier can produce the product specified in it on a basis of production to stock and can set upper and lower

stock-control limits. The commodities thus contracted for are designated as "BA" or "CA" products on manufacturing orders to show
that they are being carried in stock for the duration of the contract.

This scheme of codification is also helpful to salesmen and customer
service personnel. With it, realistic delivery promises can be made.

A. MANUFACTURE TO STOCK

This type of production is used by companies whose products are
in continued, though not always uniform, demand. These products
are usually sold in retail stores and are stocked by distributors or
dealers who have received the right to act as wholesalers in specific
areas or regions. Moreover, these products ordinarily are of the type
known as consumer goods. Canned foods, soap, textiles, hardware,
building materials, drug preparations, home appliances, and cosmetics
are familiar examples. Figure 2 shows the general development of
forecasting, planning, and budgeting used by companies manufacturing to stock.

Before manufacture to stock can be planned, a sales forecast tells
the number of each item or product likely to be sold during a future
period. The period may be a quarter (three months), six months, or
a year. The second step is the preparation of a master production
schedule. In this, the sales forecast is adjusted according to back
orders and inventory. If, for example, the sales forecast calls for
200,000 of a certain item, and 20,000 are carried as a normal stock
and 10,000 are on back order, the two latter numbers are added to
the forecast, giving a master production schedule of 230,000. On the
other hand, if there are no back orders and 30,000 of this item are in
stock, the 10,000 in excess of normal inventory are subtracted from
the forecast, and the master production schedule becomes 190,000.

When the master production schedule is set, detailed planning follows. From production routings, which are records of basic manufacturing information and bills of materials, information is tabulated
for machine-load charts, equipment, personnel, and material requirements. These breakdowns can be made simultaneously.

Each of the tabulations has its purpose. When production times
are arrayed on it, the machine-load chart, for example, tells whether
or not the equipment on hand is adequate for the work that must be
done. If it is not, the company may subcontract some parts or operations. It also may buy new machines, even though they demand
additions to the existing factory.

The personnel and equipment tabulation or breakdown shows the man-hours or shifts as well as the machine-hours or shifts required. Based on these requirements, hiring schedules, department schedules, and operating budgets are prepared.

The raw-material tabulation or breakdown adjusted for inventories of materials on hand establishes the procurement plan.

Based on these plans, purchase orders, personnel requisitions, and work orders are issued. If necessary, equipment is ordered and new construction authorized.

B. JOB-ORDER PRODUCTION

In this type of production there is no assurance of a continued demand for specific items. Goods are produced to definite customer orders. In some instances there are no repeat orders for exactly the same item. Perhaps the simplest example of job-order production is in the small machine shop which is generally called a job shop. Here orders are accepted for 1 or 100 or 1,000 or more specially machined parts for which there may never be another order. Other machined parts or mechanisms may be ordered from time to time, but with no certainty of exactly when, or even if, they will be reordered.

Figure 3 shows the basic system of planning and scheduling employed in job-order production. Figure 4 presents a schematic arrangement of planning and scheduling job-order production in a chemical company; Figure 5 indicates the system employed in a machine-tool company. Though the last two systems differ greatly in details, they meet the basic needs and perform the essential functions provided for in Figure 3.

These figures also show how planning and scheduling may be clarified. In many companies, there is no clear-cut separation of functions in this field, nor are they clearly coordinated. There also may be uncertainty as to the sources of certain forms or papers, their routings, and their effects. Diagrams that use circles for functions, rectangles for forms or documents, and solids for raw or processed materials eliminate much of the confusion. These diagrams also portray the whole system so clearly that its faults become obvious and therefore can be cured.

Industries producing capital goods such as heavy, special-purpose machinery generally use the job-order method of production. As an extreme example, it would be too risky and expensive to make to stock 10 or 12 waterwheel generators like those used in Hoover Dam, in the

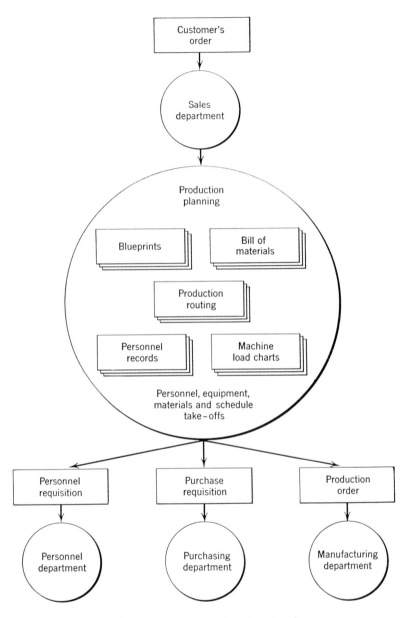

Fig. 3. General arrangement for job-order planning.

hope that there would be other dam installations that would be exactly similar.

Some goods made on a job-order basis are sold to customers who manufacture to stock. This is true of cans, bottles, paper boxes, and a variety of specially designed containers. Although these goods are usually made by high-speed, continuous processes, they are made only on definite orders. Obviously it would be risky for a carton or component manufacturer to stock special items for sale to a producer-customer, only to find that the customer has made some packaging or engineering change.

Examples of a few of the categories of goods made on the job-order basis are large electrical generating and power equipment, large printing presses, special-purpose equipment such as solvent-recovery units, cartons and boxes, special machined component parts, bottles, cans, road-building equipment, fire engines, and locomotives.

Planning for job-order production cannot begin with a sales forecast giving the number of items that may be sold in a planning period. The steel fabricator, for example, has no way of estimating how many roof trusses of certain dimensions will be sold during the first quarter of next year. He will have some estimate of the tonnage that will be sold, based on general business conditions, past experience, and an idea of what his sales effort will be. He may even produce both structural and ornamental items in which the sales value per ton is different. He may then have to forecast in terms of dollars of sales. Some form of forecasting in terms of items, tons, or dollars is necessary to determine in advance whether the company will operate at a loss or earn a profit. The production schedule will include only those items that have actually been ordered by customers and will not be based on sales estimates, as it is when manufacturing to stock.

Another difference is in the machine-load charts. When manufacturing to stock, load charts are prepared in advance of production for the period. In job-order production, orders are placed on the load chart as they are received. Similarly, department schedules are not made for a complete production period but are prepared and authorized after customer orders are received. Personnel schedules also cannot be worked out in advance; additional help is hired as schedules for orders on hand indicate an actual need. Budgets generally have to be flexible, based on the general tonnage or dollar forecast, but adjusted to the actual current rate of activity.

Aside from minimum balances of basic materials used in filling almost every order, there is no procurement schedule in job-order production, as there is in manufacture to stock. The breakdown of each

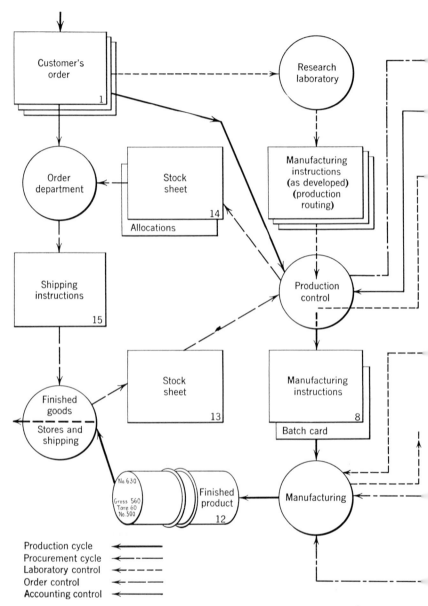

Fig. 4. Typical arrangemen

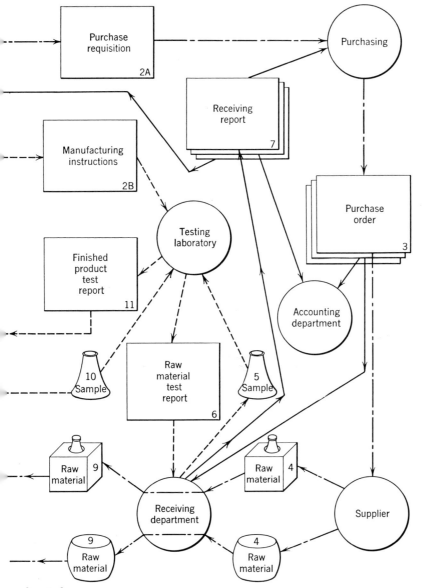

a chemical company.

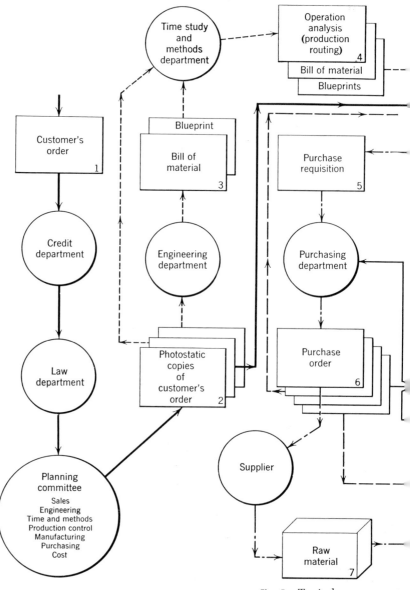

Fig. 5. Typical arrangement

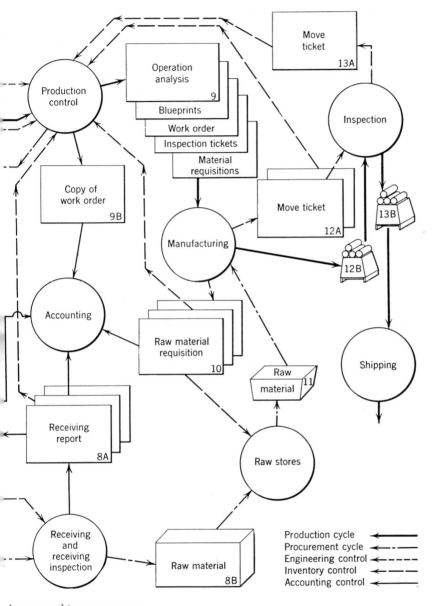

heavy-machinery company.

bid or estimate shows its material requirements. Requisitions for materials go out only after the customer's order has been confirmed.

SUMMARY

The principles and objective of forecasting, planning, and control are uniform throughout industry. Methods and operations differ, however, especially in the two basic types of production, which are manufacture to stock and job-order production.

Production to stock has one great advantage: sales forecasts can be made in terms of the number of each item to be sold. In job-order production this is impossible. Sales forecasts, therefore, are made in terms of tonnage or dollar volume, neither of which gives a precise picture of requirements.

In manufacture to stock, production schedules based on sales estimates may be prepared in advance. In job-order production, production schedules must await confirmation of customers' orders.

In manufacture to stock, procurement schedules also may be made in advance. In job-order production, only limited stocks of basic materials may be built up in anticipation of business to come. Other materials are bought after confirmation of customers' orders. Personnel schedules must be similarly delayed, for workers cannot be hired to make things for which orders have not been received.

Some companies use both manufacture to stock and job-order production either for different products or to meet both current demand and special orders from governmental agencies.

QUESTIONS TO CHECK COMPREHENSION

1. What external factors determine whether a company should produce on a job-order or a to-stock basis?

2. What are the essential differences in the basic systems used to forecast and plan for production to stock and job-order production?

3. A company in the job-order category is called upon to produce many items of different value per item and per pound. What can it use as a basis for forecasting?

4. A contract for an item for the U.S. Armed Forces permits a 10 per cent overrun. Would it be wise to produce in excess of this limit in the hope of obtaining another contract for the same item?

PROBLEMS

1. Select a company with which you are familiar that operates on a job-order basis and assume that you have been called upon to analyze its production control system. Prepare a graphic representation of the flow of documents and materials through the various organizational functions.

2. You have been asked to study the production planning and control system of a company that manufactures to stock. Annual production is about $10,000,000 worth of 200 varied products. You find that company executives develop and maintain good sales forecasts, master production schedules, material and equipment breakdowns, and machine load charts. Manufacturing foremen adjust manpower requirements by requisitioning additional employees as they seem to be needed. When there appear to be too many employees in one department, the extra people are sent to the personnel office, which acts as a clearing house for job placement in the various departments. Employees who cannot be placed are laid off or their employment is terminated. What do you recommend?

3. The bill of material for steel part 4675 shows that 0.24 pounds of cold rolled steel bar CR 267 are needed to produce 100 pieces of part 4675, and 225,000 of these parts are scheduled for production during the last quarter of this year. There are 250 pounds of this material in stock; 200 pounds are required as a minimum balance. What quantity of this material should be listed on the procurement schedule?

DISCUSSION CASE

The Billson Container Company manufactures metal boxes on a job-order basis. The process consists of blanking the metal to size, enameling it, lithographing customers' product names and other information on the enameled surfaces, and finally forming the boxes and covers.

One customer has ordered about 1,000,000 boxes of a certain type and size each month. The price per 1,000,000 boxes includes $1,000 for setting up the equipment. The Billson production manager had

been producing 3,000,000 boxes per setup, shipping one-third immediately and one-third in each of the following months. Storage space
for the excess boxes was available and was considerably less valuable
than the $2,000 saved by the elimination of two setups in 3 months.
The customer benefited by prompt deliveries but advised Billson that
only boxes for which orders had been placed would be accepted.

The Billson production manager reasoned that $11,000 in setup time
in addition to about 16 days of production on other work could be
saved if 12,000,000 boxes, or a year's supply, were produced in one
continuous run. He therefore scheduled a run of 12,000,000 boxes and
rented space in a terminal warehouse at $100 per month to store them.

After the production run had been completed, the customer announced a new, large, economy-size product in a paperboard box to
replace the more expensive metal box. Billson begged for the change
to be withheld for 11 months until the metal boxes could be used up.
The customer had already spent a large sum of money on advertising.
Any delay, moreover, would have placed the customer at a competitive disadvantage.

The out-of-pocket cost per box to Billson was $0.06.

Assume that a meeting has been called to discuss this situation
and that you are participating in the discussion. List the causes for
this situation and decide what must be done to correct each fault.

4

Manufacturing Planning

The success of any industrial enterprise depends largely upon its current control plus its past planning. In order for both to be effective, planning must precede performance, or production, and must be kept separate from it. Moreover, production planning cannot begin until two other phases of planning are completed. These prerequisites are manufacturing planning and factory planning.

When a research department releases a new product from its pilot plant, manufacturing planning must lay the ground for factory and production planning. The same holds true when the machine-design division of an engineering department completes a working model for a new machine. Even in a small factory with neither a research nor an engineering department, some form of manufacturing planning should precede the introduction of a new product. If the business is new, manufacturing planning should precede its establishment.

Manufacturing planning generally involves eight steps, taken in the following sequence:

1. Revise the product design and requirements to fit manufacturing equipment and methods.

2. Develop plans for new processes and equipment where no precedent exists.

3. Determine the operations to be performed in manufacturing, and their proper sequence.

4. Determine the equipment and personnel required for each operation.

5. Measure the time required to perform each operation.

6. Determine the materials required for each part or unit.

7. Estimate costs at various levels of activity.

8. Finalize planning based at the level indicated by price and prospective sales volume.

A fascinating chain of events follows when the machine-design section or the research and development department delivers a tableful or even a roomful of blueprints, bills of material, and specifications to the industrial engineering or planning department for the planning of a new product or group of products. Suppose we examine the steps in some detail:

A. MODIFICATION OF DESIGN

Before any planning is done, the industrial engineer and the manufacturing personnel will review the blueprints and models to determine whether the design conforms to what they know can be produced by effective manufacturing practices. Possibly the model may have been made by conventional toolroom methods and so designated on the blueprints and bills of material. Possibly a researcher may have had satisfactory results on a small scale with certain processing that the manufacturing people know will present difficulties in large-scale production. For economical production the industrial engineer and the manufacturing personnel may have to modify the design to suit existing production equipment. For example, a large forging may be specified, requiring one or a number of large chucking machines that are not available. Flame-cutting profilers and copper-hydrogen brazing equipment may be available and known to be much more effective in producing a part like that in Figure 6.

An excellent example of design modification is presented in Figure 7, which tells how the Pontiac Division of General Motors applied its

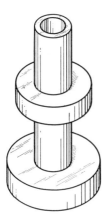

Fig. 6. A typical forged part.

Cylindrical forging, tube, scrap, and finished casing using improved method.

Casing and scrap formerly produced from 56-lb solid forging.

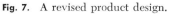

Fig. 7. A revised product design.

automotive experience to the manufacture of a recoil spring casing for an automatic aircraft cannon. The original design, developed in Europe, required a 6-pound casing to be machined from a 56-pound forging. This meant that 50 pounds of steel chips became scrap and wasted hundreds of thousands of production hours of valuable machine-tool time. The Pontiac engineers welded a steel tube to a 14-pound cylindrical forging, from which only 8 pounds of metal had to be removed. The Navy subjected the new casing to grueling tests and found that its performance met the Pontiac engineers' expectations. On an order for hundreds of thousands of guns, it also made possible great savings in metal, production time, and machines.

B. PROCESSES AND EQUIPMENT WHERE NO PRECEDENT EXISTS

New products frequently demand operations for which no equipment exists. Special equipment must then be provided for in planning, with an adequate statement of requirements from the industrial engineer. He must also secure authorization for the necessary machine-design work and construction or purchase, to make sure that equipment will be available when it is needed for production.

C. OPERATIONS AND THEIR SEQUENCE

The third step in manufacturing planning is to list the operations required by each component part and assembly and to determine the logical sequence in which they should be performed. Tolerances will be included in descriptions of operations. This, of course, is the first step in the preparation of a production routing.

Throughout this analysis of operations the engineer asks four basic questions about each operation:

1. Can the operation or any part of it be eliminated?
2. Can it be combined with some other operation?
3. Can the sequence or order of operations be changed for better effectiveness?
4. Can the operation be simplified?

A. H. Mogensen, in his work simplification conferences at Lake Placid, New York, has found that asking these four questions in this order leads to the discovery of improved work methods. Satisfactory answers, therefore, should be found before further planning is done and before equipment or fixtures are ordered.

In assembly-line production, operations must be balanced so that the assignments of each workman will require about the same time. If this is not done, end production will be determined by the inordinate time required for the longest operation. Operation breakdowns are therefore needed not only to establish current production rates but to fit increased or reduced rates if they become necessary. For example: in a production line balanced to produce 20 units of output per hour, work will be divided into 3-minute operations for each workman. If the production rate is to be increased to 30 units of output per hour, the work must be divided into 2-minute operations for each workman. This means splitting operations into elements requiring less time. Thus one workman may assemble nuts only finger-tight and another man may tighten them, instead of having one man perform the full operation. Or one man may place a component part in position and another bolt the part in its place.

There are, of course, limitations to economical division of operations. Critical study may show that certain production rates are not consistent with satisfactory balancing of operations. For example, in a specific instance production rates of 20, 26, 34, and 40 units per hour may be economically balanced. Production rates between these figures cannot be well balanced and are therefore avoided.

D. EQUIPMENT AND PERSONNEL REQUIREMENTS

After operations have been listed in their proper sequence, the industrial engineer must indicate the type of equipment on which each operation is to be performed, as well as any jigs and fixtures that may be required.

The engineer will also list personnel requirements. In doing so, he will specify the number of people needed to perform each operation and will tell whether the work is suited to women or to men. He will also indicate the labor grade of each operation, to show the degree of skill required, and to indicate what the basic hourly wage rates will be. The completed equipment and personnel specification will read somewhat as shown on page 36, with "F," in the last two columns, indicating female workers.

In the Garment Industry

Operation No.	Operation	Machine	No. of Men	Labor Grade
6	Sew lining to facing— 12 stitches per inch.	Singer Special	1 F	3 F

In the Machine Tool Industry

Operation No.	Operation	Machine	Fixtures	No. of Men	Labor Grade
3	Hot roll (6 passes)	Special No. 42	Rolls No. 78–8	2	8

In the Chemical Industry

Operation No.	Operation	Machine	Fixtures	No. of Men	Labor Grade
8	Empty filter press	Shriver 70 plate	Special acid- proof cloth	2	5

E. OPERATION TIMES

The time-study engineers or estimators are now ready to determine the time required to set up and perform each operation. During the early 1900's it was necessary to start production and then make time studies from actual operations—a method that neither allowed planning to precede performance nor kept the two separate. Since that time, techniques of time and motion study have been improved so much that it is no longer necessary actually to time each operation with a stop watch in order to know what personnel and equipment will be required. Formulas and tables will provide these facts and— what is more important—will reveal production costs at various levels of activity.

Many companies have fundamental time data for practically all classes of work in their patterns of activity. Figure 8 shows a simple standard for determining the time for operations to be run on punch presses. Moreover, the Methods Engineering Council in Pittsburgh, Pennyslvania, has developed a scientific method of motion-time analy-

STANDARD TIME CALCULATION SHEET FOR PRIMARY PUNCH PRESS OPERATIONS FOR USE IN CONJUNCTION WITH STANDARD NO. 18

Determine the following facts from an inspection of die, blueprint, and routing:

(A) Class of die __Progressive__

(B) If progressive, number of stages __12__

(C) Machine No. __159__

(D) Is press run "under motion" with the trip lever held down and the ram dropping and returning with each press revolution __No__

(E) Number of pieces blanked from each strip __180__

(F) Are finished parts dumped or stacked in containers __Dumped__

(G) Are parts screened to remove slugs or flash __Yes__

Table 1					Table 2	
Machine No.	Press Time	Machine No.	Press Time		Pieces per Strip	Minutes per Piece
158	.0600	170	.0140		10	.0080
159	.0195	171	.0129		10 to 12	.0085
160	.0167	172	.0129		12 to 15	.0090
161	.0167	173	.0133		15 to 20	.0095
162	.0134	174	.0158		20 to 25	0100
163	.0131	175	.0158		25 to 35	0105
164	.0195	176	.0158		35 to 80	.0110
165	.0105	180	.0128		80 to 200	.0115
166	.0147	181	.0158			
167	.0061	182	.0148			
168	.0492	183	.0139			

CALCULATION

(J) *Reach* for strip and *move* to die. *Locate* and *blank* first piece. *Move* strip from floor to table. *Oil* strip. *Dump* finished pieces into pan. *Discard* scrap.

For compound and two-stage progressive dies... $\dfrac{0.38}{E}$ = ────── ──────

For three- and four-stage progressive dies...... $\dfrac{0.42}{E} = \dfrac{0.42}{180}$ 0.0023

(K) Punch-press time; refer to Table 1 ....   0.0195

(L) Stack pieces in container if necessary (Table 2)........ ....   ──────

(M) Handling time between press cycle when a progressive die *is not* run under motion, 0.01 per piece.............................   0.0100

(N) Handling time between press cycle when a compound die *is not* run under motion, 0.0013 per piece.......... ....   ──────

(P) For more than four stages

$$\frac{(B-4) \times (K+M)}{E} = \frac{(12-4) \times (0.0195 + 0.01)}{180}$$ 0.0013

(Q) Screen-finished parts when necessary 0.0013 per piece..... . .   0.0013

Total basic minutes per piece............................   0.0344

Fig. 8. A typical basic standard time calculation.

sis that permits accurate time values to be set without use of a stop watch. After extensive research, during which hundreds of feet of motion-picture films of industrial operations were painstakingly analyzed, the Methods Engineering Council developed a comparatively simple set of predetermined time standards that indicate the time required by an operator with average or normal performance to perform the various motions that enter into most industrial operations.

To establish a standard by the methods-time measurement (M.T.M.) procedure, the analyst merely determines by observation or visualization the motions required to do a given job. He then assigns a time value to each motion from the tables of methods-time data. The sum of these time values plus standard allowances is the standard time for doing the job.

The procedure is quite simple and is usually much quicker to apply than conventional time study. When properly employed, it gives time values that seldom require revision when production gets under way. One word of caution is in order, however. The developers of the procedure constantly warn that its tables will give satisfactory results only in the hands of people who have been trained to use them properly. The training course is not unduly long, but it is essential.

Methods-time measurement lends itself particularly well to production planning, especially when new products are involved. It is not necessary to observe the operation being performed to develop an accurate standard. If the analyst is familiar with the methods used in similar work, he can visualize the motions that will have to be made in order to do the new job, and he can then calculate the time required for production. Thus, production planning based on sound and realistic standards becomes practical, even on new work, when methods-time measurement is used.

Figure 9 shows some M.T.M. application data as developed by the inventors, Harold B. Maynard, G. J. Stegemerten, and John L. Schwab, and illustrated and described by *Fortune Magazine*, October, 1949, in a feature article entitled "Timing a Fair Day's Work."

Other systems for the development of standard time data such as the *work factor* and *basic motion times* are also used. Time values developed by any of these systems can improve the consistency of planning figures. They do not, however, take account of variations in operating effectiveness. As an example, one department in a factory may be a new one with many workmen learning new operations. Therefore, production planners would adjust standard time values to reflect current operating effectiveness in accordance with the following formula:

$$\frac{\text{Standard hours produced} \times 100}{\text{Actual hours worked}} = \% \text{ Operating effectiveness}$$

Assume:

Standard hours produced (units of output

$$\times \text{ standard hours per unit}) = 6{,}000$$

$$\text{Actual hours worked} = 9{,}000$$

Then:

$$\frac{6{,}000 \text{ std. hours produced} \times 100}{9{,}000 \text{ actual hours worked}} = 66.6\% \text{ Operating effectiveness}$$

In planning production for the situation given in this example, 66.6 per cent of standard output values should be used. Conversely, actual performance in other operations may exceed standard output values. Operating effectiveness will then exceed 100 per cent of standard, and planning figures must be adjusted accordingly. Whether operating effectiveness is high or low, production planners will use adjusting factors to obtain values that reflect current expected outputs.

Until the volume of production has been established within reasonably close limits, the time-study man will generally include in his analysis several different methods or machines to perform many of the operations. If, for example, only a few pieces are to be turned per lot, an engine or a bench lathe may be satisfactory because setup and tooling are simple. If lot sizes are larger, a hand screw machine may be indicated, and if still larger lots are processed, an automatic screw machine may be most economical.

1. Multiple Machine Operation. In the textile industry and in operations in which products such as wire and cable are produced in continuous lengths, different methods are used to calculate the time to produce given outputs. These operations are generally complicated by the fact that they are multiple machine operations.

When, in multiple machine operation, a number of machines can be attended by one person, factors and formulas can be used to calculate predictively both machine capacities and production outputs. A primary consideration in planning is, of course, the number of machines or machine units to be attended by one or more operators. If too few machine units are assigned, labor costs will be excessive. If too many are assigned, the excess will be idle and the cost of this excess machine capacity will become burdensome.

Before this important subject is discussed, several terms and symbols must be defined:

Multiple machine operation is the simultaneous operation of more than one machine or machine unit by one or more persons. The term "machine unit," or "head," is used to designate either individual machines or one of a number of identical mechanisms on one common base or frame. In the equations which follow, the symbol N will be used to represent the number of machines, or heads.

Running time is the time necessary for a machine unit to run without interruption to produce one unit of output. This factor will be represented by R.

Working time is the time an attendant must work in conjunction with the machine unit to produce a single unit of output. The symbol for this will be W.

Interference is the time one or more machine units are idle while the attendant is occupied with work on another machine unit. Interference will be symbolized by I.

To learn how these four factors may be used to predetermine output and machine capacity, let us assume a textile winding operation, a wire insulating operation, or a bank of extrusion machines in which R, the running time per unit of output, is four minutes, and W, the working time per unit of output, is one minute. We also assume that six machine units have been assigned to one operator. The operating cycle will then be as shown diagrammatically in Figure 10. It reveals that one machine unit out of six will be idle while the operator takes care of the others. The idle machine is not the same in each cycle, but the idleness itself persists.

Next we assume that four machine units have been assigned to one person, producing the operating cycle diagrammed in Figure 11. In this case the operator will be idle one minute out of each five minutes, or twenty per cent of the time.

With five machine units assigned to one person, the operating cycle will be as shown in Figure 12. Theoretically, neither operator nor machine will ever be idle. Losses from excess labor cost and excess machine capacity are therefore optimal.

These graphic analyses show that a good first approximation of the proper number of machine units to be assigned to an operator, with-

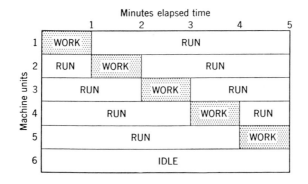

Fig. 10. Diagram showing operation of six machine units.

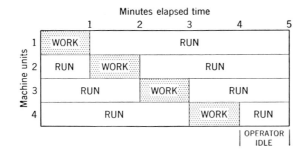

Fig. 11. Diagram showing operation of four machine units.

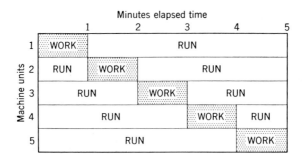

Fig. 12. Diagram showing operation of five machine units.

out considering the factor of interference, can be calculated by the formula:

$$\frac{R + W}{W} = N$$

which in the third of our assumed examples becomes

$$\frac{4 + 1}{1} = 5$$

With this simple exercise in mind, the essential steps to be taken in predetermining multiple machine assignments become evident:

First, the running time per unit of output is determined from machine speeds and material characteristics. In rewinding textile yarn or in similar operations, for example, the running time can be determined as follows:

$$\frac{\left(\begin{array}{c}\text{Net weight of one}\\\text{output unit in pounds}\end{array}\right) \times \left(\begin{array}{c}\text{Yards per pound}\\\text{of yarn}\end{array}\right)}{\text{Winding speed in yards per minute}} = \left(\begin{array}{c}\text{Running time in}\\\text{minutes per unit}\\\text{of output}\end{array}\right)$$

Second, all elements of work are studied to learn the time required for their performance. In such operations as rewinding yarn, the working time per unit of output is determined as follows:

$$\left[\begin{array}{c}\text{Minutes}\\\text{to}\\\text{change}\\\text{one}\\\text{output}\\\text{unit}\end{array}\right] + \left[\frac{\left(\begin{array}{c}\text{Minutes}\\\text{to}\\\text{change}\\\text{one}\\\text{supply}\\\text{unit}\end{array}\right) \times \left(\begin{array}{c}\text{Weight}\\\text{of one}\\\text{output}\\\text{unit}\end{array}\right)}{\begin{array}{c}\text{Weight of one}\\\text{supply unit}\end{array}}\right] +$$

$$\left[\left(\begin{array}{c}\text{Minutes}\\\text{to re-}\\\text{pair one}\\\text{break}\end{array}\right) \times \left(\begin{array}{c}\text{Breaks}\\\text{per}\\\text{pound}\\\text{of}\\\text{yarn}\end{array}\right) \times \left(\begin{array}{c}\text{Weight}\\\text{of one}\\\text{output}\\\text{unit}\end{array}\right)\right] + \left[\begin{array}{c}\text{Walking}\\\text{time in}\\\text{minutes}\\\text{per}\\\text{output}\\\text{unit}\end{array}\right] = \begin{array}{c}\text{Working}\\\text{time in}\\\text{minutes}\\\text{per}\\\text{take-up}\\\text{unit}\end{array}$$

The time spent walking from one machine unit to the next one requiring attention is also work and must be estimated. In general, the distance to be walked between machine units per operation is approximately one-half the sum of the longest and the shortest distances between machine units.[1] This approximation will be used in the calculations that follow.

Unit	Unit	Unit	Unit	Unit
1	2	3	4	5

$\leftarrow 1' \rightarrow$

$\longleftarrow \quad\quad 4' \quad\quad \longrightarrow$

Under these circumstances, in operating four machine units the probable distance is 2.0 feet; in operating five machine units the probable distance is 2.5 feet and the increase per machine is 0.5 feet.

This increase in distance per machine unit multiplied by 0.008 minutes per foot produces a unit walking time to be multiplied by the approximate number of machine units requiring attention as determined by the first approximation $\dfrac{R + W}{W}$ (exclusive of walking time); the product, when multiplied by the number of times per unit of output each machine unit requires attention, gives the walking time in minutes per unit of output.

Third, interference is determined for a number of ratios of working time and running time as illustrated in Figure 13 or computed from probability tables. For convenience the values for interference should be portrayed in graphic form.

Fourth, the load or burden cost of a machine unit is determined as follows:

Let

A = Cost of machine plus installation costs

B = Number of units or heads on machine

C = Number of manufacturing hours per year

D = Number of square feet occupied by machine and attendant

E = Rent or other cost per square foot per year

F = Allowance for investment, depreciation and obsolescence, taxes, fire protection, machine insurance, supplies, tools, and maintenance (all as a percentage of A)

G = Power cost per KWH $\times$ KWH per hour used by machine

H = Steam cost per M pounds $\times$ M pounds per hour used by machine

J = Air cost per M cubic feet $\times$ M cubic feet per hour used by machine

[1] This holds true for the arrangement of machine units and their random demands for attention in the operation under consideration. If machine units are in rows that face each other or if they require attention in orderly cycles, other values for the average distance to be walked between them must be developed for these different situations.

K = Water cost per M cubic feet $\times$ M cubic feet per hour used by machine

L = Gas cost per M cubic feet $\times$ M cubic feet per hour used by machine

Then

$$\frac{(AF) + (DE)}{CB} + \frac{G + H + J + K + L}{B}$$

$$= \text{Load cost per machine unit per hour}$$

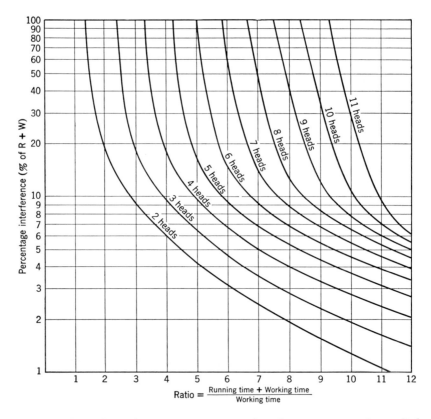

Fig. 13. Chart of interference curves. Note that these curves can be applied only (1) to machines having individual stopping mechanisms on each head or machine unit; (2) to operations in which some of the elements of work are demanded at random; and (3) when less than 75 per cent of the work can be performed while the machine units are running.

As the number of heads or machine units per attendant is increased, the gain in output is a decrement to unit cost until the load becomes so great that one or more machine units become continuously idle. The loss from excessive interference is an increment to unit cost. The point of economic balance between burden and labor cost can be determined by the following calculation:

Let

L = Labor cost per attendant per hour (with any increment imposed by vacations, paid holidays, etc.)

B = Machine load cost per machine unit per hour

R = Machine running time per unit of output in hours

W = Work time per unit of output in hours

I = Interference per unit of output with N heads

I_1 = Interference per unit of output with $N - 1$ heads

I_2 = Interference per unit of output with $N + 1$ heads

N = Number of machines per attendant $\left(\dfrac{R + W}{W} \right)$

Then

$$\left(\frac{L}{N} + B \right) (R + W + I) = \text{Cost per unit of output with } N \text{ heads}$$

and

$$\left(\frac{L}{N - 1} + B \right) (R + W + I_1)$$
$$= \text{Cost per unit of output with } N - 1 \text{ heads}$$

and

$$\left(\frac{L}{N + 1} + B \right) (R + W + I_2)$$
$$= \text{Cost per unit of output with } N + 1 \text{ heads}$$

and N heads is the economic number to assign to one attendant when

$$\left(\frac{L}{N - 1} + B) \right) (R + W + I_1)$$
$$> \left(\frac{L}{N} + B \right) (R + W + I) < \left(\frac{L}{N + 1} + B \right) (R + W + I_2)$$

The points at which

$$\left(\frac{L}{N} + B \right) (R + W + I) = \left(\frac{L}{N - 1} + B \right) (R + W + I_1)$$

have been determined for a general class of multiple machine opera-

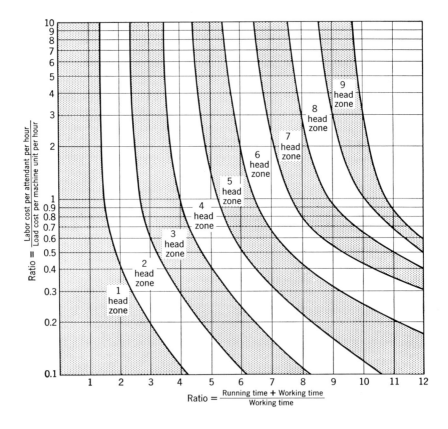

Fig. 14. Chart showing the economic number of machine units to be assigned to one experienced attendant. (*Note:* Limitations of use are the same as for the chart of interference curves in Fig. 13.)

tions up to nine heads are graphically portrayed as boundary lines between economic head assignment zones in the chart shown in Figure 14.

Since various items are generally produced on one bank of multiple unit machines or one group of similar individual machines, forms or work sheets for the determination of expected production outputs are of great convenience. They also prevent omission of factors needed in the calculation. A typical output calculation sheet for 25B rewinding machines is shown on page 47.

OUTPUT CALCULATION SHEET FOR 25B REWINDING MACHINES

A = Winding speed in yards per minute (constant)   = 600 yards
B = Time to change one finished unit of output   = 0.18 minutes
C = Minutes to replace one supply unit   = 0.31 minutes
D = Minutes to repair one yarn break   = 0.36 minutes
E = Breaks per pound of yarn: No. 10–1 ply   = 0.065 breaks
                              No. 20–1 ply   = 0.142 "
                              No. 60–1 ply   = 0.420 "
                              No. 100–1 ply   = 0.560 "
F = Walking unit (spindles on 12″ centers)   = 0.004 minutes
G = Net weight of one output unit (see specification)
H = Net weight of one supply unit (see specification)
K = Load cost per spindle per head per hour   = 0.30 cents

SAMPLE CALCULATION

Winding No. 10–1, 8,400 yards per pound, 0.5 pound   Minutes per
supply units into 0.2 pound output units   output unit

L = Wind one output unit = $\dfrac{G \times \text{yards per pound of yarn}}{A}$

$= \dfrac{0.2 \times 8,400}{600}$ = 2.80000

M = Change one finished output unit = B = 0.18000

N = Change one supply unit = $\dfrac{CG}{H} = \dfrac{0.31 \times 0.2}{0.5}$ = 0.12400

P = Repair yarn breaks = $D \times E \times G = 0.36 \times 0.065 \times 0.2$ = 0.00468

Q = Walk = $F \left(\dfrac{L + M + N + P}{M + N + P} \right) \times \left(1 + \dfrac{G}{H} + EG \right)$

$= 0.004 \left(\dfrac{3.1087}{0.3087} \right) \times \left(1 + \dfrac{0.2}{0.5} + 0.65 \times 0.2 \right)$ = 0.06163

R = Ratio of $\dfrac{\text{Run} + \text{Work}}{\text{Work}} = \dfrac{L + M + N + P + Q}{M + N + P + Q} = \dfrac{3.1703}{0.3703}$
$= 8.56$

S = Ratio of $\dfrac{\text{Labor cost per hour}}{\text{Load cost per hour}} = \dfrac{J}{K} = \dfrac{1.80}{0.30} = 6$

T = Ratios R and S referred to Figure 14: economic no. of heads
$= 8$

U = Referring to Figure 13: interference for 8 heads = 10%   = 0.31703

V = Total minutes per output unit with 8 heads
$= L + M + P + Q + U$ = 3.48734

W = Total minutes per output unit per head = $\dfrac{V}{T} = \dfrac{3.48734}{8}$
$= 0.4359$

Y = Minutes per pound = $\dfrac{W}{G} = \dfrac{0.4359}{0.2} = 2.1795$

Z = Expected output per head per hour in pounds = $\dfrac{60}{TY} = \dfrac{60}{8 \times 2.1795} = 3.4411$

F. MATERIALS REQUIRED

Design engineers frequently specify, on the bills of material or assembly parts lists, the kind and quantities of the various raw materials for each part. These quantities are based on the raw materials needed for each part, but they make no allowance for shrinkage that occurs at every stage in the manufacturing process. Even the best workman is bound to turn out some parts or products that do not meet specifications, especially when tolerances are close. An estimate of expected losses will, therefore, have to be made, and experience is the best guide for that estimate. In the manufacture of cotton cloth, for example, experience may show that a particular type generally has a 6 per cent loss during the processing. The finished cloth may weigh 25 pounds per 100 yards, but the manufacturing analysis should indicate that 26½ pounds of cotton are actually needed to produce 100 yards of the cloth.

Some companies prefer to have their industrial engineers show the exact quantity of material required with no allowance for shrinkage or waste. When the production-planning engineers take off material requirements for the procurement schedule or for purchase requisitions, they increase the figures to allow for processing losses. The cost department makes an equivalent allowance in computing costs. These steps increase the work of determining costs and planning production, a disadvantage that sometimes is very burdensome. On the other hand, when the industrial engineer allows for process losses, his estimates are likely to remain fixed while production men reduce losses. As a result, orders are placed for more material than is actually needed, and figures for production planning and costs cease to be accurate. A discussion of the subject by executives concerned with it can often indicate the best method for use in a given situation.

G. ESTIMATED COSTS AT VARIOUS LEVELS OF ACTIVITY

The industrial engineer now has sufficient information to estimate some total costs, using equipment and methods suited to various levels of production. The standard time required to perform each operation, multiplied by the hourly wage rate indicated by the labor grade, produces a direct labor cost. The direct material quantities for each part or item extended at the price per purchase unit produces the direct material cost. The sum of these two is a prime cost to which must be added burdens computed for various production levels and methods, as in the tabulated example.

	Hand Work	Semi-automatic Equipment (2 Setups per Month)	Semi-automatic Equipment (Permanent Setup)	Fully Automatic Equipment (2 Setups per Month)	Fully Automatic Equipment (Permanent Setup)
Direct labor	$3.20	$1.40	$1.40	$0.60	$0.60
Direct material	0.60	0.60	0.60	0.60	0.60
Factory burden	6.10	3.30	3.00	2.30	1.80
Factory cost per unit	$9.90	$5.30	$5.00	$3.50	$3.00
Monthly production	10,000	22,000	48,000	110,000	230,000

H. FINALIZING PLANS

Further cost calculations will lead to estimates of selling prices at various levels of production, as is shown graphically in Figure 15.

If consultations with the sales department indicate that between 130,000 and 150,000 units can be sold per month at a price of $6.00, the industrial engineer will proceed to finalize the production routing using fully automatic equipment. If actual sales are subsequently higher than this estimate, his planning will still be satisfactory. Fewer setups of the automatic equipment will be required until 230,000 per month are sold. If sales exceed 230,000 per month, duplicate equipment may be required, but the planning will remain unchanged unless more productive equipment has been developed in the meantime.

If monthly sales are estimated at 15,000 to 60,000 and the product can be sold for $8.50, the planning will be set for semiautomatic equipment. If sales promise to be less than 15,000 per month and the product can be sold for about $11, hand work may be appropriate.

Of course, the company may decide to set a low initial selling price in order to force a good market within a year or two. This will require considerable financial planning in order to sustain a loss throughout the introductory period. On the other hand, economic prospects may be so doubtful that the whole project is sent back to the research or engineering department for redevelopment, or is dropped as impractical.

Such thorough manufacturing planning calculates risks before subsequent planning starts. Although it costs money and takes time, it

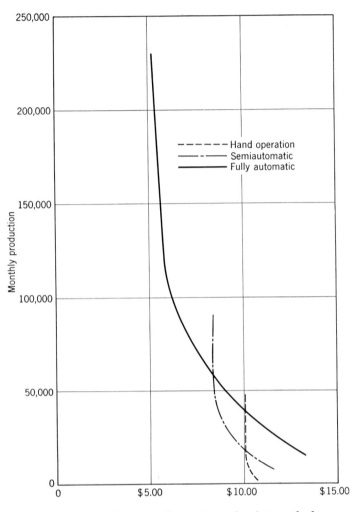

Fig. 15. Chart showing selling prices related to methods.

reduces the danger of failure or loss, with the accompanying employee dislocations.

SUMMARY

Manufacturing planning follows research, development, and product engineering. It includes rationalizing and adjusting the product design to manufacturing equipment and methods that are known to be most economical or effective. It may also require the development of new processes and equipment to meet new production needs.

In this type of planning, essential manufacturing operations are listed in the sequence in which they must be performed. The type of equipment and the personnel requirements necessary for each operation are specified. Assembly line operations must be balanced so that each workman has a fair and equitable assignment. The time required to perform each operation is established by estimate or by means of fundamental time values.

The quantity of each type of raw material is determined, as well as the expected losses of material from defective work.

Costs are usually estimated for different methods of manufacture. Hand methods are generally used when suitable machines are lacking, and when the sales volume is expected to be low. Semiautomatic equipment is likely to be indicated by a moderate sales volume, with fully automatic equipment if sales are expected to be high.

The relationship between estimated selling prices based on various manufacturing methods and the sales volumes that various selling prices will produce determines whether a given project is practical or not. If it is, manufacturing methods and equipment are planned at the appropriate level.

QUESTIONS TO CHECK COMPREHENSION

1. The Alien Property Custodian has granted an American company the right to produce a European product. The design requires considerable machining and nut and bolt assembly. The manufacturing pattern of the American company is forming on breaks and presses and electric welding. Should the manufacturing planning be on the basis of the European design, or should it be modified in conformity with the production processes of the American company?

2. A company has been in production for twenty-five years. It has scientifically studied the time required to perform all its manufacturing operations and has basic times for loading and unloading the machines and for making necessary adjustments, as well as working times of the various machines on its various products. Can this company, using basic time data, estimate with reasonable accuracy the time required to produce new products of the same general type, or must it await actual production to time the elements of work?

3. Fully automatic, semiautomatic, and hand work can be used to manufacture a particular product. What factors will dictate the method to be employed?

4. Can the profitability of a product be estimated with reasonable accuracy before production actually begins? Give reasons for your answer.

5. What four questions should be asked about each operation as it is studied in manufacturing planning? Why is it important to ask these questions in a definite sequence?

6. What are the arguments for and against including allowances for additional material to cover defective work in the manufacturing-planning analysis?

7. What are the advantages to be gained by careful manufacturing-planning analysis before a decision is made to start production of an item or a line of items?

8. Which should be completed first, factory planning or manufacturing planning?

PROBLEMS

1. A new product has been developed. The sales department estimates a demand for 10,000 per month. Manufacturing planning has provided the following data for three methods to produce the product:

Method	A	B	C
Material cost per piece	$ 0.60	$ 0.60	$ 0.60
Tooling cost	500.00	120,000.00	250,000.00
Cost per setup	300.00	1,000.00	12,000.00
Labor cost per piece	2.00	1.00	.30
Burden cost per piece	3.00	1.60	.50

Assume the tooling cost to be absorbed in one year and one setup per month. Which method should be selected on the basis that the product may become obsolete in one year?

2. A metal stamping is to be produced with a three-stage progressive punch and die on machine number 164. The press is not run under motion. The number of pieces punched from each strip of stock is 110. The finished pieces are stacked in containers and no slugs need removal by screening. Refer to the calculation sheet in Figure 8 and compute the basic number of minutes per piece required to produce these stampings.

3. Referring to the calculation form and data explained under multiple machine operation, compute the expected output, in pounds per hour per head, of a textile rewinding operation in which No. 10–1 ply yarn, with 8,400 yards per pound in 0.4 pound supply spools, is rewound into 0.3 pound output units. Assume the ratio of S to be 6.

DISCUSSION CASE

The Alpha Iron Works started business as a job-order foundry in 1912. In 1920 it purchased some war-surplus machine-tool equipment and produced machined castings on a job-order basis. In 1926 it developed some heavy machinery used in the automobile industry.

Its business was spotty and seasonal. In 1935 it purchased the patent rights to an automobile accessory. The inventor had estimated the cost of the accessory on the basis of the use of special equipment in a progressive production arrangement. Sales estimates were based on a selling price calculated from this cost.

When models and blueprints were received, Charles Jones laid out the operations using existing equipment except for two new conventional machines which were purchased. Production was planned on a class-of-work basis. That is to say, parts were trucked back and forth between departments specializing in drilling, milling, grinding, etc.

After 100 units of the product were manufactured, the cost was found to be more than double the inventor's estimate. Salesmen, meanwhile, had developed considerable interest among automobile manufacturers, but when the 100 units were used for demonstration, interest cooled, because the price was much higher than the one originally set.

A lawsuit against the inventor was considered, but counsel indicated a poor chance of winning the case.

After three years of unsuccessful effort to sell the product through automobile-accessory chains, the whole project was abandoned. The patent rights were sold to an automobile-accessory manufacturing company. This company replanned manufacture using special equipment. The selling price was reduced to one-third of that set by Alpha. Sales were good and profits satisfactory.

The chairman of Alpha's board of directors has called a meeting to consider this matter. You have been invited to attend this meeting. Discuss causes for the failure to successfully exploit this patent and list the precautions to be taken to avoid repetition of errors.

5

Automation

For many people the term automation raises a vision of the completely automatic factory in which no manual work is performed. This is perhaps the ultimate in automation, but the term also is applied to the gradual evolution of individual automatic machines and groups of automatic machines that have been integrated into processes of production or computation.

It would be presumptuous to attempt a thorough general consideration of automation in a single chapter. Many articles deal with separate phases of the subject, and many books treat it comprehensively. This chapter can offer only a brief explanation of automation and indicate its impacts on production, forecasting, planning, and control.

The idea of automation is not new nor are applications of its principles. Figured fabrics and carpets have for many years been woven on Jacquard looms by arrangements in which loops of perforated cards control the design. The old-fashioned pianola, or player piano, was an early example of automation, in which perforated rolls of paper actuated hammers that struck strings and thus played difficult musical compositions. Although both piano playing and the making of carpets or cloth were standardized, it is evident that what traditionally had been human skills were transferred to machines. What is not so obvious, especially to critics of the "machine age," is the superior skill required to design and build the actuating apparatus and properly perforate the paper rolls or cards.

Yes, the idea of actuating processes automatically is old; what is new is the element of feedback, in which sensing devices tell when a process is out of control and signal control devices to make proper adjustments. The automatic player piano can play a composition without error only when the strings are properly tuned. We can get a simple picture of feedback by assuming that a pianola has been modified so that when a string not in tune is struck a signal is carried to a control mechanism which then loosens or tightens the string, as may be required.

A. AUTOMATIC MACHINES

The oldest form of automation is found in machine tools that perform certain operations or functions automatically. Modification of the engine lathe, for example, produced the screw-cutting lathe, the turret lathe, and the automatic screw machine into which bar stock is fed automatically and which continuously produces complicated component parts without further attention until tool wear requires the tools to be adjusted or dressed. Automatic copying lathes, profiling machines, and automatic grinding machines all were advances in automation, which was carried still further by the addition of sensing devices to adjust for tool wear and by automatic tool dressing.

At the Massachusetts Institute of Technology, research made it possible to add an electronic type computer to a standard milling machine. Scientists who are skilled in programming translate drawings of a part to be machined into paths along which a cutting tool must move to perform the operation. Three-dimensional control of the work table movement is accomplished by servomechanisms. These devices receive their instructions as impulses from the electronic computer, which is in turn instructed by a punched tape or a magnetic tape. Without a model or prototype, therefore, the machine will perform operations that have been only engineering concepts in the form of drawings.

The "Record-Playback" developed by the General Electric Company records on magnetic tape the behavior of a machine performing a specific machining operation under the guidance of a skilled workman. When the tape then is played back, the operation is automatically performed without control or attention from the workman.

These individual automatic machines possess flexibility that permits them to be used in many different operations on many different parts. Some machines are designed to produce automatically a variety of completed parts.

B. AUTOMATIC TRANSFER

As the limit to which turrets, cross slides, and other mechanisms could be added to machine tools was approached, engineers undertook the automatic transfer from one machine to another of parts being machined. The movement of cylinder blocks for automobile engines shows how effectively this has been accomplished. The cylinder block, which is a rough casting when it is introduced at one end of a series of automatic machines, passes automatically from one machine to the next until all milling, drilling, tapping, boring, and lapping operations have been completed.

When groups of automatic machines are integrated into a system by automatic transfer mechanisms, there is always the chance that the malfunction of one unit or tool may halt the whole parade. This threat can be met in several ways. One is by preventive maintenance which keeps machines in good working condition and makes repairs before operation can become faulty. Another provides for auxiliary tool heads to be held in readiness to replace any that go out of adjustment. Still another way is to space machine units so that several pieces of work are in process between them. The number of these pieces between machine units multiplied by the unit cycle time is the time available for a highly skilled maintenance group to correct the malfunction without reducing final output.

C. PROCESSES THAT CORRECT THEIR OWN ERRORS

The introduction of low-energy electronic circuits has made it possible to feed information to mechanisms that will actuate these mechanisms quickly, accurately, and from locations remote from the actual operations. Thus, men in control centers can observe instruments, monitor processes, and make adjustments in them.

Feedback control, which establishes the relation between the reference input and the command for action, permits the development of processes that correct their own errors. Sensing devices in the system, connected in closed-loop circuits, tell the controlling device when to make adjustments that would otherwise have to be sensed and made by human monitors. This constitutes automatic control, which has been defined as "a system in which the value of a controlled condition or a related condition is compared with the desired value, and corrective action is taken dependent upon the deviation from the desired value. Without the inclusion of a human element, the operation is performed by comparing and correcting chains of elements in a closed loop."

Disturbances can be introduced into automatic systems of servomechanisms and analogues [1] that actuate and make adjustments to a given process. The effects produced by these disturbances can foretell the operating characteristics and limits of speed and accuracy of the process before it is actually put into production. It is therefore evident that process capabilities can be better predicted with automatically controlled processes than with manually operated or semiautomatic processes.

D. APPLICATION OF AUTOMATION

Every day, more and more automatic devices are being added to individual machines. A primary objective is to retain flexibility, so that many different manufacturing operations may be performed as machines become more automatic. Many of these machines produce component parts of commodities without any manual intervention except for loading, setting tools, unloading, and moving the finished pieces to assembly sites. Other single machines or machines in series automatically produce and package finished commodities.

Combinations of automatic machines and transfer devices produce items such as completely machined cylinder blocks for automobiles, crankshafts, metal stampings, oil pump bodies, pistons, and many other items. The bottling and canning of foods and beverages is another example of this type of automation. As shown in Figure 16, the Coca-Cola Corporation provides large show windows at the front of its bottling plants so that everyone who wishes to may watch the sequence of bottling operations. Many automatic systems of assembly have also been tried. Some, for example the automatic assembly of automobile frames and telephone apparatus, have succeeded. Others are theoretically possible but await perfecting and economic need.

For completely automatic processes and even automatic factories we look first to the chemical and petrochemical industries. Automation permits the consistent and continuous precision that is essential where products are the result of chemical reactions, as well as automatic correction of maladjustments or failures that would otherwise be disastrous to equipment or would lead to unsatisfactory products. Remote control with low power-level electronic circuits is an added advantage in these process industries.

Automatic formaldehyde factories that produce as much as ten million pounds of product per month with only one engineer and a

---

[1] These analogues may be in the form of electronic networks.

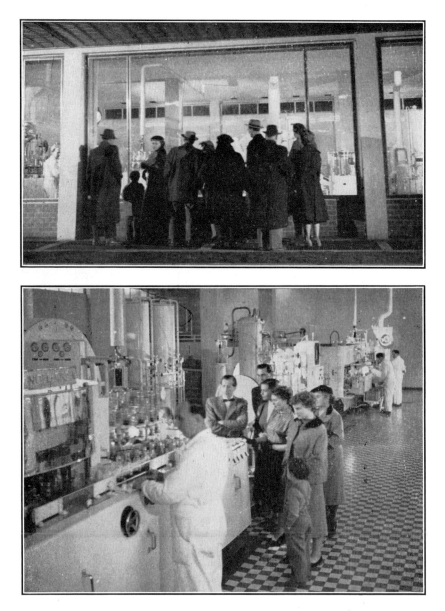

Fig. 16. Views of Coca-Cola automatic bottling plant in Nuremberg, Germany. (Courtesy Coca-Cola Export Corp.)

small maintenance crew per shift amaze us even though they also are well established and economically successful. Many of these chemical and petrochemical processes are governed by electronic computer-type controllers. The steel industry, too, employs many servomechanisms and feedback circuits to control its basic operations, which are still performed essentially by batch-type production methods. Finishing operations in the steel industry have for many years been controlled by modern automatic systems.

E. AUTOMATIC HANDLING OF INFORMATION

Handling information is of vital importance in commercial operations and in forecasting, planning, and control of production. Many companies use punched card equipment to classify sales and production information and to summarize it so that decisions can be quickly and accurately made. Computers are used to prepare payrolls, analyze sales trends, report production progress, and to perform many other operations. Electronic computers of the calculator type can solve probelms of production scheduling and sales forecasting. Electronic computers of the memory type permit storage of detailed inventory records and similar data that must be preserved for reference.

A large mail order company employs a magnetic drum system that provides stock control for 12,000 different items; with the aid of ten men it can handle 80,000 orders per day. Airlines also handle passenger reservations by magnetic drum devices, and the Pennsylvania Railroad makes passenger reservations automatically. Since handling of travel reservations is essentially similar to equipment loading in production planning, equipment and methods devised for airlines and railroads can be applied to factory scheduling of production. Stock control in a mail order company is similar to raw material and finished goods stock control in factories. Magnetic drum devices designed for mail order operations can therefore be applied to factory operations.

F. ACCURACY OF AUTOMATIC SYSTEMS

Two types of errors are made in clerical and manufacturing operations performed by human beings. The first type is the *"accidental"* error, which generally results from diverted attention, fatigue, impaired health, or emotional stress. Everyone knows that some errors are introduced into a man's work when he works overtime and he becomes fatigued. An attractive young woman passing a workplace commonly causes errors by diverting the attention of workman or clerk. Worry over debts, family quarrels, or a sick child lasts longer and has greater effect upon accuracy and quality of work. Digestive upsets, headaches, and other disturbances not apparent to supervisors (and often ignored by victims themselves) are common causes of accidental errors.

The second type is the *"systematic"* error. In operations performed by people, systematic errors come from improper training, improper instruction, and improper placement of individuals in work for which they are physically or mentally unsuited. Some people who have not learned their multiplication tables properly will systematically compute 9×8 as 73 or some other wrong number. Some persons are partial to even numbers, others to fives and tens. Some machine tool operators always work to the high side of tolerances and their errors are consistently outside upper specification limits. Some workmen will systematically ignore certain essential requirements of their jobs because they have not been properly trained or instructed to consider them and to make allowances for them. Some people with large fingers will regularly fail to make proper delicate adjustments to mechanisms. People who are muscular and strong frequently strip threads on nut and bolt assemblies, but others who are weak will assemble nuts and bolts so loosely that they lead to mechanical or electrical failures.

Accidental errors disappear as automation takes over repetitive operations once performed by people. Machines are not distracted by pretty girls, they do not worry about problems at home, and their faculties do not become fatigued by overtime work. *Systematic* errors can also be avoided by automatic devices that sense errors and either correct them or give warning that repair or adjustment is needed or that a run of errors can be expected.

G. EFFECTS OF AUTOMATION ON INDUSTRIAL ORGANIZATION

Advances in automation demand better managers and a higher ratio of managers to operating personnel. These new managers will require superior knowledge of the relationships between sales forecasting by automatic contrivances, research and process engineering based upon a whole new set of economic factors, and production based upon the programming and controlling of factors translated into signals and sensing as contrasted with present plans and schedules that are laid out in our traditional writing. Managers will also need great skill in social leadership in order to maintain a well-coordinated team of assistants. Along with all these new demands, managers will have the advantage of essential information quickly at their disposal with which to make decisions.

Production engineers will probably become the high priests of automation. They will have to understand operation and control by electronic input and feedback devices as well as the creation of analogues and the use of all types of sensing and controlling devices, such as beta-ray thickness controllers, transducers, servomechanisms, and many other innovations that will enter into automation. These engineers also will need to know the principles of physics, mathematics, statistics, mechanical engineering, chemical engineering, and electrical engineering, and they must be capable of working with specialists in these disciplines.

Industrial engineers have made important contributions to scientific management in the development of systems for work study. They will implement these systems to meet new requirements posed by automation. Measurements will be in terms of thousandths of seconds instead of decimal hours. Sequencing will be in the form of analogues and taped programming instead of physical rearrangements of equipment and manual operations.

Production engineers will know all details of the actual automatic operations. They will have to translate sales trends revealed by automatic computers into immediate adjustments of production schedules. Actual programming or cutting of tapes will change the whole scheme of production engineering from one in which action is directed by written schedules to one in which guidance takes the form of a special shorthand that can be understood fully only by the machines it controls and by persons trained to interpret it.

Operations research will undoubtedly play an increasingly important part in finding optimal solutions to problems of automatic production. Production engineers will have to work with men skilled in this new science. A brief discussion of operations research is therefore essential.

H. OPERATIONS RESEARCH

Perhaps it was only natural that military engineering, the oldest of engineering professions, should be first to recognize the need for scientists to help solve many problems of logistics, strategy, and tactics. After years of accelerated progress, operations research emerged as an applied science during World War II. Logic, mathematics, statistics, and many branches of science were used to quantify the factors of military problems. Factors and calculations expresed in numbers formed a scientific basis for decisions involving complex relationships and interactions between choice and chance.

Unfortunately, many of the operations research studies made between 1941 and 1946 remain classified because they bear upon national security. Some have been declassified and appear in the literature, especially in *Methods of Operations Research* by Philip M. Morse and George E. Kimball.[1]

The wartime success of operations research led businessmen to apply its principles and methods to problems of industry and commerce. Establishment of the Operations Research Society of America gives evidence of widespread interest in this new scientific method. The Institute of Management Sciences, founded recently, gives further evidence of the recognition that interdisciplinary approaches are needed to solve problems of production and industrial and commercial management.

Peacetime operations research is intended to develop means of securing optimal solutions to problems that involve choice and chance. Businessmen recognize that they, like military men, must take calculated risks. They also are learning that techniques of operations research can be used to determine courses of action that will aim at the greatest possible gains with the least chance of loss or disaster.

Hotel managers, for example, always face the difficult problem of accommodation reservations and cancellations. Suppose that a hotel has 1,000 rooms and that cancellations average 6 per cent. When travel reaches its peak, should the manager run the risk of letting 60 rooms stand idle, or should he overbook his capacity by 5 or 6 per cent? Probability studies will tell him how many guests are likely to come late in the evening without reservations and how often he is likely to be embarrassed by having to tell a guest who has made an advance reservation that he cannot be accommodated. All these factors can be quantified. The study is extended to include the effect of competition and the losses in profit and prestige that will be created if the hotel gets a reputation for disappointing people who have made reservations. The most difficult part of the problem, of course, is how frequently these disappointments can occur with impunity. Only by considering all these factors can the manager tell what he can

---

[1] Published jointly by The Technology Press of Massachusetts Institute of Technology and John Wiley & Sons, New York, 1951.

afford to do. What honor *permits* him to do, of course, is another matter.

Airlines are faced with similar problems. Some of them have been solved by requiring passengers to restate their intentions long enough in advance of flight time so that other reservations can be accepted to replace those of passengers who decide not to make this or that flight. The problem extends into deciding how many lunches, dinners, and even breakfasts shall be put on a certain plane in time for a given takeoff.

How, then, can operations research be used in production forecasting, planning, and control? Has it been used under some different name to solve production and sales problems? It seems obvious that this new science can combine disciplines of statistics, logic, psychology, engineering, and management and use them to solve long-range problems of sales forecasting. This interdisciplinary approach should disclose broad relationships and interactions among the factors involved. It may also lead to the development of improved systems and techniques for forecasting. It is doubtful, however, that the actual forecasting will ever be done by operations researchers.

Many problems of production engineering were studied by techniques similar to, but not as profound as, those of operations research before they received this name. Multiple machine assignments, explained in a previous chapter, form an example of the optimal solution of a production engineering problem by techniques essentially like those employed in operations research. Possibly operations researchers may be able to refine or simplify the solution of problems of multiple machine operation or may even broaden both the problem and its solution to include the psychological factors inherent in men and women who operate the machines.

Systems to determine economical production lot sizes offer another example of operations research that had had much attention before the advent of operations research as a science. The broader relationships between stocks of finished goods and customer service or stable employment have also been studied by operations research men. Some of the results have provided the basis for important decisions concerning management policies and procedures.

Production engineering also presents problems that have not been recognized as such either by businessmen or by engineers. Some problems involve complex variations and interactions that demand the assembly and calculation of huge volumes of data. Such problems had to be avoided so long as there was no adequate means of handling these essential facts and figures. However, new developments in mathematics, statistics, and computing devices are enabling operations researchers to solve an ever-larger number of increasingly complex problems.

The differences between the operations research scientist and the production engineer are great and so are their approaches to problems of production. The production engineer must solve problems in a set of conditions restricted to factors most of which are within his own sphere of activity. He does a good deal of long-range planning, of course, but this planning must be within limits set by time factors and budgets.

The operations research scientist, on the other hand, wants to study problems in their entirety without limitations of scope, time, or expense. He has learned the advantages of group research, and he must be permitted to secure consultative assistance from experts in other branches of science. He is overwhelmed neither by the complexity of problems nor by the task of feeding vast quantities of data into modern computers. His training has given him exceptional skills in developing hypotheses, and he knows how to obtain evidence on which to accept or reject them.

Production engineers must get things done. Operations research scientists are concerned with the broad contemplation of total situations so that optimal decisions can be based upon their findings. Some production engineers will acquire techniques of operations research. Whether they will ever have the time and freedom to apply them is doubtful.

Engineers have knowledge and skills needed in the work of operations research. The application of applied statistics to engineering and research problems is almost parallel to the application of operations research to production engineering problems. Teams of statisticians and engineers have solved problems that neither could have solved alone.

SUMMARY

Automation is the operation of individual automatic machines, groups of automatic machines integrated by transfer mechanisms, and completely automatic factories. Individual automatic machines can be highly adaptable and used to perform many different operations on many different products. Groups of automatic machines linked

together by transfer devices are generally designed for a single purpose and cannot be used for any other. Completely automatic processes are usually designed to produce a specific product, but they can
be modified to produce variants of it.

The most important advance in automation in recent years has been
the introduction of closed-loop, low-energy electronic circuits that can
sense what is happening in processes and can feed this information
back to control units which direct the making of adjustments. Processes are therefore able to detect and correct their own errors.

Automatic handling of information has become an important factor
in everyday business operations. One type of automatic system can
make decisions related to sales forecasting and production planning.
Systems of the memory type are used for the storage of information,
such as inventory records, that is needed for reference.

Systems that handle production and information automatically reduce accidental and systematic errors to minimums and therefore are
both faster and more accurate than those dependent upon manual
and mental skills and efforts.

Automation requires better managers than other methods do, but
information readily and reliably available helps these managers make
good decisions. Production engineers will have new and important
roles to play as automation advances. Both managers and production
engineers will have many new lessons to learn. Operations research
will play an important part in determining optimal automatic production situations. Production engineers will work in close cooperation
with operations research scientists to solve the broad problems associated with automation.

QUESTIONS TO CHECK COMPREHENSION

1. Describe an old form of automation not discussed in this book.

2. Many machines are called automatic. Are they fully so? Can the
degree of automation be increased?

3. Describe the principles of automatic transfer.

4. As automatic features are added, do machines generally retain their
flexibility to perform many different operations?

5. Explain feedback control.

6. Is it possible to design fully automatic processes that will correct
their own errors?

7. Can systems for automatic handling of information be used to forecast sales and schedule production?

8. What factors tend to make automatic systems more accurate than those operated by people?

9. What effects will automation have on industrial organizations?

10. How can operations research be used to determine optimal solutions to automatic production problems?

PROBLEMS

1. Describe a closed-loop or feedback process that operates in most modern homes.

2. Assume that you are to design the equipment for an automatic process to produce household, screw-in, electrical fuses in 5, 10, 15, 20, 25, and 30 amperages. The fuse wire or strip shall be alloyed as steps in the process and extruded in one size. Fusion points for the various amperages shall be produced by small cutting dies that neck-in or reduce the strip to special widths in sections ¼ inch long in the middle of each fusible unit. This necking shall be controlled by feedback circuits that not only permit changing from one width or amperage to another but control the fusing points within limits of $-0.1 + 0.0$ amperes. The face plates, flash barriers, contact sleeves, and contact points may be of your own design. The maker's name and the amperage designation may be hot-branded on the units or made otherwise if you prefer. Automatic feedback testing and controlling devices to check for fuse points and open and short circuits shall be included in the equipment. Prepare a rough schematic drawing and a process description.

DISCUSSION CASE

For twenty years George Martin had manufactured concrete building blocks and had sold cement, sand, and gravel. Work was strenuous, but profits from the business provided a good living and permitted his two sons to attend college.

Martin's production control system was extremely simple. Two areas in the factory yard were staked out for storage of blocks. When these areas were filled with blocks stacked ten high they each contained a normal supply for one week. When both areas were full of blocks, production was halted. When one area was empty, production was resumed. Thus without any reference to records Martin maintained an upper stock limit of two and a lower stock limit of one week's normal supply.

One son, Harold, studied medicine and therefore lost interest in his father's business. The other son, William, studied engineering and then joined his father. Soon he began to try out means of introducing automation into what had been a series of operations that were largely manual. After several attempts he designed and constructed new machinery that handled and mixed all raw materials and produced completed concrete blocks. All operations were automatic except the trucking of incoming materials and of outgoing blocks.

The operation functioned best on a 24-hour basis producing 14,000 blocks per day. An unusually large housing development nearby required blocks for about 20 foundations per day over a period of several months. This permitted efficient operation and provided excellent profits. When the project was completed, other building in the community justified only one 8-hour shift operation per day. Even this, however, permited a satisfactory profit.

William Martin undertook to keep the automatic equipment running full time by selling blocks to builders in other communities. This required the purchase of additional truck tractors and trailers because hauls were much longer than they had been to the local housing development. One trailer had to stand before the machine at all times to receive blocks as they were produced; other trailers and truck tractors were on the road with loads. This meant that more transportation equipment was needed, while profit per block diminished as the length of hauls increased. After a few months, William found that these hauls were consuming all the profits automatic machinery produced.

George Martin and his son are meeting to decide how profits can be restored and you have been invited to attend this meeting. List the causes of present difficulties and recommend the course of action to be taken. Support your recommendations with costs, selling prices, weights, transportation costs per ton mile, and some notion of the estimated cost to dismantle the automatic facility and re-erect it in another community where there is a larger volume of building.

6
Factory Planning

After the eight steps of manufacturing planning have been completed, and if the project is economically sound, consideration will be given to factory facilities for production. This phase is generally termed factory planning. Although the arrangement of equipment in the factory buildings is sometimes considered as part of manufacturing planning, it will be treated as a part of factory planning in this book, because the types of buildings and their configurations depend largely upon the arrangement of equipment in them. In most new plants or additions, the arrangement of equipment is worked out first, after which a structure is designed to house it. In plants already constructed, space is sought that will not modify the ideal arrangement too greatly. The general sequence in factory planning is:

1. Determining optimal size of factories.
2. Geographical studies to determine the best plant location.
3. Preparing equipment layout or arrangement.
4. Determining the type of structure required.
5. Determining the service facilities.
6. Scheduling construction.
7. Scheduling equipment installation.

A. OPTIMAL SIZE OF FACTORIES

Even while companies are small, their officers should find out how large operations can grow before it becomes desirable to divide the plant into more effectively manageable subdivisions. As companies become large, this problem of physical and organizational division of operations and factory facilities becomes urgent and continuous.

Insight into the magnitude of this type of planning can be gained by a study of a highly enlightened and successful company. On its fiftieth anniversary in 1951 the American Can Company prepared a composite picture of all its factories, which it called "Canco City," or its "Golden Anniversary Town." Reproduced here as Figure 17, this picture shows ninety-eight Canco factories, machine shops, and other properties scattered across the continental United States and Canada, and in Hawaii.

If these ninety-eight factories could be brought together, or if they had been allowed to grow up in one location, they would cover 820 acres. Spread out as they are, the factories contribute to the economic health and general welfare of almost a hundred communities. These scattered plants also permit more than 35,000 employees and their families to achieve economies, comforts, and social satisfactions that would not be possible in a metropolis or in one "single industry" city.

What, then, is the optimal size of a factory? It varies from industry to industry, from one company to another, and in different areas. Many social as well as economic and engineering factors must be weighed before the correct answer can be reached—and it will be correct only for one specific situation. Still, some general rules can be laid down to guide managers as they consider this industrial problem.

The first duty of any company is to meet the needs and demands of its customers. Another is to act as a good, responsible citizen of communities in which its factories are located. On the first score the American Can Company gives such excellent service that many customers need not carry large stocks of containers, yet can be fully confident of having what they want when they need it. The other obligation is met in two ways. In one, the company acts as a good and reliable employer that pays its proper share of taxes and helps in community planning. In the other, it helps maintain but never dominates employment. This policy eliminates the threat of disaster if production should cease for any reason. It also allows satisfactions of work choice that do not exist in communities where only one company operates.

These factors are somewhat uncertain, though vitally important. Economic elements are easier to calculate. Transportation costs weighed against burden costs provide most of the facts that are needed, but weight must also be given to increases in operating effectiveness that may result from subdivision. They can generally be predicted by inferences drawn from similar operations that have shown increased effectiveness after subdivision or decentralization.

Fig. 17. Canco City. (Courtesy American Can Co.)

B. PLANT LOCATION

If an existing facility is to be expanded, additions are simply made to present structures. With the current trend toward decentralization, many companies prefer to expand by constructing new plants at strategic locations throughout the country. The primary reasons for this are savings in transportation costs, quicker customer service, and the desire to keep centralized operations from becoming too large, unwieldly, and complex. It is also better for a community to be dependent upon a number of diversified industries than upon a single large one. Decentralized plants belonging to several corporations meet this requirement.

The general location may be selected on the basis of market centers. Some companies that have started operations near the New York market next select Chicago, then possibly the West Coast, and possibly the South later. Distance from supplies of raw material is also important in selecting a general location.

Final choice of a community and site depends upon several factors. Industrial zoning regulations must be considered. Water supply is of prime significance, especially when process water is to be used or much air conditioning is contemplated. Metropolitan New York City and the belt along the main line of the Pennsylvania Railroad to Trenton, New Jersey, form an example of a highly industrialized region whose water supply is no longer adequate. Many plants cannot get water for expansion, yet their operations in the region have been frozen by expensive factory buildings. Drainage must also be considered. Process wastes must have outlets, and these outlets must not be threatened by future litigation over pollution.

Railroad and highway facilities are of primary importance, as is the need for sidings to buildings. If much of the production is for export, a tidewater location is required. The cost of land, of local electric power and gas service, the availability of fire protection, the local taxes, and neighboring industries also require study. Test borings of the subsoil and the expense of grading are additional considerations.

People, their skills, attitudes, and well-being must be taken into consideration. If one community has many unions competing for membership, with continual jurisdictional disputes, it is wise to choose another in which union relations are constructive. There should be good housing, transportation, schools, and recreational facilities, for without them skilled and intelligent workers will not be attracted or will not remain. Since the company must become a part of the community, it should carefully study the attitude of the people of the community toward industry and the type of industrial activity that it has accepted. Industry of a very different type may meet with opposition.

In the United States the factors to be considered in determining best plant location are essentially those just discussed. In Europe the formation of two powerful trade confederations has necessitated study of complex additional factors in deciding where to locate plants and relocate operations for optimal results. With France, Germany, Italy, and the three Benelux countries already joined in the European Common Market, and with Britain, Scandinavia, Austria, Portugal, and Switzerland soon to join in the seven-nation Free Trade Area, previous methods for determining economic location of operations no longer yield valid results. Indeed, as this book is being written, electronic data processing centers in Europe are working full time, and most modern decision-making techniques are being applied, to reshuffle manufacturing operations.

In the past, European companies had to manufacture most of their products in each country because of import duties and quotas. These companies can now plan for high production of one product or a family of products in one of the countries in a trade federated area and ship to all countries in the area. A large electrical company like Phillips, for example, can now think about manufacturing lighting equipment in France to serve all countries in the Common Market. Thus television and radio equipment may be made in Germany, semiconductors in Italy, and other products in the Netherlands and Belgium. This can be done by transferring operations among factories that already exist. Such reshuffling is not as simple as it sounds, however, because all other normally considered factors such as transportation and competition must be included in the calculations. Careful study also must avoid dislocations to people, their employment, and their economic welfare when operations are removed from a community.

Similar determinations will be required for the Free Trade Area. Perhaps another even more difficult decision-making matrix [1] confronts companies operating in Europe:

[1] A decision-making matrix is a systematic array of choices and variables to which probabilities can be applied to give numerical values.

Variable / Choice	European trade confederations unite	European trade confederations do not unite
Operate in the Netherlands	One operation adequate for both markets	No operation to serve Free Trade Area
Operate in the Netherlands and in Britain	One superfluous operation	Both market areas adequately covered

The foregoing discussion might lead to the belief that the United States manufacturer has simpler problems in plant and operation location than his European counterpart. This is true in stateside operations, but many United States companies also have European operations and are probably feeding just as many decision-making data to their electronic wizards as are Europeans. The game is an exciting one and the stakes are high.

C. ARRANGEMENT OF EQUIPMENT

Before any plans for the new structure are begun, a detailed layout of production equipment should be made. Some companies operate with a class-of-work arrangement, in which all machines that perform the same class of work are grouped together. As an example, all drilling machines are grouped together in a drilling department that is supervised by an expert in drilling techniques. All milling machines are similarly grouped and supervised, as are those for welding, grinding, and so on.

Although the class-of-work arrangement generally permits full utilization of equipment, it makes production planning and control more difficult, since work must be routed back and forth among the machines. This type of operation is often referred to as process control, but the name class-of-work is more descriptive. Difficulties of planning and control are magnified when class-of-work operation is con-

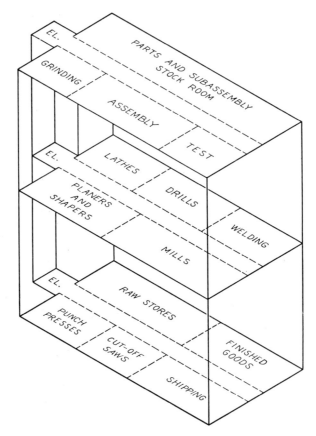

Fig. 18. Isometric sketch of a multistoried class-of-work equipment layout.

ducted in multistoried buildings. They are further increased and complicated in multistoried, multibuilding operations. Figure 18 shows a typical class-of-work machine shop in a three-storied building, in contrast to the single-storied layout of Figure 19. It is obvious that the later is simpler both to plan and to control.

The class-of-work arrangement requires that an adequate supply of materials or parts be ready for each operator. It also means that a supply of processed parts piles up after each operation, waiting for a trucker to take it to the next machine. These supplies are multiplied by every operation and machine, producing a bulk of unprocessed and partly processed material termed the work-in-process inventory. Although sometimes overlooked or accepted as evidence that "things are

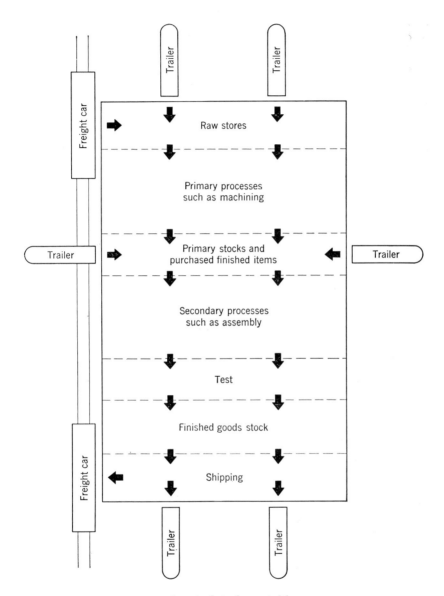

Fig. 19. A typical single-storied layout.

moving along," this inventory is a source of expense that may dwarf the obvious cost of trucking parts from machine to machine.

This was true in one particular plant organized on a class-of-work basis in eight multistoried buildings. All operations were performed on component parts, subassemblies, and assemblies of three products. Trucking costs appeared to be enormous, yet they actually amounted to $32,000 per year. Though substantial, they did not justify a major plant reorganization involving some 1,200 machine tools.

Work-in-process was another story. On the original class-of-work arrangement, those machine tools required an inventory of $10,300,000, divided as follows:

Raw materials	$ 1,500,000
Work-in-process	7,500,000
Finished goods	1,300,000
	$10,300,000

To reduce this inventory, operations were consolidated in three interconnected, multistoried buildings. Production of the three products was decentralized, and each was given an equipment layout arranged for better, more continuous work flow. At the same time, stocks of finished goods were increased to provide better customer service. Once this new plan got into operation, inventories dropped $4,500,000, to:

Raw materials	$1,500,000
Work-in-process	2,500,000
Finished goods	1,800,000
	$5,800,000

In this reorganization, improved work flow did save several thousand dollars in trucking costs. This amount was trifling, however, beside the interest on $4,500,000 that had been needlessly invested in inventories. Moreover, the production-control department spent much less time keeping track of work-in-process whose value—and volume—had shrunk from $7,500,000 to one-third of that amount. This example typifies the importance of knowing that work-in-process inventories add to the cost of running a business without adding any value to the product.

Class-of-work organization is seldom used in high-production operations or in mass production. These employ progressive production, in which materials move continuously through a series of machine operations and emerge as completed products. This eliminates stocks of unprocessed and processed materials at each machine and keeps costly work-in-process at a minimum.

Progressive production involves product control rather than the process control of class-of-work production. Another machine-tool example: the supervisor is an expert on product rather than process, and gives attention to drilling, milling, profiling, or any other operation required in the manufacture of a product. Progressive production requires large capital investments by men who have the courage and vision to seek rewards through low selling prices and volume that will keep their facilities occupied.

Figure 20 shows a progressive production arrangement in an automobile assembly plant. It is obvious that such production can be planned and controlled more easily than class-of-work production. Instead of recording and controlling many piles of semicompleted parts at many decentralized machines as in class-of-work production, there is a supply of material at the first operation in the progressive production arrangement, and a stock of finished parts or products after the final operation. The one piece in each work station remains constant and need not be considered for purposes of production control.

Progressive production can be adapted to many plants that now use only class-of-work production. Suppose, for example, that such a plant has one high-production item among several that it manufactures. Analysis shows that this item can keep 3 drills, 1 milling machine, and 1 grinder occupied most of the time. These machines, therefore, are moved out of the class-of-work arrangement and are placed next to each other. Upon completing his operation, each worker can then lay the piece on the bed of the next machine or on a small rack between it and his own. The result is simplified control, reduced inventory, and elimination of trucking.

The analysis that must precede such a change utilizes the process flow-chart developed by Frank B. and Dr. Lillian M. Gilbreth [1] and used extensively by A. H. Mogensen.[2] The Gilbreths gave us the scientific foundation for production planning. Time study was a rough measure of what was being done. Then the laws of motion,

[1] Frank B. Gilbreth, *Motion Study*, D. Van Nostrand Co., New York, 1911.
Frank B. Gilbreth and Lillian M. Gilbreth, *Applied Motion Study*, Sturgis & Walton Co., New York, 1917.
[2] A. H. Mogensen's Work Simplification conferences, Lake Placid, New York, and Sea Island, Georgia.

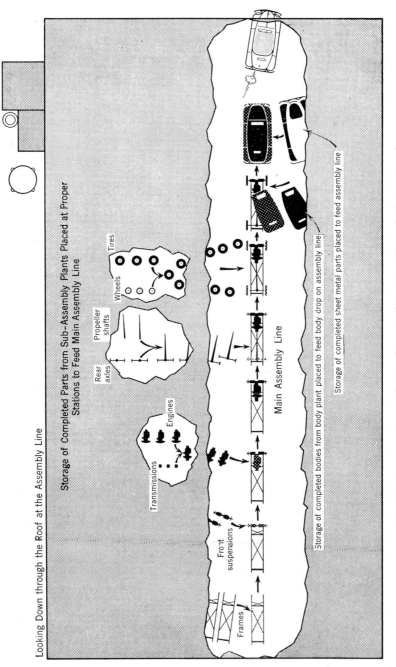

Fig. 20. A progressive production layout. (Courtesy General Motors Corp.)

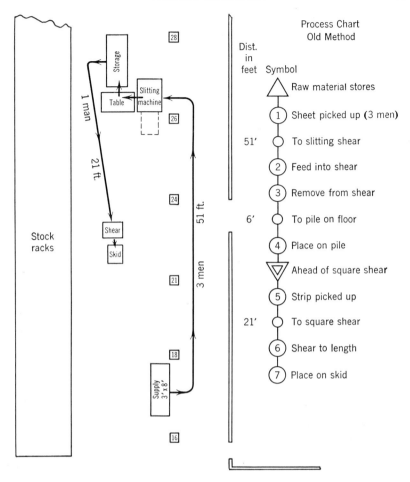

Fig. 21. Process flow-chart and card racks—old method.

micromotion analysis, and process flow analysis developed by the Gilbreths provided a systematic graphic means of study that disclosed undreamed of manufacturing capabilities. Without the laws and analytical methods of the Gilbreths it is doubtful that we would now have Methods-Time Measurement for manufacturing planning and effective process flow so essentially needed in factory planning.

The process flow-chart in Figure 21 shows an analysis of work movements in the cutting of sheet metal for card racks in a typical class-of-work arrangement. Only the machines used on this work are shown. The process flow-chart in Figure 22 shows the improved

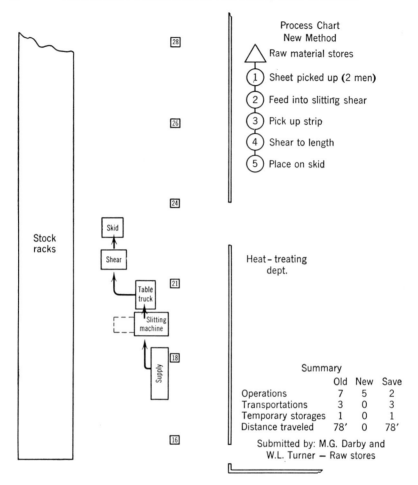

Fig. 22. Process flow-chart and card racks—new method.

work flow in which 2 operations, 3 transportations, 1 temporary storage, and 78 feet of travel were saved.

Figure 23 shows a process flow-chart of receiving and inspecting a typical part. Here the equipment has already been arranged. This does not mean that everything is frozen and no improvement can be made. The summary at the top of the chart shows that 5 moves, 5 storages, and 74 feet of travel were eliminated by a simple rearrangement of 1 workplace. Two inspections were also combined. In addition to man-hour savings, the process interval was shortened, which means that parts are more quickly available for production schedules.

Figure 24 shows the plan of the stockroom and the old and new paths of flow. It is obvious that the new method is simpler and better. Without process flow-chart studies, such potential improvements are not obvious. These simple examples indicate the validity of Mogensen's statement that he has never seen a job that could not be improved after process flow-chart analysis.

After the process flow-chart analysis has been completed, the engineer is ready to plan the arrangement of machines. For this he may use scale templates cut from cardboard, placed on a board of plywood or masonite covered with paper. If the new layout is being prepared for use in a building already constructed, a floor plan of the structure is placed on the board. Following the sequences developed with the process flow-charts, the templates are moved around on the board until the machines are properly spaced in relation to each other, and aisles and testing stations are provided. When a satisfactory arrangement is achieved, the templates are stapled fast to the board. The plan then is tested by running colored threads representing the various products to be processed from one machine to the next in the order of the operation. An examination of the threading will generally indicate some need for modifications.

The boards with the templates in position are often photostated and used in place of blueprints for rearrangement of the equipment. Figure 25 shows a typical template layout of equipment.

Some companies consider the arrangement of equipment of such importance that they build three-dimensional scale models. When these models have been arranged, such companies also erect a scale model building around them so that those who have difficulty visualizing orthographic blueprints can fully understand the proposed arrangement. Typical model layouts are shown in Figures 26 and 27.

D. THE TYPE OF STRUCTURE

The nature of the work to be performed goes far to determine the type of structure. Heavy equipment requires a single-storied building with no basement but strong floors and footings. Processing of liquids calls for a multistoried structure or a single-storied building with a basement. If large pieces are to be processed, high and wide truss spans will be needed and craneways may be required. If explosive products are to be manufactured, small structures placed some

PROCESS CHART

SUBJECT CHARTED: PARKER CROSSES ST. TEE
OPERATION: RECEIVING
CHARTED BY: JOHN SMITH
CHART NO.: 1　SHEET NO.: 1
DATE
PLANT
DEPT.: RECEIVING

CAN I ELIMINATE?
CAN I COMBINE?
CAN I CHANGE SEQUENCE?
CAN I SIMPLIFY?

SUMMARY

Method	Pres.	Prop.	Saving
No. of Operations	2	2	0
No. of Moves	11	6	5
No. of Storages	9	4	5
No. of Inspections	2	1	1
Man Hours	9.00	6.92	2.08
Distance Traveled	181	107	74
P & L	Man		Mech.
Total COST			

PRESENT METHOD

Dist. In Feet	Time In Min.	DESCRIPTION OF PRESENT METHOD
	10	On Motor Truck at Door
4'		Placed on Chute
20'	10	Slid Down Chute—Gravity
20'	20	Slid to Storage and Stacked Up (1 Crate at a Time)
		Waiting for Uncrating of Glass
3'		Place on Floor
	5	Removing Lid of Crate
		and Removing Packing List
3'		Loaded on Truck—(2 Men)
30'	5	To Receiving Bench—(2 Men)
		At Bench—Waiting for Unloading
	10	Boxes Placed on Bench—(2 Men)
3'		Cartons Removed From Box and Opened.
	15	Tees Unwrapped and Placed on Bench.

PROPOSED METHOD

Dist. In Feet	Time In Min.	DESCRIPTION OF PROPOSED METHOD
	10	On Motor Truck at Door
4'		Placed on Chute
20'		Slid Down Chute —Gravity
3'		Place on Hand Truck
20'		Move to Uncrating Area
	5	Remove Lid of Crate
30'	5	Move to Inspection Area by Truck
	5	At Bench Waiting for Unload
	20	Carton Removed From Box and
		Opened, Tees Unwrapped and Placed
		on Bench. Counted. Checked Off
		List, Gauged, and Stamped. Parts
		Replaced in Carton and Carton
		Replaced in Box.

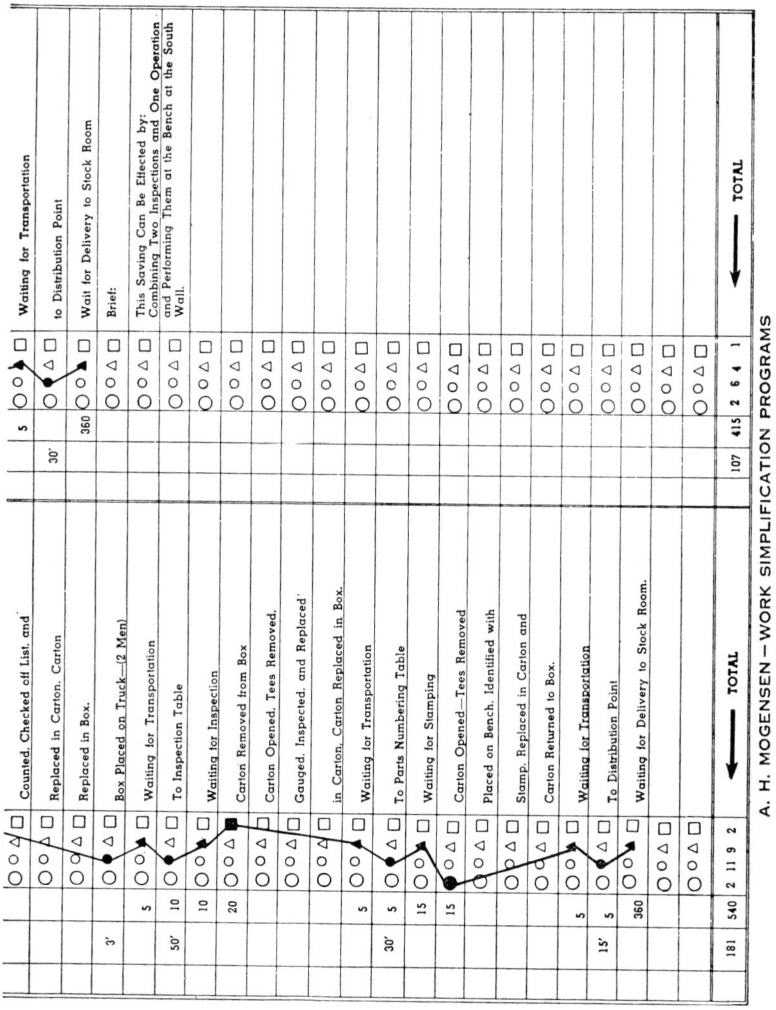

Waiting for Transportation
to Distribution Point
Wait for Delivery to Stock Room
Brief:
This Saving Can Be Effected by: Combining Two Inspections and One Operation and Performing Them at the Bench at the South Wall.

TOTAL

Counted. Checked off List, and
Replaced in Carton. Carton
Replaced in Box.
Box Placed on Truck—(2 Men)
Waiting for Transportation
To Inspection Table
Waiting for Inspection
Carton Removed from Box
Carton Opened. Tees Removed.
Gauged. Inspected, and Replaced in Carton, Carton Replaced in Box.
Waiting for Transportation
To Parts Numbering Table
Waiting for Stamping
Carton Opened—Tees Removed
Placed on Bench. Identified with Stamp. Replaced in Carton and
Carton Returned to Box.
Waiting for Transportation
To Distribution Point
Waiting for Delivery to Stock Room.

TOTAL

A. H. MOGENSEN – WORK SIMPLIFICATION PROGRAMS

Fig. 23. Process flow-chart of Parker Tee.

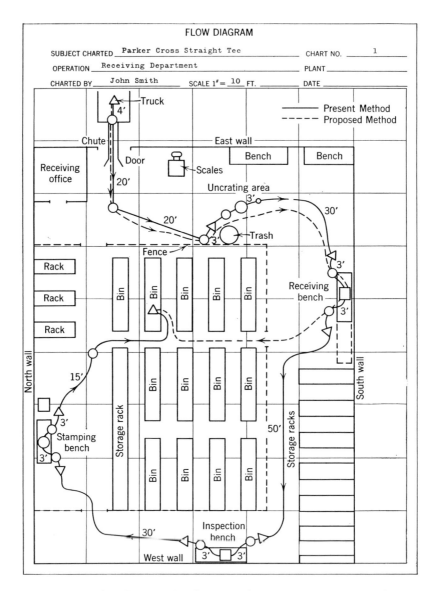

Fig. 24. Flow diagram of Parker Tee. (Courtesy A. H. Mogensen.)

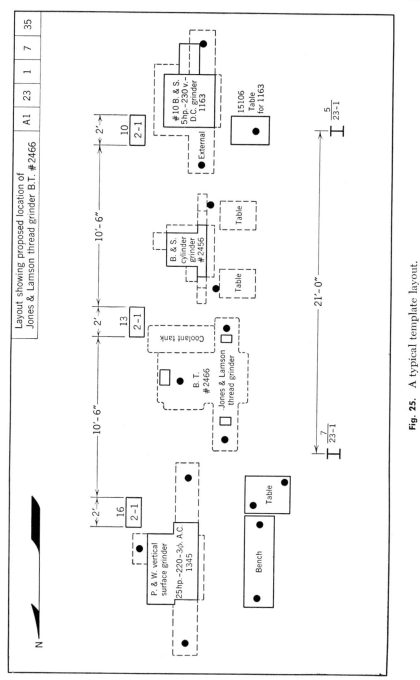

Fig. 25. A typical template layout.

Fig. 26.   Typical model of a proposed manufacturing facility.

distance apart will reduce the danger of loss and injury from explosions.

For many years, factories were purely utilitarian buildings designed to provide essential space at minimum cost, without regard for architectural beauty or pleasing interiors. Since 1930, however, management has revised its thinking in this field. In the words of Robert W. Johnson, management has learned that factories can be beautiful—and has found that beauty pays. As a result, a growing number of corporations have erected plants that are modern in design, beautiful in appearance, and efficient in their provision of space. That such buildings arouse pride and dignity among those who work in them is an oft-proved fact. This, in turn, promotes good industrial relationships and improves the quality of products.

E. SERVICE FACILITIES

Like factory design, service facilities have undergone a great change since the 1920's. They once were planned to meet only the most essential human needs as expressed in the factory codes of various and often backward states: so many toilets for a specified number of employees; no lunch rooms or even tables; if wash-up facilities existed, they were merely spigots adjoining latrines; clothes hooks were crowded into dark corners or replaced by long-handled crosstrees on which clothing was hung from rafters. The factory was a place for work, and human comforts or conveniences received minimal attention.

Today all this is changed. Modern factories contain spacious and immaculate toilet facilities with sanitary terrazzo floors and tile side walls in attractive colors. There are ample sinks and shower baths. Locker rooms are clean, orderly, and comfortable. There are smoking lounges with easy chairs. Cafeterias are spotless, comfortable, and cheerful. The food is good, better for the price than the food served in many commercial restaurants, as is evidenced by the heavy deficits

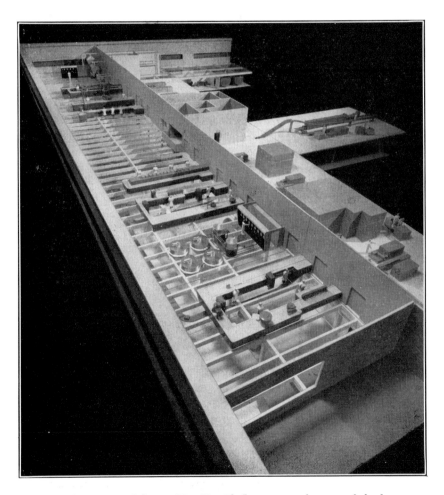

Fig. 27. The same model as in Fig. 26 with floor removed to reveal the basement arrangement.

Fig. 28. Ethicon Suture Laboratories. (Courtesy Johnson & Johnson.)

of most company-operated facilities. The landscaped grounds often are provided with picnic tables and courts for games, and there is parking space for the automobiles of employees.

All these services must be planned, as well as power, water, heat, process steam, and fire-protection necessities. (See Figure 28.)

F. SCHEDULING CONSTRUCTION

When several million dollars are invested in a new building, it is vitally important that it be completed as rapidly as possible so that it can begin to pay for its cost. Owner and contractor can cooperatively develop a schedule to insure prompt completion. Gantt charts are especially useful in such scheduling.[1]

G. EQUIPMENT INSTALLATION

If all equipment to be installed in a building is new, its arrival and installation also must be scheduled. Gantt charts will be useful in this, but supplementary devices are helpful. The author once had an interesting experience with an engineering company that had contracted to design and to subcontract the construction and installation of some highly complex equipment. Each subconstractor's work was

[1] Wallace Clark, *The Gantt Chart*, The Ronald Press Company, New York, 1922.

laid out on a Gantt chart. The engineering company handed the author fifty-six stamped postcards. Each listed a piece of equipment and the date it was due for delivery. If each piece arrived on time, this was indicated on the proper postcard, which then was mailed to the company's office. If equipment did not arrive on time, this fact also was indicated and the postcard was mailed. Actually, only two pieces of equipment were late, and the delay amounted to only two days. As soon as postcards arrived, the engineering company was able to prod the delinquent contractor, who thereupon made delivery.

If equipment is to be moved from an old factory to a new one, careful planning and scheduling are needed to prevent loss of production time and loss of time by employees. If the move will extend over several days, it generally is best to begin with equipment used in late stages of processing or production and progress toward earlier and earlier stages. In the meantime, some work-in-process can be trucked from the old location to the new one.

Each year new techniques are developed to eliminate guesswork from production engineering and strengthen its scientific foundation. As an example, until recently planners used approximations based on past performance in order to determine the number of receiving and shipping stations needed in a proposed factory. These approximations frequently gave satisfactory results. Today queuing models can be used to determine scientifically the required optimum number of these stations based upon input, output, service policy, and order of service.[1]

SUMMARY

As companies grow they should plan their factories for optimal size. Both social and economic factors must be considered when operations are to be subdivided among decentralized factories whose locations improve service to customers and whose smaller size makes them simpler to manage.

When the details of manufacturing planning have been completed, factory planning or the planning of the manufacturing facilities can begin. While the plant site is being selected, the equipment layout is established. This can be done with scale cardboard templates of

[1] Churchman, Ackoff, and Arnoff, *Introduction to Operations Research,* John Wiley and Sons, New York, 1957.

the various pieces of equipment or with three-dimensional scale models.

Frequently expansion is achieved by renting or purchasing existing structures. When this is done, the equipment layout generally is a compromise between the most effective layout and the one that can be accommodated by the structure. When new buildings are erected, however, their type and dimensions are virtually determined by the effective flow of materials through the various manufacturing processes.

If a class-of-work arrangement is to be used, large work-in-process inventories can be expected, and problems of scheduling and control will be complicated. If a continuous progressive manufacturing arrangement is employed, the problems of scheduling and control will be simplified, but planning must be more detailed than that required by the class-of-work arrangement.

Service facilities such as heating, power, wash rooms, toilets, and cafeterias are not to be slighted in factory planning. The scheduling of construction is important in order that occupancy can begin on a predetermined date and income from expanded production can begin to pay off the cost of the new facility. A schedule for equipment installation is important for the same reasons. Gantt charts can be used to schedule both construction and installation.

QUESTIONS TO CHECK COMPREHENSION

1. A company is organized to manufacture pigments for paints. Most of its raw materials will come from abroad, but some will be brought by Atlantic coastal shipping. Where should this company locate its factory?

2. Differentiate between class-of-work operation (process control) and progressive manufacture (product control).

3. What element of cost is generally high with class-of-work manufacture in multistoried, multibuilding operation? Why?

4. Process flow-charts and template layouts have been prepared for a proposed new plant. The principal executives find it hard to visualize the effectiveness of the arrangement from these two-dimensional exhibits. What technique can be used to illustrate further what is proposed?

5. Explain some of the factors that determine the type of structure required for the manufacture of high-production, low-cost items.

6. Is there a growing tendency to try to make factory buildings and their service facilities attractive? Can this pay off? How?

7. A new manufacturing facility has been planned. It will save $500,000 per year because its equipment and its arrangement will be more productive than those of an obsolete plant now in use. The new one will cost $2,000,000, borrowed at 3 per cent interest. How much will be lost if construction requires 2 years instead of 6 months? How will this affect the return on invested capital?

8. Existing equipment is to be moved from an old location to a new one. What type of chart or graphic arrangement can be used to avoid bad timing that will dislocate production and employment?

9. A manufacturing company plans to construct a factory and operate it in a certain community. Should this receive as much careful consideration as that which is necessary when two people plan to marry?

10. You are offered two positions. One requires the planning and scheduling of production in a class-of-work equipment arrangement. The other requires the planning and scheduling of production in a continuous, progressive arrangement of equipment. Which position will you choose if all other considerations are equal? Give the reasons for your choice.

11. One community has good schools, a good theater, a golf course, and adequate housing. Another has only a trailer camp site. All other considerations are equal. If you were given the responsibility for making the selection of one of these communities for a factory, which one would you choose?

12. Are process flow-charts useful in planning equipment arrangements?

13. A company plans to produce metal stampings using heavy punch-press equipment. One property with a number of multistoried buildings, another with one frame four-storied building, and a third with a single-storied building are available for rental. Which should be investigated first?

PROBLEMS

1. Assume that you are to select a location in Germany for a factory that will manufacture soap. How would you assemble facts on which to base your decision?

2. Operation of your factory has become too complex. You wish to support your request that operations be divided between two separate factories. Present your arguments in quantitative form as much as possible and add a discussion of the social and psychological factors that cannot be put into figures. If you can, select a company with which you are familiar or select one that is described in current technical literature.

DISCUSSION CASE

In 1946 the Ketcher Chemical Company, operating a plant in Illinois, had reached the limit of its plant and equipment capacity. Since many of its raw materials were imported, a location on the Atlantic seaboard was indicated. Also, a substantial part of the company's market was in the eastern states.

Some of its processes consisted of reflux condensations releasing hydrogen sulfide to the atmosphere, and filtrations requiring considerable water to wash out impurities. The wash water had an objectionable odor and color.

The company selected and purchased property beside a river flowing into the Atlantic Ocean. The plant site was ideal in that it was close to a state highway and close enough to the main line of a railroad for a rail siding. The water supply came from a local reservoir that was independent of the city water supply.

No discussions were held with the municipal officials except to obtain a building permit. The state factory inspection department approved the plans of the new factory.

Operations were started in the new plant late in 1947, several key operators being brought east as the nucleus of a new force. These men had belonged to an independent union in the Illinois plant. The mechanics and maintenance men who were hired locally belonged to a national trade union. The remainder of the new employees, also hired locally, did not belong to any union.

After a few weeks' operation there was a jurisdictional dispute between the maintenance men and the operators who had come from Illinois. At the midwestern plant, operators had occasionally repaired and adjusted equipment. This had been permitted by the independent union because maintenance men often worked a shift or two when operators were absent. The local mechanics claimed that their work was being taken away from them. They walked off the job, taking the non-union operators with them.

Some process intervals were 56 hours. The operators who had been brought from the Midwest remained on the job until all processed material was run to completion.

After a month's inactivity all differences were settled by agreement that the work of the mechanics would not be done by the operators. A few weeks later a condenser went out of control because the operator in attendance did not immediately repair a jammed valve. The odor of hydrogen sulfide caused the inhabitants for miles around to become nauseated.

Early in 1948 most of the nearby dwellings painted with white lead began to turn gray. Many of the owners brought suit against the Ketcher Company and recovered damages, on the ground that hydrogen sulfide had damaged their paint.

Citizens of the community had had only a mild interest in the walkout, but when paint discoloration was added to the epidemic of nausea they complained about the ill-smelling, colored water being discharged into the river. An order was issued restraining the company from dumping in the river unless the wash water was first treated. The order allowed six months for the installation of the water-treatment plant. The order was appealed.

Late in 1949 the local water supply, as well as the city water supply, became inadequate, and the company was forced to take river water and treat it before use. A meeting of the board of directors was called to decide what should be done about these problems. Assume that you took part in this meeting. List the causes for what is wrong and recommend remedial action.

7

Specialization, Standardization, and Simplification

Industry does much costly but nonessential planning and controlling at the manufacturing level. Most of this can be avoided through integrative planning by the men in upper levels of management, where products can be seen in relation to the company's overall structure and growth, its objectives, and its potential for profits. The benefits of such planning can be realized, however, only if policy-making officials provide organization to deal with recurrent problems of specialization, diversification, standardization, and simplification.

Attention to *specialization* is needed to keep companies from making too many diverse products. Companies often add so many unrelated products to their lines that their enterprises become unmanageable and unprofitable. However, companies that give too little consideration to the addition of related products to their lines cannot hope for any great growth. The optimal degree of specialization is such an important factor in the welfare of a company that decisions to add or to discontinue products outside its present skills and facilities should be made by a management committee which includes men trained in the several disciplines of finance, manufacturing, engineering, sales, and research.

Attention to *standardization* does not imply that a company must make only one type or model of a commodity. A leading British advocate of standardization defines it as *"only meant to be an instrument to manufacture the maximum variety of products out of a minimum variety of components by means of a minimum variety of machines and tool."* [1] Standardization of raw materials and component parts is an important factor in reducing working capital requirements

[1] Edward G. Brisch, "Standardisation without Tears," *The Manager*, September, 1951.

for raw material and work-in-process stocks. Manufacturing costs are decreased when fewer standard components are produced in larger lot sizes. Planning and control complexities and costs are reduced when fewer standard components have to be produced. To obtain the benefits of standardization someone or some group within each company should be responsible for questioning the addition of any new raw material or component used in the manufacture of finished products.

Simplification as the term is used in this chapter means the simplification of types, sizes, colors, and other varieties of finished products to obtain the lowest manufacturing and distribution costs consistent with serving essential human wants and needs. It can be done within companies and it can be done within industries producing similar commodities. Industry committees can determine the types, sizes, and varieties of products that will effectively meet consumer requirements. Recommendations based upon these determinations can be accepted or rejected by individual companies. It is generally more profitable, however, to restrict varieties of products to those within simplification recommendations.

A. SPECIALIZATION

An important part of planning is the determination of the extent to which a company should specialize. If this consideration is neglected, an enterprise is likely to grow to unmanageable and unprofitable proportions. As a rather farfetched example, the small manufacturer of metal products would be unwise to start a steel mill simply because his major raw material is steel. If he were to operate a steel mill he might then extend his enterprise to include a coal mine to supply the major material used in making steel. The result of such expansion would probably be three enterprises, two of which are outside the scope of the original company. Instead of unwisely expanding for the sole purpose of controlling its primary material, the small metal products company will purchase steel from other companies that are large enough in the specialty of steel making to own mines and even railroads.

Less farfetched is the decision to be made by companies that manufacture refrigerators, washing machines, home workshops, and many other products requiring electric motors. Should such a company manufacture its own motors or purchase standard motors made by other companies specializing in the manufacture of electric motors?

The decision will, of course, be based on several factors. Cost is a primary consideration and so is quality. In some cases the company specializing in the manufacture of electric motors can deliver a superior product at a price equal to or less than the cost of manufacture in the equipment companies' factories. Field service and replacements are also factors to be considered.

One good reason for expansion away from specialization is a company's need to grow. It has but two choices in orderly planned growth. It can add new products to its present line of products, or it can perform more of the operations required on its present products by working back to the raw materials that are used in them. Another reason is the company's need to improve the quality of raw materials, parts, or assemblies used in the manufacture of finished products and thus have more of the manufacturing operations within its own control.

It is obviously unwise for a machinery company to make standard nuts, bolts, screws, lock washers, springs, and similar items that can be purchased more cheaply from others, but it is not so easy to decide whether or not to manufacture other items such as electric motors, compressors, pumps, and standard units made by specialists.

Good planning will, of course, keep companies from expanding beyond the framework of their specialty, manageability, and profitability. When the addition of new products is suggested, any company must ask itself whether or not these new products will fit into present facilities without diluting skills or unduly increasing the complexities of the business. Assume, for a simple example, that a company manufactures bar soap. The suggestion is made to manufacture soap flakes. This added product will not require too much new equipment or too many new skills. After a careful analysis this company may find it wise to add the new product. But the soap company that contemplates expanding into the television business will find the decision more difficult to make. It might more properly consider forming a new company to specialize in television.

Good long-term planning also makes provision for declining sales or reduced profits from a major product. Suppose, for example, that a company has made only paint, which once brought a proper profit. But increased competition and other factors have reduced these profits so greatly that they offer no satisfactory future. The managers therefore decide to withdraw gradually from the paint business and expand, also gradually, into another field. Officials thereupon list other products that can be made with some of their existing facilities and skills. Food processing may meet the requirements; so may the manufacture of polishes. Other products, such as plastics, may utilize too little that is old and need too much that is new and are quickly eliminated. Promising products are then re-examined in detail. The company at last selects the one that combines advantageous use of present facilities and skills with the best prospective profits and long-range stability.

As companies grow, add products, and expand manufacturing to include more and more of the operations required to convert raw materials into finished products, they often find profits declining and complexities of operation increasing. They must then consider specialization and the objectives of the enterprise. Development of an accurate cost system can generally discover the products that are contributing to losses. Even after unprofitable *products* have been dealt with, there may still be *operations* that reduce profits on other products. As an example, a company may have started as a foundry. During the passing years it has emerged as a machining and assembly company. Although much reduced in magnitude, foundry production is retained. Competitive prices from other companies specializing in foundry work may show that it will be cheaper to purchase castings than to make them. Production of castings should therefore be discontinued. The foundry equipment can be retained until the advantages of outside purchases are assured. Then consideration can be given to disposing of this equipment.

One company manufacturing consumer products also made its own packaging materials and did its own printing. Analysis of the profitability of its *operations* as well as its *products* showed that printing and box-making operations were almost unprofitable. The company thereupon bought boxes and printed matter from specialty companies in competition with its own production. When purchase prices were compared with the company's own manufacturing costs they showed the analysis to be correct. The same effort, space, and working capital devoted to the company's specialty could earn a greater profit. The company therefore disposed of its printing and box-making equipment.

These are but a few examples of the need for careful planning to insure maximum benefits from specialization.

B. STANDARDIZATION

Industrial progress has required the establishment of nationally accepted standards for such things as screw threads, fits, finishes, colors, and many other characteristics. In addition to these each company should standardize its own raw materials and component parts. Standardization of its methods and techniques are a part of a company's individuality.[1]

Creative ingenuity of the truly inventive mind turns to the novel apparatus, process, or product. It seldom concerns itself with conventional methods, components, or materials. Soon after new products and processes are accepted with great enthusiasm by top executives, the more practical manufacturing executive starts to consider modifying factors that will adapt the new creation to manufacturing techniques, materials, and standard components of proved effectiveness and value. Indeed, a most important step in the evolution of a new product or process should follow invention and should precede or should be accepted as an integral part of manufacturing planning. This step is *standardization*. If invention or research is followed by development, standardization should be included in development.

Many companies are so keenly aware of the advantages of raw-material standardization that they require a complete study of situations requiring the addition of any new raw material to their stock lists. Some companies even compute the added working capital requirements and costs of adding new raw-material items and compare them with any disadvantages that would result from the use of some other material currently stocked and used for other purposes.

Assume, for example, that a newly designed machine is accepted for production. The inventor thinks that a certain part would be subjected to considerable wear, and therefore specifies that it be made of SAE 65 phosphor bronze. This material is accepted by everyone until the standards committee or the purchasing department points out that the size of phosphor bronze needed for this part is not used for anything else made by the company. On the other hand, SAE 72 brass and other types of bronze in this size are presently used for other parts and are regularly carried in stock. Will free-machining SAE 72 brass be satisfactory for this part? If it will, material costs will be cut more than half, labor costs will be reduced, larger orders of brass may effect purchase savings, and no new item need be carried in stock. This, of course, will reduce the working capital required.

The inventor and his design engineers are consulted. After wear and machine performance are reconsidered a decision is reached in which functional quality characteristics are retained in the machine

---

[1] The following portions of this chapter have been adapted from E. H. Mac-Niece, *Industrial Specifications*, John Wiley and Sons, New York, 1953, Chapter Four.

design and the currently stocked material is substituted for SAE 65 phosphor bronze.

The standards committee must also give careful consideration to standardizing the many parts that are produced by a company. It is expensive to tool up for a newly designed nonstandard part. Some other part already being produced may serve as well. In addition to tool costs, added work-in-process inventories of the new part must be carried, requiring added working capital. Machine setup is also expensive. Another part will cut down the lot sizes produced in one run and increase setup time.

For an example of this, assume that a company produces many different mechanisms that include cast-iron side frames that form the bearing supports for and between which rolls operate. The rolls are of different lengths, but, in spite of this, designers produce a frame that can be used interchangeably on either side of the machine. It reduces the number of patterns needed and permits simplification of foundry operations. One group of milling and drilling equipment and machine setups can be used. And when a new machine is considered, the first question to be asked may well be, "Will our present existing side frame be suitable for it, even though the shaft bearing holes are drilled on different centers from those in the other machine?"

To obtain some notion of how extensively some companies standardize component parts, inquire about some automotive replacement part at a General Motors repair shop. If you ask him, the stockroom attendant will probably tell you that the part to which you refer is used on several different General Motors cars and in several different models or years. It may also be used in the cars of two or three other manufacturers. Cost improvements achieved by standardization and large production runs are one reason why automobiles cost less per pound than beefsteaks.

C. SIMPLIFICATION

Simplification in the variety and characteristics of finished products keeps manufacturing and distribution from becoming unmanageably complicated and makes lot sizes large enough to permit satisfactory profits. This is such an important economic consideration for both industry and the nation that a Commodity Standards Division was established in the U.S. Department of Commerce a number of years ago under the Honorable Herbert Hoover. The purpose of the division is the reduction of waste in manufacturing and distribution through the simplification of unnecessary varieties in nonstyle articles of commerce. Hoover showed keen insight into the importance of helping industry and commerce help themselves without any dictatorial pressure by federal agencies. Simplified Practice Recommendations are sensible nonbinding agreements democratically arrived at by cooperative action of American industrial and commercial companies.

Fabulous economies were effected by reducing the number of sizes, shapes, styles, and types of commodities. As one example, the study of folding paper boxes (used by department and specialty stores) revealed that 683 sizes were made, though 52 per cent of the annual consumption was concentrated in 9 sizes. Fourteen sizes would meet the other needs, with the result that sizes were cut from 683 to 23, a reduction of 96.5 per cent.

Standardizations were agreed upon by the industries affected and were made public in the form of Simplified Practice Recommendations. These are generally reviewed every three years to permit the dynamics of changed conditions and improved products and processes to be realized. Companies within each industry are not forced to comply with the Simplified Practice Recommendations, but most of them do comply because of the economic advantages and because nonstandard items are not always easily disposed of in the open market.

Inevitably, since standardization is not compulsory, some companies decide that they want to obtain a commodity having closer tolerances or higher quality characteristics than those listed in the Simplified Practice Recommendations. Suppliers will, of course, resist creating nonstandard quality characteristics unless the purchaser wants large quantities of the material and the economics of the proposition are sound.

Resistance crumbles when one or more suppliers may find a proposition so attractive, modifications to production processes so inexpensive, and their quality-control assurance already so good that they elect to make the changes and so gain a new market. When Simplified Practice Recommendations are next reviewed, the companies in a particular industry or at least all of the progressive ones will probably wish to drop the old broader commodity requirements and adopt the new narrower limits. Progress is thus cooperatively achieved.

The benefits of simplified practices are many and may be grouped as follows:

To the Producer and Manufacturer

1. Large amounts of capital are not tied up in slow-moving stocks of great variety.

2. Economical manufacture due to simplified inspection requirements, longer runs with fewer changes, a reduction of idle equipment, less stock to handle, and reduced clerical overhead.

3. Continuous employment instead of temporary or seasonal employment when this or that size or model was needed.

4. Large units of production and less special machinery.

5. Prompt delivery.

6. Reduction of errors in shipment.

7. Less obsolescence of materials and machinery.

To the Jobber, Wholesaler, and Retailer

1. Increased turnover.

2. Elimination of slow-moving stock.

3. Staple lines that are easy to buy and quick to sell.

4. Concentration of sales efforts on relatively fewer items.

5. Decreased capital invested in stocks and repair parts on hand.

6. Reduction in amount of storage space required.

7. Decreased overhead, handling charges, and clerical work.

To the Consumer

1. Better values than otherwise possible.

2. Better service in delivery and repairs.

3. Better quality of product.

When new products are developed the standards committee can use many contrivances to assure that consumers will have a reasonable selection from which to choose. Preferred numbers are helpful in determining a series of dimensions, areas, volumes, temperatures, flow units, current, amperages, voltages, speeds, horsepower, and many other characteristics. Every standards engineer and committee should have a copy of the ASA booklet entitled "Preferred Numbers Z17.1," 1931. (See Figure 29.)

To learn how a preferred series of numbers can be used, assume that a company is organized to manufacture ribbons. It elects to enter the broad-ribbon field, supplying widths from 1″ to 4″. If widths increasing in $\frac{1}{8}″$ increments between these two dimensions were adopted this company would manufacture and stock 24 different widths. It might also require 24 sets of equipment, each of which would be utilized only part of the time. The final result could be failure of the company.

Instead of establishing widths in an even arithmetic progression, the company conservatively starts manufacturing 4 widths selected from the 5-series of basic preferred numbers, as shown in Figure 29, which are in approximately 60 per cent steps. The 4 widths so

TABLE 2

Basic Preferred Numbers—Fractional Series (⅛ to 40)

⅛ to 1

5-Series (60% Steps)	10-Series (25% Steps)	20-Series (12% Steps)	40-Series (6% Steps)
	⅛	⅛	
		9/64	
5/32	5/32	5/32	
		11/64	
	3/16	3/16	3/16
			13/64
		7/32	7/32
			15/64

1 to 10

5-Series (60% Steps)	10-Series (25% Steps)	20-Series (12% Steps)	40-Series (6% Steps)
1	1	1	1
			1 1/16
		1⅛	1⅛
			1 3/16
	1¼	1¼	1¼
			1 5/16
		1⅜	1⅜
			1 7/16
1½	1½	1½	1½
			1⅝
		1¾	1¾
			1⅞
	2	2	2
			2⅛
		2¼	2¼
			2⅜

10 to 40

5-Series (60% Steps)	10-Series (25% Steps)	20-Series (12% Steps)	40-Series (6% Steps)
10	10	10	10
			10½
		11	11
			11½
	12	12	12
			13
		14	14
			15
16	16	16	16
			17
		18	18
			19
	20	20	20
			21
		22	22
			23

TABLE 1

Basic Preferred Numbers—Decimal Series (10 to 100)

5-Series (60% Steps)	10-Series (25% Steps)	20-Series (12% Steps)	40-Series (6% Steps)
10	10	10	10
			10.6
		11.2	11.2
			11.8
	12.5	12.5	12.5
			13.2
		14	14
			15
16	16	16	16
			17
		18	18
			19
	20	20	20
			21.2
		22.4	22.4
			23.6

25	25	25	25	1/4	1/4	1/4	1/4	2 1/2	2 1/2	2 1/2	2 1/2	24	24	24	24
			26.5				17/64				2 5/8				26
		28	28			9/32	9/32			2 3/4	2 3/4			28	28
			30				19/64				2 7/8				30
	31.5	31.5	31.5		5/16	5/16	5/16		3	3	3		32	32	32
			33.5				21/64				3 1/4				34
		35.5	35.5			11/32	11/32			3 1/2	3 1/2			36	36
			37.5				23/64				3 3/4				38
40	40	40	40	3/8	3/8	3/8	3/8	4	4	4	4	40	40	40	40
			42.5				13/32				4 1/4				
		45	45			7/16	7/16			4 1/2	4 1/2				
			47.5				15/32				4 3/4				
	50	50	50		1/2	1/2	1/2		5	5	5				
			53				17/32				5 1/4				
		56	56			9/16	9/16			5 1/2	5 1/2				
			60				19/32				5 3/4				
63	63	63	63	5/8	5/8	5/8	5/8	6	6	6	6				
			67				21/32				6 1/2				
		71	71			11/16	11/16			7	7				
			75				23/32				7 1/2				
	80	80	80		3/4	3/4	3/4		8	8	8				
			85				13/16				8 1/2				
		90	90			7/8	7/8			9	9				
			95				15/16				9 1/2				

Preferred Numbers below 10 are formed by dividing the numbers between 10 and 100 by 10, 100, etc.
Preferred Numbers above 100 are formed by multiplying the numbers between 10 and 100 by 10, 100, etc.
Percentage steps in headings are approximate averages.

Fig. 29. American Standards Association Preferred Numbers.

selected are 1″, 1½″, 2½″, and 4″. After sufficient sales data are obtained, the company may find that sales may be increased profitably by adopting widths to conform with the values in the 10-series of basic preferred numbers which are in approximately 25 per cent steps. Under this arrangement there are 7 widths: 1″, 1¼″, 1½″, 2″, 2½″, 3″, and 4″. If still more widths are justified, the 20-series in 12 per cent steps or the 40-series in 6 per cent steps can be adopted. It will be noted that in converting from the 5-series to the 10-series of preferred numbers it is only necessary to add 3 new sizes without changing any sizes already existing. The same holds true in converting to the 20- and 40-series. All existing sizes are retained; new ones are added.

SUMMARY

Long-range planning for specialization, standardization, and simplification eliminates the need for subsequent day-to-day planning and control of kinds and varieties of items that should never have required this continuing attention in the first place.

Attention to specialization can keep companies from unwise expansion into complex, unrelated, unmanageable, and unprofitable operations. It can include orderly planning for expansion and for transition from one type of activity to another that is more promising or more profitable.

Companies grow normally by winning a larger and larger share of the market for their present products. Forced growth involves the performance of an increasing number of operations, the production of raw materials for finished commodities, or the addition of new products to established lines. Attention to specialization is not intended to restrict any forms of company growth but rather to provide direction for profitable growth.

Standardization keeps companies from using more types, sizes, and other varieties of raw materials than are really needed for production. Reduction in varieties of raw materials means reduced investment in stock and less attention to stock control. Standardized production components reduce tool costs, permit larger and more economical production lot sizes, avoid losses from obsolescence, and reduce capital requirements for work-in-process.

Simplification that reduces the number of varieties of finished products is important to both industry and the public. Simplified Practice Recommendations cooperatively developed by companies within different industries and published by the U.S. Department of Commerce have benefited industry by reducing costs of manufacture and distribution and have helped consumers by lowering prices. The several series of preferred numbers can be used to determine nonstyle varieties most likely to satisfy consumer wants.

QUESTIONS TO CHECK COMPREHENSION

1. A textile company wishes to expand vertically. It can do this by producing some of its raw materials (which are cotton, rayon, and nylon) or it can produce finished products such as dressgoods, draperies, towelings, and other items made from its fabrics. Discuss the advantages and disadvantages of each course. Which do you recommend?

2. Another textile company uses 6 different warp sizes of yarn, ranging from No. 30 ± 5 to No. 60 ± 5, and 5 different filling yarn sizes, ranging from No. 20 ± 5 to No. 50 ± 5, to produce 30 different fabrics. A reduction in the number of yarn sizes is urgently needed to avoid confusion and financial losses. What do you recommend?

3. Assume that you, a production-planning engineer, and a development engineer have been nominated by your company to represent it on a Committee for Simplified Practices of the United States Department of Commerce. How can you help the design engineer to suggest standards that will be acceptable to consumers and satisfactory to your company?

4. Your company is licensed to make and sell a product patented by another company. The bill of materials for this product shows that several parts are made with materials essentially and functionally similar to but not identical with materials currently stocked by your company. Assume that the license agreement stipulates that the product shall be made in strict accordance with the licensor's specifications for materials, processes, and performance tests. What action should be taken?

5. A company that produces its own machined metal parts for a variety of assembled products has so many short production runs that setup or preparation time almost equals machining time. Designers have never considered standardization of component parts or interchangeability of subassemblies. There also is no standard terminology for piece parts.

A casual study made by a production-planning engineer shows that parts differ from each other by only a few thousandths of an inch. Many other parts are identical but have different names and numbers and are therefore scheduled separately for production. What organizational arrangement can eliminate this undesirable and unprofitable practice? How should the accumulated errors be corrected?

PROBLEM

A clock company finds that it produces 312 sizes of clock dials with diameters ranging from 3 in. to 48 in. Except for the 6-in. dial, production lots have been so small that their cost is unreasonably high. The company decides to reduce sizes to as few as 25 or 30. Determine the sizes that should be retained, using a preferred series of numbers.

DISCUSSION CASE

The Ruolf Company has manufactured and distributed cereal food products since 1856. Through the years it has developed great skills in purchasing and milling various grains and in processing and packaging its end products. The company has also developed excellent skills and arrangements for the marketing and distribution of its products.

Choice grains are obtained by cooperative agreements with farmers for whom the company tests seed grain and recommends fertilizers in accordance with soil analyses. Much of the work of the purchasing department is done out in the field with farmers, helping them to improve quality and yields and developing relationships to assure adequate and continuing sources of choice grains. Crop loans are frequently made to reliable farmers who need financial aid.

Manufacturing is on a grand scale, involving enormous silos, effective mechanical handling, well-controlled modern processes, and high-speed mechanical packaging. So many improvements and controlling devices have been introduced during the years that manufacturing is almost fully automatic.

Sales and distribution are modern and effective. The company's products are sold through wholesale grocery companies and by direct contracts with chain stores and supermarkets. Company representatives cooperate with retail outlets in developing up-to-date merchandising methods to stimulate sales.

Several years ago the Ruolf Company developed an electric mixer, an electric toaster, and a small combination electric grill and oven. Since these items seemed to assure that the company's food products would be better mixed and cooked, they were manufactured and marketed. To round out this new line, electric irons, heating pads, and a number of other electric products were also developed and sold.

The management committee of the Ruolf Company has met to evaluate the results of this expansion of its business. Manufacturing executives complain that the electrical products cannot be produced with any degree of automation and that costs are high by competitive standards. Purchasing executives have had difficulties in adjusting from an agrarian environment to the mechanical and electrical field. Marketing executives have found that a whole new arrangement of distribution, differing radically from that of the food industry, is needed to sell electrical household equipment.

The chairman of the committee emphasizes the need for company growth and reports that the electrical household products division now accounts for 3 per cent of the company's total business. A decision must be made whether to continue this new division of the company or to seek growth in the field of liquid, dehydrated, and frozen foods.

Assume that you are participating in this meeting. List the causes for what is wrong and determine what actions are necessary to correct each fault.

8
Sales Forecasting

In our discussion of manufacturing planning (Chapter 4), we found that costs are high when sales volume is low, but drop rapidly as volume increases. In some economic systems this fact would mean little, but in our mass-production economy it brings a long chain of consequences. As costs go down, selling prices are reduced; this brings further increase in volume, with attendant problems of procurement, employment, factory housing, financing, and so on. To know what a business will do, we must know its future sales, which means that we must have sales forecasts. Without them, both short- and long-range planning rests on foundations much less substantial than sand.

A. LIMITATIONS OF FORECASTING

Critics sometimes question the value of all economic forecasts because those made on a national or international scale frequently end in failure. In 1944, for example, an eminent economist with a fine staff of experts stated that, to have full employment in 1946, we Americans would have to eat almost twice as much food as we did in 1940, heat and light our houses twice as well as in 1944, use 30 per cent more gasoline, and wear three shoes. During the next two years Americans remained bipedal, ate little more than they did in 1940, and responded to urgent requests that they conserve heat and electric power. In spite of this, employment rose along with the rise in the civilian labor force, as is shown in Figure 30.

In the same year an economist at one of our leading universities predicted that payrolls would shrink by more than $20,000,000,000 at the end of World War II even if hourly wage rates remained unchanged. Average hourly wage rates increased from $1.00 per

108

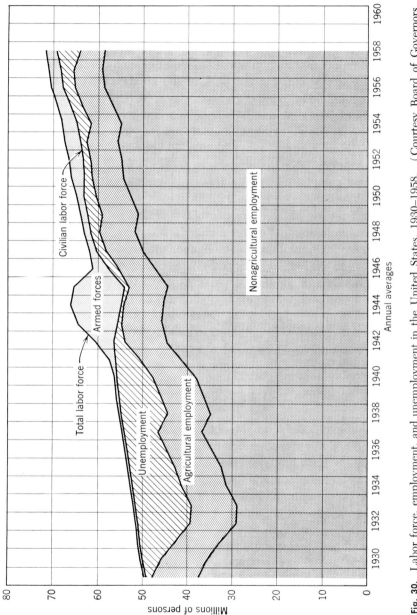

Fig. 30. Labor force, employment, and unemployment in the United States, 1930–1958. (Courtesy Board of Governors, Federal Reserve System.)

hour in 1944 to $1.40 at the end of 1948. Rising employment boosted payrolls from about $120,000,000,000 at the end of 1944 to about $135,000,000,000 at the end of 1948.

On December 21, 1946, the Associated Press reported: "The Bureau of Economic and Business Research of the University of Illinois said today in a report that facts support the belief of many authorities that the country is approaching the peak of the inflationary phase of the business cycle." During the following year several other forecasts brought headlines such as: "We have reached the inflationary peak of the business cycle"; "United States is heading into a minor depression"; and "Hard times to arrive in 1947." Actually, as everyone now knows, consumer prices continued to increase until the latter part of 1948 and then fell only slightly, and personal income increased similarly.

Indeed, a review of long-range forecasts almost suggests that many economists were using *Farmer Benner's Business Forecast* for the years 1816 to 1967. Although Mr. Benner died in 1884, he predicted the depression of 1929 only 2 years late, but closed it in the same year, 1931. During the next 4 years, business would be on the up-grade, and the next great panic would occur in 1947. Actually, as everyone knows, we had minor depressions, or recessions, as they were called, between 1929 and 1947, whereas 1947 was a year of prosperity. (See Figures 31 and 32.)

B. THE FIELD FOR LIMITED FORECASTS

Despite these failures to predict the national economic situation, production and sales forecasts for individual industries and companies can be made within limits of accuracy that allow them to be used as a basis for planning industrial production. Of course, plans based on such forecasts must be adjusted to fit conditions as they actually develop, but the fact remains that carefully prepared forecasts seldom err more than 5 to 15 per cent. With the probable limits of error known in advance, such variances are generally not serious.

C. DATA USED TO DETERMINE TRENDS

Several agencies, both public and private, compile data on economic trends. Foremost among the subjects covered are:

Industrial production	Manufacturers' sales	Exports
Volume of trade	Manufacturers' inventories	Imports
Commodity prices	Employment	Building permits
Wholesale prices	Bank deposits	Business failures
National income	Car loadings	Consumers' prices

Though assembled as detailed statistics, these data commonly make their appearance in print in the form of index numbers. In determining these numbers, figures for a certain year or series of years are taken as the norm, and deviations are expressed in terms of per cent of the norm. Index numbers for prices, general business, and other factors appear in business publications along with ordinary business statistics expressed in terms of barrels, dollars, bushels, and so on.

The Federal Reserve Board publishes an index of industrial production adjusted for seasonal variations. This shows the trend of industrial production graphically. It can be followed each month as the lines on the charts are extended. This index, moreover, is broken down into indexes for several general types of production as follows:

Consumers' perishable goods	Capital goods
Consumers' semidurable goods	Fuels
Consumers' durable goods	Materials and supplies
Construction materials	

With these indexes for the general types of production, each manufacturer may consider the trends in his own special field without being confused or even deceived by trends in other fields that have little or no meaning for him. During the period 1939–1943, for example, the general index of industrial production rose from 100 to about 240. Because of wartime demands, however, most of this increase was in capital goods, while consumers' durable goods shrank substantially. Had he followed the general index only, a manufacturer of capital goods would have underestimated activity in his field, whereas one producing consumers' durable goods would have overestimated it. Use of the correct indexes, however, was enough to prevent these errors.

The industrial forecaster must have these prepared indexes and must be skilled in interpreting them. He must also have all significant facts relating to his specific business, his company's past performance, and its past and current policies. Moreover, he must prepare periodic analyses of the various lines and products of his company to make sure that production will not continue on an item for which there is no longer a demand, or one for which the demand is being greatly

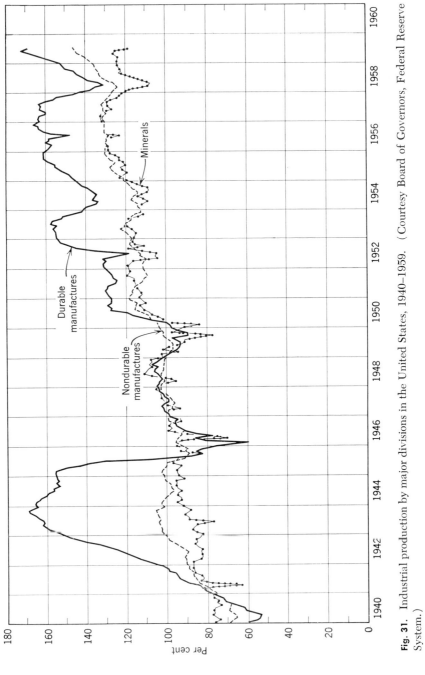

Fig. 31. Industrial production by major divisions in the United States, 1940–1959. (Courtesy Board of Governors, Federal Reserve System.)

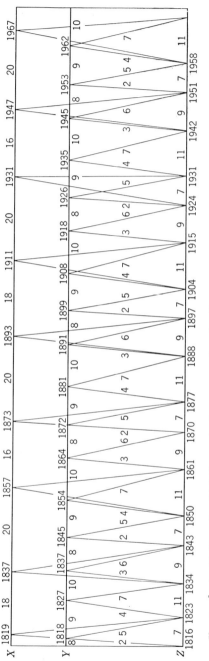

Key to chart. X—Years in which the panics have occurred and will occur. Their regular cycles are 18, 20, 16, and 20 years. Y—Years of good times, high prices, and the time to sell stocks and values of all kinds. Their cycles are 8, 9, and 10 years. Z—Years of hard times, low prices, and a good time to buy stocks, corner lots, etc., and hold until the boom, then unload. Their cycles are 9, 7, and 11 years.

The man who made this chart died in 1884, and this chart was first published in Cincinnati, Ohio, in 1871–60 years ago. If you will study it carefully, you will note the accuracy with which this chart has hit the business cycles.

Fig. 32.   Farmer Benner's business forecast.   (Courtesy Dayton Review Publishing Co.)

reduced by competition. He must also be familiar with seasonal fluctuations in demand and must understand their causes.

D. TECHNIQUES OF SALES FORECASTING

No one method of sales forecasting can be applied to all industrial enterprises, nor can all factors that establish a sales forecast be supplied by one individual or even one statistical department. Finalized sales forecasts generally include the contributions of many men of varied experience. Committees including executives from production, sales, purchasing, finance, and research generally study, discuss, and revise sales estimates after they have been prepared by a statistical group. Basic data for sales forecasts are usually developed by combinations of techniques. In many companies forecasts also are developed independently by various groups, each employing one or more different methods. The results check and balance each other, thus limiting possibilities of error. A description of the five most common techniques follows:

1. Opinion. Perhaps the oldest type of sales forecasting is a broad guess made by executives in charge of a business. Although such forecasts can be made quickly and at little expense, they lack scientific validity and can be deceptive or even disastrous when considered without supporting facts. Even seeming exceptions to these statements actually support them, for the opinions of seasoned executives—which often prove to be right—are generally based upon a store of fully digested information. Nevertheless, the best use of opinion today is to check the overall estimates of sales developed by other methods. If the consensus among top executives disagrees with those forecasts, the forecasts should be critically reviewed to make sure that they involve no hidden errors.

Although top executives may have a reasonably good idea of what the total sales volume will be, they are seldom sufficiently intimate with the details to estimate sales by product lines or items. They also generally lack the intimate knowledge necessary to estimate sales by territories. Yet breakdowns by items are important in financial, production, procurement, and promotional planning, and breakdowns by sales territories are essential to intelligent direction of sales efforts. These demands also limit the use of opinion forecasts by executives.

2. Estimates by Salesmen. Many companies base their sales forecasts upon estimates submitted by salesmen. These men presumably know more about their own sales districts than anyone else in the organization. Moreover, the salesman who has a hand in setting the forecast is likely to be ready to meet a sales quota established in accordance with it. Each district salesman therefore submits his estimate of the sales to be expected in his district for the period being forecast. These estimates are reviewed by divisional managers, who make any changes that may seem necessary. The estimates of all salesmen in a division are then tabulated by items and months. They are also totaled and sent to the regional or territorial sales manager. After further review, discussion, and revision, they are sent to the executive in charge of sales. He and his associates in management review the figures in the light of general economic conditions and other modifying factors, after which they prepare the final forecast.

Although salesmen are not considered to be good estimators, their errors generally balance each other. The result is a body of information that becomes a fairly reliable forecast as it goes through the hands of managers and executives in the central office.

3. Statistical Sampling. When salesmen lack time to collect figures, sampling can be used to develop total sales estimates. It must be preceded, however, by analyses of sales to determine the areas to be sampled and the extent of the sampling. The mechanics of sampling itself are revealed by the following examples:

A company producing consumer goods has 10 sales regions and 120 sales districts. It might design its sampling plan to obtain careful sales estimates in 1 district in each region. This would give geographical coverage, the districts selected being representative of the various economic levels related to the income and spending habits of the population. If sales estimates of these subgroups are rational, the data may be extended to produce the total sales estimate. Other factors, such as general business trends, should also be considered.

Our second company manufactures producer goods. A sales analysis shows that 500 of this company's 10,000 customers buy 60 per cent of its output. One hundred of these 500 major customers are selected and carefully interviewed to determine their future requirements, and the results are extended to produce a forecast that will be reasonably accurate for 60 per cent of the total business. The remaining 40 per cent are adjusted in proportion. Thus, if the sample as extended indicates total sales of $3,600,000, the remaining 9,500 customers probably will buy two-thirds as much, or $2,400,000 worth of the company's products. When the sample indicates an increase to $3,900,000, sales to the unsampled customers should rise to $2,600,000.

Neither of these sampling methods should be adopted without critical testing. For several years they should be tried out in comparison with whatever method has been employed, and all should be checked for accuracy. Only when the record becomes convincing should a decision to adopt the sampling method be made.

What and how much of a product category consumers are currently buying are important factors that can indicate sensitively how sales forecasts should be adjusted. Information about these factors also points to steps that need to be taken with respect to sales policies, advertising, product redesign, and performance requirements. It is true that these factors are reflected in a company's sales figures, but the sensitivity of these figures is generally reduced and disturbed by the time intervals between sales to distributors, retailers, and consumers. Several organizations, such as the A. C. Nielsen Company, provide services to industrial and commercial companies in which sales of their products to customers are continuously sampled. The sampling plans have been designed to permit inferences, within close limits of accuracy, concerning the universes represented by the samples. Data assembled from these point-of-sale samplings are sensitive indicators of trends in consumer preferences, current sales, and the share of the market enjoyed by a company's products. Such information increases the accuracy of sales forecasts and permits timely adjustments to them.

4. Historical Background and Statistical Projection. Some companies have detailed sales records by items and sales territories or, if they make producer goods, by types of industrial consumers. Such companies can analyze trends in their sales, using statistical treatment of sales data to reveal growth or decline. Moving averages, which will be described later in this chapter, serve as sensitive indicators of trends. Further statistical treatment projects the probable continuation of trends by calculating and plotting their fitted curves. Even without recourse to complex statistical methods, forecasts may safely predict increased sales, if a product has doubled in sales every 5 years, if no diverting products have been invented, and if no new or unusual competition has developed. As with other methods of forecasting, future predictions based on past sales should not be used alone but should be checked and balanced with the results of other methods that are available and reasonably reliable.

Historical data will be used to predict both level and pattern of sales. Sales trends and extensions of them into the future must be known. Histories may sometimes present fluctuating or erratic records for certain products or product lines. As an example, one product may have had the following annual sales:

	Millions of Units		Millions of Units
1928	50	1938	88
1929	60	1939	65
1930	42	1940	96
1931	70	1941	49
1932	65	1942	77
1933	50	1943	56
1934	81	1944	82
1935	86	1945	60
1936	72	1946	65
1937	68	1947	58

Graphically, these data present a ragged picture (shown in Figure 33), which indicates that the sales department so overstocked dealers in years such as 1936, 1938, 1940, 1942, and 1944 that orders lagged during the following years.

Computation of a 10-year running average of sales for 1938–1947 gives a picture that will reveal growth or decline. This can be done by computing the total of the 10 years from 1928 to 1937, subtracting sales for 1928, adding sales for 1938 to obtain the 10-year running average for the year 1938, and pointing off to reduce the 10-year total to the average.

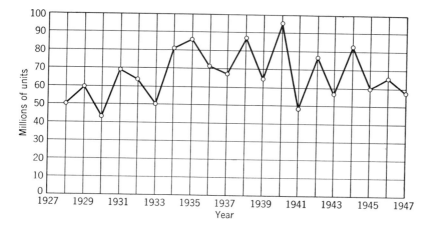

Fig. 33. Graph showing annual sales.

```
        644   Total sales, 1928 to 1937 inclusive.
−1928    50
        ───
        594
+1938    88
        ───
        682   68.2 = 1938 ten-year running average
−1929    60
        ───
        622
+1939    65
        ───
        687   68.7 = 1939 ten-year running average.
−1930    42
        ───
        645
+1940    96
        ───
        741   74.1 = 1940 ten-year running average.
−1931    70
        ───
        671
+1941    49
        ───
        720   72.0 = 1941 ten-year running average.
−1932    65
        ───
        655
+1942    77
        ───
        732   73.2 = 1942 ten-year running average.
−1933    50
        ───
        682
+1943    56
        ───
        738   73.8 = 1943 ten-year running average.
−1934    81
        ───
        657
+1944    82
        ───
        739   73.9 = 1944 ten-year running average.
−1935    86
        ───
        653
+1945    60
        ───
        713   71.3 = 1945 ten-year running average.
−1936    72
        ───
        641
+1946    65
        ───
        706   70.6 = 1946 ten-year running average.
−1937    68
        ───
        638
+1947    58
        ───
        696   69.6 = 1947 ten-year running average.
```

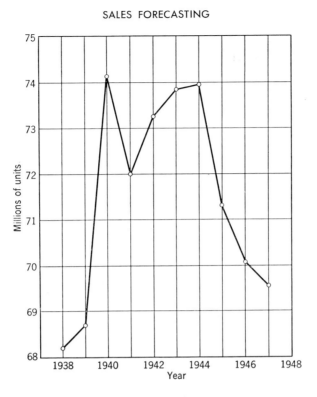

Fig. 34. Ten-year moving average.

Transformed into a graph (Figure 34), these figures show that decline began in 1941. This decline may mean that the product has encountered decreasing consumer demand, or it may mean that policies and practices of management are unsound. Before the company resigns itself to gradually decreasing sales that will end in discontinuance of the product, it should review management policies and practices and should study consumer acceptance.

The historical background must be complete with information about events, policies, product quality, and sales promotional effort, as well as the number of units sold. The tabulation shows several good reasons for certain irregularities in the volume of annual sales from year to year. It can be used as a basis for checking the forecast for sales level established by other methods.

The 1948 forecast of 146,000 gross was based upon a competitively superior product, upon continued radio and other advertising, upon samplings of dealers' stocks (which indicated normal inventories), and upon an analysis of the trend of economic indexes that had proved to be significant for this particular item.

PRODUCT XXX   AVERAGE VALUE PER GROSS, $80

Period	Total Unit Sales	Important Factors
1938	60,250	
1939	65,320	
1940	47,163	Strike in March and April
1941	71,326	
1942	65,657	Two new competitors
1943	68,451	
1944	72,943	
1945	94,247	Introduction of radio advertising
1946	127,430	Improved product
1947	138,243	
1948	146,000	Forecast

Thus a forecast for the *level* of sales is established. Historical data can also be used to study the seasonal *pattern* of sales.

If the 146,000 gross could be sold in 12 equal portions, 1 each month, planning, procurement, and manufacture would be simplified. Actually, however, sales have ranged from 7,300 gross per month to 29,200 gross, in irregular sequence (see Figure 35), and numerically as shown in the following tabulation:

	Number of Gross	Per Cent
January	7,300	5
February	7,300	5
March	7,300	5
April	14,600	10
May	29,200	20
June	7,300	5
July	7,300	5
August	7,300	5
September	7,300	5
October	7,300	5
November	29,200	20
December	14,600	10
	146,000	100

Fig. 35. Monthly sales of Product XXX as a percentage of annual sales.

At first glance it seems simple to schedule an average month of 12,166 gross and maintain this level throughout the year, storing production not needed in lean months to meet the demands of April, May, November, and December. Capital charges for finished goods and storage expense, however, may make this impossible. Assuming a 30-day finished-goods inventory (12,166 gross) as normal, a level production of 12,166 gross per month would produce excesses in 7 of the 12 months (see Figure 36). In October the excess inventory of finished goods would reach 19,460 gross. At $80 per gross this would represent $1,556,800 of working capital. Many companies neither have such a sum of money on hand nor command the credit to obtain it. Moreover, after a period of inflated values, raw-material prices might drop and in doing so wipe out the profits of the entire year.

Our hypothetical company neither has $1,500,000 to sink in excess inventories, nor can it take the risk of deflation. Yet this does not mean that it must resign itself to "rush" seasonal production alter-

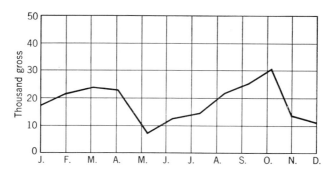

Fig. 36. Monthly inventories of Product XXX with level production.

nating with curtailed production and layoffs. Sales of Product XXX fluctuate because they are stimulated by spring weddings and Christmas, and facilities unused at other seasons form a large part of the overhead on the product. The forecaster, therefore, suggests that the company add Easter items to stabilize production during January, February, and March, with beach and vacation products to help out during the summer. With these, and with some accumulation of excess finished goods inventories during August and September, the company can hope to achieve sales stability and a level production rate without excessive demands for working capital.

Stability of sales and production means stable employment and economic security for workers. Both are vitally important, and the level production that begets security is equally advantageous to employers. These subjects, therefore, will be discussed in more detail in Chapter 22.

5. Regression or Correlation Analysis. As industrial and business indexes are refined, many companies find that sales of certain products show a remarkable relationship to one index or a correlation between others. As an example, products that compete for the dollars available for spending only after basic necessities have been purchased show sales that are closely correlated with national income when it is high. Sales of gasoline are related to automobile registrations, and so on. Some indexes, indeed, lead or follow the sales of certain goods so closely that predictions can be made in advance. For a simple example, there should be a predictive correlation between population and the sale of dentifrices. Assume a mortality of 500,000 people and births of 3,000,000 babies in a year. With allowances for infant mortality and the fact that children have some teeth to brush, one year later a prediction of about 2,225,000 new potential consumers for the new year would not be too inaccurate. Each company must calculate its share of this potential market according to its position in the field, its expected sales and advertising effort, the expected quality of its product, and its sales policies.

A manufacturer of electric storage batteries who knows the average life expectancy of storage batteries in general can predict replacement sales from correlations with automobile registrations, the number of industrial battery-operated trucks, and usage data on other types of batteries. To forecast his sale of automobile storage batteries, he first notes the number of automobile registrations—say 32,000,000 in a given year. He also finds that 5,000,000 of these registrations were for new cars, and he knows that the average life expectancy of a battery is 18 months. During the coming year, total replacement sales will be 5,000,000 for the batteries of automobiles sold 2 years before, plus the replacements for older cars. A correlation in which car sales and registrations lead replacement sales by 18 months allows ample time for each storage-battery company to forecast its share of the business and to plan for production.

Thus the information about one activity that leads another activity can be used in forecasting the sales of the latter. When indexes such as business failures or unemployment follow sales trends, they give little assistance in correlation studies that are intended to check sales forecasts.

The following tabulation shows a simple correlation analysis among national income, national sales by one type of industry, and the sales of one particular company. This analysis must be supplemented by studies of the company's sales districts or selected areas in them, to determine shifts in population and income.

Simple Correlation Analysis of National Income and Sales

Year	National Income (Millions)	National Income Index	Sales This Industry		Sales This Company	
			$	Index	$	Index
1929	82,617	100	10,000,000	100	1,000,000	100
1930	73,303	89	9,000,000	90	870,000	87
1931	61,966	75	7,800,000	78	730,000	73
1932	47,367	57	5,500,000	55	500,000	50 *
1933	46,273	56	5,300,000	53	510,000	51
1934	52,865	64	6,300,000	63	520,000	52
1935	58,493	71	7,200,000	72	750,000	75 †
1936	67,957	82	8,100,000	81	830,000	83
1937	72,275	87	8,800,000	88	900,000	90
1938	66,117	80	8,400,000	84	920,000	92 ‡
1939	70,601	85	8,400,000	84	940,000	94
1940	76,220	92	9,000,000	90	1,110,000	111
1941	91,910	111	11,200,000	112	1,150,000	115 §

* Price reductions.
† Quality of product improved.
‡ New dealer policies, sales force increased.
§ Introduction of radio advertising.

There are limitations to the use of preliminary analyses based upon national income and company sales. Suppose, for example, that this preliminary analysis indicates a 10 per cent increase in total sales; the forecaster may not assume that each product or line of products will show this increase. Some may, but others may not; an analysis therefore must be made for each product or closely related line.

E. CONSIDERATIONS IN INTRODUCING SALES FORECASTS

Neither annual nor monthly production figures can be used for the analyses on which forecasts are based, since *production* and *sales* often do not coincide. Thus a heavy backlog of orders at the end of one year will increase production during the next, with no corresponding increase in sales. On the other hand, advance orders from a few big customers may boost sales far above month-to-month production. Even sales figures must be adjusted to allow for excessive dealer inventories. Though the goods have been both sold and made, their presence in stockrooms is bound to reduce future consumer sales.

Forecasts also are not static; they cannot be made for six months or a year and neglected until their period ends. Forecasting provides a basis for planning during the first quarter; both plan and forecast are often followed with little or no modification. During that period, however, the forecaster receives data secured by sampling dealers' inventories. These data tell him whether the movement of goods accurately reflects sales and consumption, or whether part of these goods is piling up in warehouses and stockrooms. Plans and forecasts for the second quarter are then adjusted, both to compensate for differences between actual sales and those predicted, and to offset abnormal inventories in the hands of wholesalers and retailers.

The accuracy of forecasts depends upon need and the cost of refinements. Some companies get along with forecasts whose limits of accuracy are 10 per cent, plus or minus. Others set limits of 5 per cent plus or minus, and still others set 2 or 3 per cent limits. Much depends upon the period covered and the use to which the forecasts are put. The following table shows the three types of forecasts most commonly used and the limits of accuracy that generally are required.

Too much must not be expected from sales forecasts during the first year or two after their introduction. Until salesmen and sales managers realize that the forecast is a vitally important tool of management, they are inclined to be overoptimistic in promising cases and

Accuracy Requirements of Different Forecasts

Type	Period	Use	Accuracy
Long-range	5 to 10 years	Planning for plant expansions	±15%
Annual	1 year	Preparation of production, financial and sales budgets	±5%
Short-term	3 or 4 months	Planning immediate operations	±2%

insensitive to sales potentials in others that on first appraisal seem unattractive. Only experience will convince them of the need for accuracy in the estimates that they send on for analyses. They will also find that accurate forecasts eliminate back orders and late deliveries for their customers.

SUMMARY

Attempts to forecast the economic future on a national or international scale seldom achieve success. In spite of this, many industrial and commercial indexes reliably indicate trends and may be used with confidence in preparing sales estimates for specific companies or products.

Sales forecasts are essentially first approximations in production planning; they provide foundations upon which plans may rest and adjustments may be made. As the accuracy of these approximations increases, however, adjustments are reduced and production planning is simplified. To do his work, the forecaster must have accurate records of sales showing both level and pattern, must be familiar with company policies, and must be acquainted with its past and proposed sales promotion as well as its future advertising program. He learns the sales potential of his company by correlating its sales and those of its industry with national and regional income.

Sales for each month must be estimated, as well as those for the quarter and year. If sales are traditionally and irremediably seasonal, analysis may show the need for new products to be sold in other seasons. Level production sometimes can be achieved in spite of seasonal sales by building up inventories during off seasons. This demands increased working capital and involves the risk from obsolescence and falling prices.

Annual or monthly figures of past production should not be a basis for forecasting sales. Actual sales figures should be employed, and even they should be adjusted to account for excessive or short dealers' inventories.

Statistical treatment of sales data such as 5- or 10-year moving averages help reveal and measure growth or decline.

Sales forecasting usually will not yield accurate results during the first few years. As experience is gained, and as the need for accurate sales estimates becomes evident, the results will become more reliable and meaningful.

QUESTIONS TO CHECK COMPREHENSION

1. Should production or sales figures be used in forecasting?

2. Do trends in indexes of industrial production, national income, manufacturers' sales, and manufacturers' inventories indicate changes in the economic position of certain businesses?

3. Do seasonal fluctuations place limitations on planning and level production.

4. What may prevent companies that produce seasonal goods from achieving level production?

5. Will 5- or 10-year running averages show trends more clearly than the usual annual sales figures for each year?

6. Do limitations of predictions on a national and international basis mean that a manufacturing company cannot make sales forecasts with sufficient accuracy to plan its operations?

7. How are industrial and financial indexes prepared?

8. How is the index for industrial production broken down so that an increase in one type of goods will not confuse a manufacturer who produces another type?

9. What is the oldest technique used in sales forecasting? What are its limitations?

10. What are the arguments in favor of sales forecasts developed by salesmen?

11. Can statistical sampling be used in developing sales forecasts? Should such forecasts be checked by some other means?

12. Explain the difference between sales forecasts for level and pattern.

13. Some industrial indexes lead and some lag certain industrial activities. Which are useful to the sales forecaster?

PROBLEMS

1. A company has been operating for 10 years with the following gross sales:

1st year	$3,250,000	6th year	$ 4,300,000
2nd year	3,600,000	7th year	6,000,000
3rd year	4,000,000	8th year	8,200,000
4th year	4,000,000	9th year	12,300,000
5th year	4,100,000	10th year	17,500,000

Assume that national income for the eleventh year is estimated to be 110 per cent that for the tenth year. The company's competitive position is normal; it makes consumer products that are not "bread-and-butter" items and that therefore compete for dollars left over after basic necessities have been bought. Forecast this company's sales in its eleventh year.

2. List sales figures of the past 10 or 12 years for a company with which you are familiar or obtain them from the annual statement of some company. List also the sales figures of those same years for the type of industry to which this company belongs; then list national income for these years. Convert these figures to indexes. Determine whether the company's sales have been growing or declining in relation to industry sales and to national income. Try to account for any abnormal variations in the company's sales.

DISCUSSION CASE

The Marsco Manufacturing Company has manufactured hand tools for the past 23 years. Until 8 years ago, William Marshalton, the president, established the production plan by calling the manufacturing, sales, and accounting executives together in December. He would tell them that in his opinion sales demand for the next year would be a certain percentage above or below sales of the year then closing. Schedules for all items of production were then based on this blanket increase or decrease.

Mr. Marshalton's estimates always were very conservative, for he had been deeply impressed by a bad experience back in 1930 when low inventory turnover forced the company deeply into debt. Since low forecasts prevented adequate planning, back orders always piled up during the latter half of each year. The factory then operated at night and on Saturdays, and Sunday work was common. At the same time, blanket planning produced excessive inventories of items for which there was little demand.

When Mr. Marshalton at last retired, a Mr. Wade, who had studied the subjects, proposed that the company adopt scientific sales forecasting and production planning. A planning department was therefore set up with Mr. Wade as its head.

Throughout World War II the planning was good but forecasting was artificial, because both sales and production were regulated by the War Production Board's Controlled Materials Plan. Because there was a scarcity of consumers goods, excess inventories were exhausted. When wartime restrictions were lifted, Mr. Wade made ambitious sales forecasts based on the housing shortage and all available indexes of national income, new construction, etc. The factory operated at full capacity until the latter part of 1948, when sales fell off about 20 per cent. Production for the remainder of the year added to inventories so greatly that working capital was almost exhausted.

Mr. Thompson, the president, therefore directed Mr. Wade to visit hardware supply distributors throughout the country and learn the cause for this sudden falling off of sales. Wade has returned and Thompson has called a meeting to discuss the problem. As a participant in that meeting, state the difficulties clearly, give the causes for them, and suggest steps to be taken so that errors will not be repeated.

9

New Methods for
Forecasting Sales
and Distribution

Facts and figures of industrial and commercial operations have been shouting warnings about future events. But as yet we have not fully learned the significance of these warnings. As we do learn the symbols in a mathematical and statistical scheme of communication and understand their meaning we will solve better the riddles of what the future holds. Meanwhile, some techniques have been developed that let us operate relatively well within areas of uncertainty.

The methods discussed in Chapter 8 will adequately serve the needs of many companies. These methods will also serve to check and supplement newer methods as they are developed. Statistical decision-making methods implemented by data processing capabilities heretofore undreamed of are, however, providing scientifically effective means of prediction. Extension of these capabilities is now limited only to our knowledge of the problems that these electronic wizards are ready to solve for us. Two simple examples that typify some of these methods will be discussed in this chapter.

A. A MODERN SALES FORECASTING TECHNIQUE

As has been said sales are characterized by level and pattern. Until recently, forecasters held to the notion that monthly or weekly sales through a given year would follow the pattern of previous years and that the primary requirement in forecasting was, therefore, an estimate of the sales level for a coming year. The characteristic sales

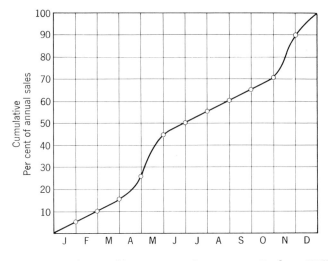

Fig. 37. Cumulative characteristic sales pattern, Product **XXX.**

pattern could then be adjusted to the estimated sales level.   This assumption gives only minor importance to sales pattern.   The newer scientific and dynamic technique for sales forecasting pays critical attention to pattern and the deviation of sales from pattern as a means of determining the level that sales are likely to reach in a forecast period.   If a first estimate of level is wrong, this new method shows quickly the error, and it, moreover, indicates the proper correcting adjustment.

Graphic representations are made dynamic by cumulative plotting of forecast and actual sales.   Seasonal monthly or weekly patterns are shown as straight lines by constructing seasonal sales variations in the time order scales on the charts.   This new method for sales forecasting is being used by several prominent companies.   Mr. Frank J. Carr [1] of Westinghouse states, "We are using this technique with considerable success in many different parts of our company."

To explain this new forecasting technique in a somewhat oversimplified manner, suppose we use the information for Product XXX in Chapter 8.   We then can take figures from a current operation and study the application details first in a simulated situation and then in a real one.

The information for Product XXX contained in Figure 35 is plotted dynamically as cumulative values in Figure 37.   No one wants to

[1] Frank J. Carr, director, Business Systems Research and Development, Westinghouse Electric Corporation, Pittsburgh, Pa.

frequently convert unit or dollar values to percentages and then reconvert them to unit or dollar values. Sales for each month, as percentages of annual sales, are, however, the best figures for establishing characteristic sales patterns for use with various sales levels. A lower time order scale is, therefore, constructed on the chart so that each month's percentage of annual sales is represented by a length equal to a corresponding perecentage of the total length of the time order scale. In other words, a lower time order scale of 100 divisions is established on the chart. Then in the case of Product XXX, the first 5 divisions will represent January, the second 5 February, the next 10 March, and so on, as shown in Figure 38.

In that figure, a straight line is then drawn from a point on the right hand vertical scale, representing the forecast of 146,000 sales units, to the origin of the chart. Cumulative sales units can then be read

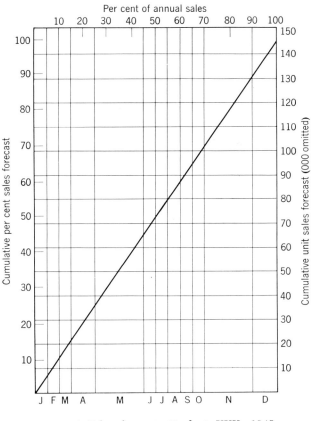

Fig. 38. Sales forecast, Product XXX, 1948.

on the right-hand vertical scale and cumulative percentage sales on the left-hand vertical scale.

As sales for Product XXX are reported they can be plotted on the chart. If the forecast level of 146,000 sales units is correct, the plotted points will closely follow the forecast line. If they do not follow this line an adjustment is indicated and so is the direction of the adjustment.

Let us now explain an actual industrial application of this new technique in some detail. Sales figures for 1955, 1956, and 1957 were assembled at the end of the first quarter of 1958. They were used to determine the characteristic monthly pattern of sales and to set control limits. The figures for the first three months of 1958 were saved for a simulation exercise.

	Sales ($000) Omitted	Cumulative Sales	Per Cent of Annual Sales	Cumulative Per Cent of Annual Sales
		1955		
Jan.	2,980	2,980	7.84	7.84
Feb.	3,078	6,058	8.10	15.94
Mar.	3,278	9,336	8.62	24.56
April	3,500	12,836	9.20	33.76
May	3,240	16,076	8.52	42.28
June	3,004	19,080	7.90	50.18
July	2,878	21,958	7.57	57.75
Aug.	2,596	24,554	6.83	64.58
Sept.	3,440	27,994	9.05	73.63
Oct.	3,662	31,656	9.63	83.26
Nov.	3,286	34,942	8.64	91.90
Dec.	3,080	38,022	8.10	100.00
Total	38,022		100.00	
		1956		
Jan.	3,050	3,050	7.71	7.71
Feb.	3,250	6,300	8.22	15.93
Mar.	3,024	9,324	7.65	23.58
April	3,484	12,808	8.81	32.39
May	3,354	16,162	8.48	40.87
June	3,324	19,486	8.40	49.27
July	3,070	22,556	7.76	57.03
Aug.	3,002	25,558	7.59	64.62
Sept.	3,420	28,978	8.65	73.27
Oct.	3,550	32,528	8.98	82.25

	Sales ($000) Omitted	Cumulative Sales	Per Cent of Annual Sales	Cumulative Per Cent of Annual Sales
Nov.	3,674	36,202	9.29	91.54
Dec.	3,348	39,550	8.46	100.00
Total	39,550		100.00	
		1957		
Jan.	3,484	3,484	8.05	8.05
Feb.	4,240	7,724	9.80	17.85
Mar.	4,172	11,896	9.64	25.49
April	3,834	15,730	8.87	36.36
May	3,812	19,542	8.81	46.17
June	3,654	23,196	8.44	53.61
July	3,328	26,524	7.69	61.30
Aug.	3,456	29,980	7.99	69.29
Sept.	3,328	33,308	7.69	76.98
Oct.	3,430	36,738	7.93	84.91
Nov.	3,560	40,298	8.23	93.14
Dec.	2,966	43,264	6.86	100.00
Total	43,264		100.00	

The characteristic sales pattern was determined by averaging the three years 1955, 1956, and 1957.

	Sum of Per Cent of Annual Sales	Characteristic Average Per Cent of Annual Sales	Cumulative Characteristic Average Per Cent of Annual Sales
Jan.	23.60	7.84	7.84
Feb.	26.12	8.71	16.55
Mar.	25.91	8.64	25.19
April	26.88	8.96	34.15
May	25.81	8.61	42.76
June	24.74	8.25	51.01
July	23.02	7.67	58.68
Aug.	22.41	7.47	66.15
Sept.	25.39	8.47	74.62
Oct.	26.54	8.85	83.47
Nov.	26.16	8.72	92.19
Dec.	23.42	7.81	100.00
Total	300.00	100.00	

Work by Frances B. Newman in 1952 [1] based upon principles of Shewhart Statistical Quality Control [2] since confirmed by many other applications, has shown that when cumulative sales values remain within the limits of two standard deviations above and below the cumulative forecast line, the sales activity is in a state of control. No adjustment of the sales forecast nor the production plan need then be made. Application of the theory of runs as presented by Dr. Paul S. Olmstead [3] will generally tell also when the sales level is changing even before any points on the chart fall outside the control limits.

Control limits were computed as follows and are shown as broken lines on the chart in Figure 40:

	3-Year Average Per Cent Sales	1955		1956		1957	
		Per Cent Sales	Deviation^2	Per Cent Sales	Deviation^2	Per Cent Sales	Deviation^2
Jan.	7.84	7.84	0.0000	7.71	0.0169	8.05	0.0441
Feb.	8.71	8.10	0.3721	8.22	0.2401	9.80	1.1881
Mar.	8.64	8.62	0.0004	7.65	0.9801	9.64	1.0000
April	8.96	9.20	0.0576	8.81	0.0225	8.87	0.0081
May	8.61	8.52	0.0081	8.48	0.0169	8.81	0.0400
June	8.25	7.90	0.1225	8.40	0.0225	8.84	0.3481
July	7.67	7.57	0.0100	7.76	0.0081	7.69	0.0004
Aug.	7.47	6.83	0.4096	7.59	0.0144	7.99	0.2704
Sept.	8.47	9.05	0.3364	8.65	0.0324	7.69	0.6084
Oct.	8.85	9.63	0.6084	8.98	0.0169	7.93	0.8464
Nov.	8.72	8.64	0.0064	9.29	0.3249	8.23	0.2401
Dec.	7.81	8.10	0.0841	8.46	0.4225	6.86	0.9025
Total	100.00	100.00	2.0156	100.00	2.1182	100.00	5.4966

$$
\begin{array}{ll}
\text{1955 sum of deviations}^2 & 2.0156 \\
\text{1956 sum of deviations}^2 & 2.1182 \\
\text{1957 sum of deviations}^2 & 5.4966 \\
\hline
\text{Total sum of deviations}^2 & 9.6304
\end{array}
$$

$$
\text{Standard deviation} = \sqrt{\frac{\text{Sum of deviations}^2}{\text{Number of months} - 1}} = \sqrt{\frac{9.6304}{35}} = 0.524\%
$$

[1] Frances B. Newman, "Better Production Planning from Controlled Sales Forecasts," *Factory Management and Maintenance,* June, 1952.

[2] Walter A. Shewhart, *Economic Control of Quality of Manufactured Product,* D. Van Nostrand Co., Inc., 1951.

[3] Paul S. Olmstead, "Distribution of Sample Arrangements for Runs Up and Down," *Annals of Mathematical Statistics,* March 1946; "Runs Determined in a Sample by an Arbitrary Cut," *The Bell System Technical Journal,* January, 1958.

Then the control limits at the end of the year were:

$42,000,000 + (2 × 0.524% of $42,000,000) = $42,440,160 Upper limit

$42,000,000 − (2 × 0.524% of $42,000,000) = $41,559,480 Lower limit

These limits were plotted on the cumulative sales scale for the end of the year, and broken lines were extended from them parallel to the solid sales forecast line. These broken lines thus formed the control limits.

Actual cumulative monthly sales figures for the first three months of 1958 were then posted on the chart in Figure 40. The third point

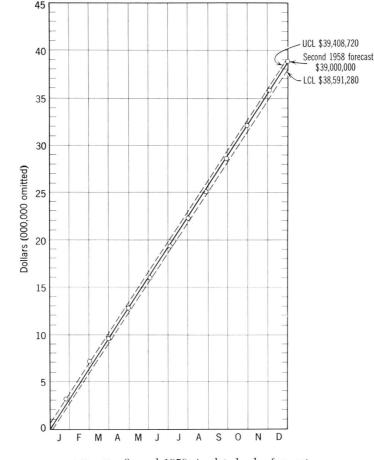

Fig. 41. Second 1958 simulated sales forecast.

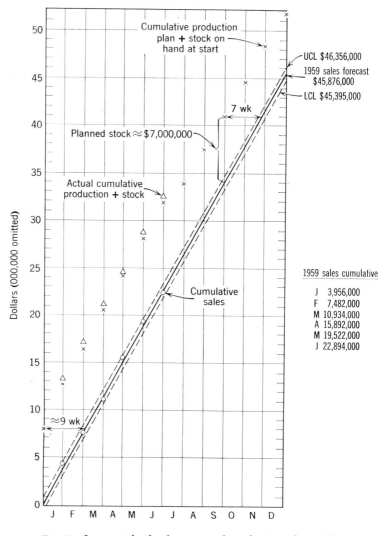

Fig. 42. Integrated sales forecast and production plan, 1959.

sary. There should be just enough detail to avoid seeking trouble where none exists. This will leave enough time and energy to make some ad hoc, special studies when the prime indicators show they are needed.

Persons who try to apply this method will probably find that the sales patterns of their operations are not as stable as those in the last example. They may also find that deviations in percentage sales will be greater and generally more erratic. The historical reasons for these abnormalities, such as changing the date in one year for year-end discounts or the whole sales force going on vacation in September in another year, can often be found. When assignable causes for such irrational sales behavior are found they can generally be calculated out of the pattern development.

Some executives will accept this modern technique as the answer to all their forecasting, planning, and control problems. It will, of course, extend their analytical capabilities, and it will simplify their work, but it will not eliminate the need for critical attention to external factors such as general business conditions, strikes, competition, and everything that may tend to restrict or increase sales.

B. SIMPLIFIED DISTRIBUTION FORECASTING

Problems in distribution allocations often cause annoying dislocations to plans based upon good sales forecasts of both pattern and level for items sold in broadly scattered locations throughout the country. Companies with nationwide distribution systems generally have several warehouses in locations that permit prompt customer service and minimize transportation costs. Since centralized forecasting of each item for each warehouse is cumbersome, each warehouse generally estimates its own stock requirements. These estimates, which often are only guesses, usually lead to overstocks of certain items in some warehouses, whereas others are understocked or find themselves without these items. Goods must often be reshipped from one warehouse to another to correct the unbalanced situations.

A simple technique used by several companies significantly reduces errors of this kind. It is so simple that the staff of each warehouse can use it without help from a central office. In this method,

$$F = [F_p K] + [S_o(1 - K)]$$

in which F = Forecast for next period
F_p = Forecast for last period
S_o = Sales for last period
K = A factor somewhere between 0.7 and 0.9

The factor K to be used can be determined experimentally or from an analysis of past sales and forecasts. A factor of 0.8 is a good one with which to begin. It gives an importance of 80 per cent to the most recent forecast and 20 per cent to the most recent sales.

Let us now assume that we are operating a small bakery. Twenty deliverymen distribute bread to customers on twenty routes every day except Sunday. At about three o'clock each afternoon the deliverymen return with their trucks and hand the office clerk an estimate of the number of loaves of each kind of bread they will require at six o'clock the next morning. Analysis shows that 13 per cent of our bread is returned because of overoptomistic estimates by our deliverymen. This bread is sold at half price to retail stores in poor neighborhoods. No data are at hand to show how often deliverymen underestimate their needs and have too little bread for their customers. Since trucks seldom return empty, however, we assume that this factor can be ignored. Further analysis shows that we are operating at 110 per cent of our normal baking capacity. In other words one eleventh of our baking is done by overtime work for which premium wages must be paid.

We decide to try the simplified forecasting method to reduce both returns and overtime. Each deliveryman is asked to submit separately for each coming day his estimated normal requirements and any unusual additional demands such as bread for banquets and organizational picnics. We must be certain that the simplified forecasting method will bring worthwhile benefits before we adopt it. So for several weeks we list actual results with deliverymen's estimates comparatively with what would have resulted if the new method had been in effect. For one deliveryman and a specific day —say Wednesday—the comparison may be as follows:

Actual sales last Wednesday	260
Forecast for last Wednesday	242
Expected unusual sales next Wednesday	20
Deliveryman's estimate for next Wednesday	290
Simplified forecast, using K factor 0.8	

$$F = F_p K + [S_o(1 - K)] = 193.6 + 52 = 246$$

Plus unusual sales	20
	——
Total loaves, simplified requirement	266
Actual sales	263
Loaves actually unsold	27 or 10.27%
Loaves that would have been unsold with simplified forecast	3 or 1.03%

The foregoing calculation has been simplified by including figures for only one deliveryman on a single day, without regard for the different types of bread he sells. It also shows the last forecast was low. As we continue calculations for several more weeks these errors start to smooth out and we are convinced that calculated estimates are much more accurate than a deliveryman's hopes or hunches.

After the new system is carefully explained to all employees, it is formally introduced. Errors in overestimating are significantly reduced. Although deliverymen are occasionally a few loaves short of their needs, our enterprise has been transformed from one of marginal profit to one of attractive reward.

SUMMARY

Sales forecasts, production, and stock plans can be integrated graphically to show their relationships and interactions. Charts of these data are made dynamic by plotting values cumulatively. Seasonal sales patterns are built into time order scales, eliminating need for seasonal adjustments to figures. Statistically calculated control limits for sales are included in the charts, forewarning of changing sales levels and indicating the direction in which adjustments should be made. This new method supported by attention to changing economic factors will improve accuracy in prediction and permit more effective planning of production and finished goods stocks.

A simple forecasting method can be used to reduce errors in estimates for distribution of goods to warehouses of a company. Major weight is given to the last period forecast and minor weight to sales for the last period.

QUESTIONS TO CHECK COMPREHENSION

1. What advantages are offered by viewing monthly or weekly sales figures cumulatively?

2. How can seasonal sales variations be included in graphic representations to show cumulative sales forecasts as straight lines?

3. Can statistical control limits be calculated for and used with sales forecasts?

4. How can statistical methods be used to improve accuracy of allocations to warehouses?

PROBLEMS

1. Assume that your company has had sales as follows:

	1957	1958	1959
January	$ 100,000	$ 110,000	$ 120,000
February	120,000	128,000	136,000
March	125,000	135,000	142,000
April	140,000	155,000	160,000
May	160,000	175,000	187,000
June	160,000	170,000	185,000
July	165,000	182,000	200,000
August	170,000	191,000	210,000
September	150,000	152,000	160,000
October	130,000	133,000	140,000
November	120,000	125,000	132,000
December	100,000	112,000	115,000
	$1,640,000	$1,768,000	$1,887,000

Compute monthly sales as percentages annual sales for their respective years. Compute a cumulative average sales pattern and incorporate it as a seasonally adjusted scale on a chart. Assume a 1960 forecast of $2,075,000 and show the cumulative forecast as a straight line on the chart. Compute the standard deviation of monthly sales and construct upper and lower control limits on the sales forecast chart. Assume sales of $140,300, $168,000, $175,800 in the first 3 months of 1960. Would you adjust the 1960 sales forecast? If so, what adjustment would you make?

2. Your company has five warehouses strategically located in the United States. You produce only one product in one size. Despite this simplicity stocks in the warehouses have been unbalanced.

	Warehouse				
	1	2	3	4	5
Average units sold, last 10 periods	20,000	15,000	17,000	8,000	12,000
Forecast last period	19,000	15,500	18,000	8,000	11,000

You have 71,600 units to distribute among the warehouses for the current period.   How will you allocate these units if a 0.8 K factor has been satisfactory in the past?

DISCUSSION CASE

The Thomas Jones Company had doubled its sales every five years for the past twenty years.   The characteristic seasonal pattern of sales contained two peak months; one in May and another in September:

	Per Cent of Annual Sales		Per Cent of Annual Sales
January	5	July	4
February	6	August	6
March	7	September	21
April	7	October	8
May	20	November	5
June	8	December	3
			100%

Mr. Watsatz, company president, had simplified sales forecasting and production planning with the following directive:

Our sales forecast for any coming year shall be 120 per cent of sales in the previous year.   Production shall be at a level rate and stock equal to two months' average sales shall be maintained to allow for peak periods.   Monthly production shall be 8.33 per cent of annual production to provide stable employment.

Watsatz's plan had succeeded for a long time.   No one questioned it except Joe Parsons, Production Manager, who had been employed previously by progressive companies and who kept up-to-date on forecasting and production control.   Parsons had advocated a six-weeks' stock allowance instead of a two-months' allowance.   He had also disagreed with Watsatz's oversimplified sales forecasting plan and had advocated a more scientific plan and market research studies.

Sales for the first four months of 1959 were about 12 per cent below forecast.   Stocks of finished goods began to pile up.   Operating expenses exceeded income. Working capital was further reduced because of plant expansion costs. A bank loan was negotiated.

Mr. Parsons had collected privately information about competitive products and sales. He asked for a meeting to present his ideas about what was wrong and the correction that should be made. Assume that you have been invited to this meeting. Present your analysis and recommendations for production control, sales forecasting, and market analysis.

10

Control

Many people think of production control as a function embracing both planning and control. Since these functions and operation feed upon each other, it is quite natural to accept this notion. Operation is fed objectives by planning, and planning replans action based upon feedback from operation. Others think that control begins before anything is done. As we have said, however, control is a regulative or adjusting process. It follows operation just as operation follows planning. Because control is so intimately related with manufacturing planning, operation, and replanning, a discussion of control and review is essential.

The principles of control are the same for production control, quality control, budgetary control, cost control, and other managerial controls. There is a growing tendency to consider *control* as the dynamic function of operating management and *review* as the broad administrative management function that studies the relationships and interactions of the results of dynamic controls as they affect the total enterprise.[1]

The basic cycle of events in control are *Action, Feedback, Evaluation,* and *Adjustment.* Since these events are dynamically in continuum they take the form of a closed-loop circuit. There are seven essential steps in the establishment and application of operating controls. These steps will be discussed in their normal sequence.

A. OPERATION

The first step in the control cycle (after careful preliminary manufacturing and planning) is operation. In this step, the act of doing

[1] A. W. Rathe, *Top Management Planning and Review,* American Management Association, 1954 and 1955.

something, some faults will be obvious and, therefore, easily corrected. Other faults will be more deceptively concealed requiring the steps that follow to reveal them so that they can be dealt with.

B. MEASUREMENT

Think of almost any factor in business and commerce and industrial engineers will find some way to measure it and represent it in numbers. The second step is to measure what is being done. In the field of quality control, for example, variations in physical, chemical, electrical, dimensional, and other properties are measured. In production control, all operations are measured to determine the time required for their performance and the capacities of equipment with which work is done. In budgetary control, measurement produces ratios of expenses to direct operation costs. In cost control, factors measured in terms of quality, waste, operating effectiveness, and expenses tell what costs are as operations are currently performed. In automation, electronic and mechanical operations must be measured accurately in terms of milliseconds before a whole system can be integrated.

C. CAPABILITY STUDIES

Analysis of measurements in step two, aided by many reliable statistical techniques, gives an accurate projection of what actually can be done. Managers frequently try to achieve the imposible in a given system. Just as frequently they could produce much more effectively if they knew the true capabilities of their production systems.

Take quality control for example. Measurements and statistical techniques can tell quickly whether or not a process can produce within required limits. If it cannot and if tolerances are realistic, steps can be taken to contrive processes or equipment that will produce effectively. As Dr. Joseph Juran [1] says, "The product tells on the process."

If one or two machines among several of the same kind have the capabilities for producing within required limits and the remainder produce outside-limit material, it becomes obvious that the remainder need repair or modification. When the percentage of defects gen-

[1] J. M. Juran, *Quality-Control Handbook,* McGraw-Hill Book Company, New York, 1951.

erated by some workmen is significantly higher than those of other workmen on the same operations, we conclude that there has been improper selection and placement of workmen or that job training is required. It is almost frightening when we learn how little some managers really know about their production and quality capabilities and how long these men continue to produce ineffectively. It is even more disturbing to contemplate the probable number of similar situations which are never discovered.

In production control we need to know quality process capabilities so that scrap and defect losses can be figured. The measurements made in step two must also be analyzed and output capabilities computed in terms of operation times, machine capacities, production mixes, and many other factors. These studies of process capabilities tell us what we *can* do.

In budgetary control, some general ratios for supervisory, staff, and other expenses can be set on a pro forma basis, but best results are obtained when proved capabilities are demonstrated by operation and are agreed to by those who are accountable for operating performance.

Cost control uses the measurements of time study, material utilization, and expense ratios to compute objective costs. Actual costs are used for current financial planning, but progressive cost engineers set targets based upon measurement.

In automation, process capabilities must be measured accurately. Fortunately, disturbances can be introduced to simulate the performance of automated processes under adverse conditions; this reveals true process capabilities.

D. OBJECTIVES

After we discover what we *can* do, we are ready to figure out what we *should* do. This may be either more or less than our capabilities. This decision then leads to plans for using excess capabilities or other plans to increase capabilities either for quality or quantity so that the objectives can be met.

E. FEEDBACK

If we shoot at a target but cannot tell how close to the bull's-eye our bullet hits, our next shot is likely to be no better than the first.

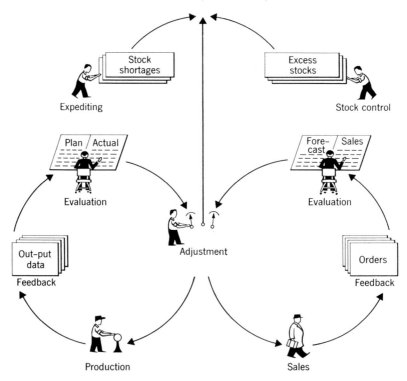

Fig. 43. A diagrammatic representation of production control.

circuits on the same basis of *Action, Feedback, Evaluation,* and *Adjustment.*

In automation, the results of closed loop control with feedback are easily understood because adjustment rapidly follows action. But this rapidity makes it difficult to see what is actually happening. The study of a simple automated circuit will give the student a clearer insight into the whole subject of controls.

The value of dynamic control and administrative review is that it keeps us from searching for trouble where none exists. But one caution about controls and review. Adjustments should not be set for too close control. In mechanisms, too close control will create *hunting,* which results in machines wearing themselves out by too frequent adjustments and their controlling devices becoming fatigued and confused. And so it is with engineers and managers. If their adjustments are too frequent they wear out, become tired and confused, and fade away.

SUMMARY

Control is the dynamic operating management function comprising the elements of *Action, Feedback, Evaluation,* and *Adjustment.* The basic principles of control are the same for quality control, production control, budgetary control, cost control, and other operating controls. Controls are set and operated in the following sequence:

1. We perform some act.
2. We measure the factors associated with the act.
3. From these measurements we determine what can be done.
4. Then we figure out what we would like to or should do.
5. Information about our current actions is fed back for evaluation and review.
6. This information is evaluated by comparing performance with capability.
7. Adjustments are made in accordance with this evaluation.

The dynamic cycle of *Action, Feedback, Evaluation,* and *Adjustment* can be applied to almost all of our efforts to achieve and maintain control. Control is the day-to-day function of operating management. When properly applied it keeps us from searching for trouble where none exists.

Review is the broad administrative management evaluation of *all* factors in the operation of an enterprise. Since there are complex interactions between these many factors, review will indicate corrective action deliberately and more slowly than operating control.

QUESTIONS TO CHECK COMPREHENSION

1. Are the principles of control the same for quality, production, budgetary and cost control?

2. Distinguish between control and review.

3. What is the basic sequence of events in a control cycle?

4. What are the seven essential steps in establishing and operating controls?

PROBLEMS

1. Based upon the operation of a company with which you are familiar or another operation that you visualize, prepare a procedure for the establishment of a control system for production.

2. Based on the information in problem 1 and other information on quality, cost and budgetary control, describe a method for review that will show the integration and interaction of these controls.

DISCUSSION CASE

The Melton Company produces precision machinery. It has recently established a system for quality control and one for production control. J. B. Matthews, Melton's president, gave his enthusiastic support to the establishment of these controls. He reasoned that with them in operation he and his administrative staff could give their full attention to matters of policy and long range planning.

Fred Johnson had been appointed Manager of Quality Control and Howard Wilson Manager of Production Control. These men tried to cooperate fully in the solution of each other's problems.

Wilson knew that President Matthews wanted increased output so that additional contracts could be taken. Wilson, therefore, kept increasing the factory production load. At first this increased load apparently led to a significant increase in output. Since there was no standards for work measurement or piece work rates, workmen assumed that the increased load meant a large backlog of orders with no possibility of running out of work. So they increased their efforts and effectiveness.

Johnson found that as he reduced tolerances more precise dimensions resulted. Workmen produced parts with dimensions on the high side so that remachining could correct any dimensions that happened to fall above the upper tolerance limits. Scrap losses from dimensions below minimum limits were low but rework increased.

Mr. Matthews accepted a large contract for precision machinery based upon a statement by Wilson that the extra load could be absorbed and the advice of Johnson that parts could be produced within still closer limits. When production on the new contract started, it soon became evident that costs would be higher than those estimated and that delivery dates on other orders as well as on the new contract could not be met. Wilson blamed Johnson because of the expensive rework caused by closer dimensional limits. Johnson replied that more work was being scheduled than could be produced.

The situation became so serious that J. B. Matthews called a staff meeting to determine causes for the trouble and to take remedial actions. Assume that you have been invited to this meeting. Present your ideas.

11

The Basis
of Production Planning

Production planning translates sales forecasts into master production schedules that every well-run factory follows in turning out goods for the market. Production planning also uses information developed in manufacturing planning and factory planning in order to perform its functions, which generally include:

1. Preparing production forecasts
2. Preparing master schedules
3. Preparing procurement schedules
4. Preparing department or area schedules
5. Preparing personnel schedules
6. Establishing stockroom procedures
7. Preparing authorizations for production
8. Establishing finished goods inventory controls
9. Preparing alternative plans for action

Production planning is used continuously in the operation of existing facilities to continue manufacture of goods that already are in production. It is also used in modifications and expansions of an existing industrial activity and in the introduction of a totally new activity.

There are three distinct types of production planning:

A. PROJECT PLANNING

This plans the manufacture of articles that probably will never be produced again in exactly the same form. Examples are special-purpose machines, solvent-recovery systems, and special turbogenerators.

Even this type of planning requires some basic manufacturing-planning information.

B. LOT OR BATCH PLANNING

This covers the planning of special customer or stock orders for lots of parts, batches of chemicals, lots of textiles, etc. Repeat orders may or may not be received, but it is important to have the necessary data from manufacturing planning on file for repeat orders if they do come in. Such data provide basic information needed for prompt, simple planning to meet orders for new products.

C. PROGRESSIVE OR CONTINUOUS PRODUCTION PLANNING

This is used on quantity production items that can be arranged to flow through equipment in continuous production. This type of planning requires extensive manufacturing-planning information.

Many companies use progressive-production planning and techniques on job orders. Manufacturing space is assigned to job orders for thousands or even millions of units. Equipment is put into place, the order is run off, and machines then are rearranged for the next order. If no large order is ready to be run, small lots are routed to the equipment where it stands, and rearrangement is postponed until large orders again are received.

Production planning and scheduling would be extremely difficult, if not impossible, unless the pertinent information were listed and recorded for ready reference and identification by part and product names and numbers. There may be some instances where operations are so simple and production planners so intimate with the operations that production planning can be done without having any manufacturing planning listed in some convenient form. These instances are few and they are dangerously dependent upon the intimate knowledge of one or a few men.

Try to imagine a production-planning engineer with no reference except blueprints and bills of material with which to establish production plans and schedules. He would be required to determine many complicated factors. This would be time-consuming. He also would have to go through the same complicated procedure at the beginning of each planning period and whenever any schedules required modification or correction.

It is evident, therefore, that all the manufacturing-planning information, including the raw materials listed on bills of material and assembly-parts lists, should be consolidated and listed in some convenient reference form. Such a reference form should contain:

1. Operations to be performed
2. Sequence of operations
3. Time required to set up or prepare for them
4. Time required to perform them
5. Number of men required
6. Tools, jigs, and fixtures required
7. Machines required
8. Capacities of the machines
9. Raw material required
10. Material waste to be expected
11. Number of units of production to be expected from a given input of raw material
12. Allowable manufacturing tolerances

This information is not only necessary for planning but is also continuously needed for reference in operation. Perhaps the oldest name used for this record is production routing. Other terms for it are manufacturing detail, manufacturing-planning analysis, and operation analysis.

The production routing, when properly designed, can serve many purposes:

1. It provides a basis on which a system of incentive wage payment may be administered.

2. It can serve as the basis for summarizing information from bills of material and thus be used in take-offs or breakdowns of material requirements.

3. The production routing can be used to determine personnel requirements in a take-off or breakdown of man-hours.

4. It can be used to determine equipment, tools, and fixtures required in the operations of machine-load charts.

5. It can be extended to show labor and material costs and thus serve as a cost sheet.

6. It can serve as a record for infrequently made products and so eliminate dependence upon fallible human memory.

A typical production-routing sheet is shown in Figure 44.   In referring to it, the reader will assume an order for 6,000 of these cross shafts, Part 296A.   The take-off of requirements would be as follows:

MATERIAL TAKE-OFF

6,000 units × 0.24 pound per unit = 1,440 pounds

A purchase requisition for 1,440 pounds of ½-inch cold-rolled steel bars in 10-foot lengths is issued.

MACHINE-LOAD TAKE-OFF

	Setup Hours	Units	Hours per Piece	Hours	7½-Hour Shifts
Abrasive cutoff saw	0.25 +	(6,000	× 0.0032)	= 19.45	2.60
Bench lathe	0.40 +	(6,000	× 0.0067)	= 40.60	5.41
Avery 1-spindle drill	0.30 +	(6,000	× 0.015)	= 90.30	12.04
Norton centerless grinder	0.25 +	(6,000	× 0.0023)	= 14.05	1.87

These hours or shifts are placed on the machine-load chart and there show that the specified machines will not be available for other work during those periods.   This subject will be treated in detail in Chapter 13.   The machine-load chart also indicates the number of people of the various skills required and the dates when they will be needed.

Figure 45 shows the production-routing procedure used in a heavy machine tool company producing both to stock and to order.   This company used the term operation analysis instead of production routing.

Production routings are generally prepared by the engineering department.   In any type of manufacturing activity there will be many engineering changes affecting materials, dimensions, tolerances, methods, and incentive wage rates.   It is logical, therefore, for the engineering department to issue revised routing sheets including these changes.   In some companies, however, routings are revised by the production-control department in accordance with notices of engineering changes issued by the engineering department.

In companies producing to stock, production-routing sheets generally are issued by the engineering department as soon as changes become effective, and are sent to all departments concerned.

PRODUCTION ROUTING

Part Name: Cross Shaft

Used on Assembly: 262509

Sheet: *1 of 1* Sheets

Part No.: 296A

Direct Labor per Unit $1.03891

Dept. No.	Oper. No.	Description	Mach.	Tools & Fix.	No. of Men	Set-up Hr.	Std. Hr. per Oper.	Std. Hr. per Unit	DL Cost per Std. Hr.	DL Cost per Unit	Material
1	1	Cut ½″ Cr to 6″ ± 0.003″ length	AB Saw	None	1	0.25	0.0032	0.0032	$1.40	$0.00448	*Purchase Description* ½″ Cold-rolled bars in 10′ lengths
6	2	Turn 0.250″ ± 0.003 slot 2.3″ ± 0.003 from end to depth of 0.125″ ± 0.002	S.B. Bench Lathe	Std. Tool Bit	1	0.40	0.0067	0.0067	1.55	0.010385	
3	3	Spot, drill, and ream ⅛″ ± 0.002 hole 1″ ± 0.003 from opposite end through center	Avery 1 SP D.P.	Fix. 296-A-3	1	0.30	0.015	0.015	1.35	0.02025	*Quantity per Unit* 0.24 lb.
7	4	Grind to .485″ ± 0.001	Norton C.L. Gr.	None	1	0.25	0.0023	0.0023	1.65	0.003795	*Purchase Price* $0.06 per lb.
26	5	Inspect			1F						*Material Cost per Unit* $0.0144

Fig. 44. A typical production routing.

Many companies engaged in job-order production prefer to have all manufacturing information cleared through the production-control department, as is indicated by Procedure A of Figure 46. Other companies use the procedure shown in B.

To simplify production routing and increase flexibility, definite machines usually are not specified on production routings. Instead, machine groups or centers are specified. Each machine in the group is capable of performing the work, but some jobs, in certain quantities, should properly be done on certain machines. As an example, machine group 7 may include engine lathes, hand screw machines, and automatic screw machines. If the job is a simple one in small quantity the foreman will produce it on an engine lathe. If the quantity is larger the foreman may wish to produce the job on a hand screw machine. If the quantity is large enough to justify the setup cost he may wish to produce the job on an automatic screw machine.

Freedom in selection of machines also allows the manufacturing foreman to utilize his full machine capacity. It may be, for example, that an order for some screws comes through at a time when all hand screw machines and automatic machines are loaded. If machines are not specified, the foreman may run this particular job on an engine lathe even though this is not the most efficient equipment. By so doing, he gets the order out without delay and does not let the engine lathe stand idle.

Many companies producing on a job-order basis seldom have repeat orders. In such instances there can be no production routing based on past performance. The engineering department must analyze each invitation to bid, prepare a sequence of operations, estimate the material requirements, and estimate the operating man-hours required, as well as the machine loading. From this information a price is computed; if an order is received, all essential information is issued to the manufacturing department. A comparison of estimates and the actual operation is made to determine the accuracy of the estimate and is filed as background information for future estimates. Estimators generally use as much fundamental data as possible. Helped by data on machine feeds and speeds, and with their own knowledge of the personnel and equipment capacities, these men produce surprisingly accurate estimates.

Referring back to Figure 44, it can be seen that production routing is vitally important in planning and scheduling. It is the basic reference used in taking off or breaking down the machine requirements, the personnel requirements, and the material requirements.

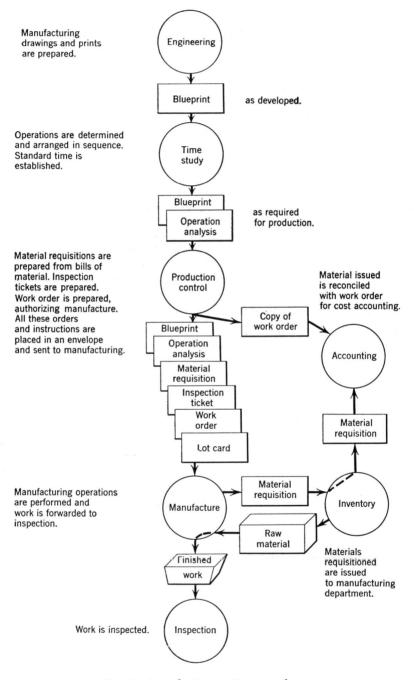

Fig. 45. A production-routing procedure.

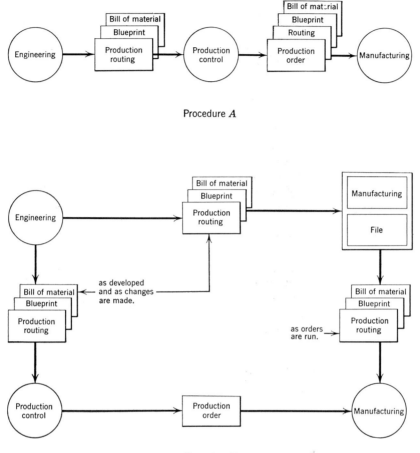

Procedure *A*

Procedure *B*

Fig. 46.   Other methods of issuing manufacturing information.

SUMMARY

Production planning, which translates sales estimates into master production schedules, depends largely upon basic information developed in manufacturing planning. This basic information is kept in a ready reference form generally called a production routing.

Production planning prepares procurement, personnel, and department schedules, establishes stockroom procedures and controls, prepares and issues work authorizations, establishes finished goods inventory controls, and maintains alternative plans of action.

Production routings list operations to be performed in their proper sequence. The time required to set up the equipment and the time to perform each operation are also listed. The number of men required and their skills, the machines to be used together with the tools, jigs, and fixtures required for each operation, the raw materials, and the gross amount to be used are also specified. The manufacturing tolerances are included in the description of each operation.

Production routings are almost indispensable in production planning. They can also be used for incentive wage administration and cost accounting, and they form a record of basic manufacturing information for current and future reference.

Because of engineering and process changes, production routings must be kept up to date. Some companies issue new production routings each time an order is to be produced. Other companies issue new production-routing sheets as engineering changes are made.

QUESTIONS TO CHECK COMPREHENSION

1. What information should be included in a production routing?

2. What purposes can the production routing serve?

3. Operation 6 on a production-routing sheet shows 0.60 hour per setup and 0.036 hour per piece. If 27,000 pieces are to be produced, how many 7½-hour shifts will be required?

4. In what organization are production routings generally prepared?

5. Do you think that the cost department should keep a separate listing of operations, the payroll another, the manufacturing another, and the planners still another? Or should one listing to serve all purposes be prepared cooperatively?

PROBLEMS

From the basic information contained in the production routing shown in Figure 44, solve the following problems:

1. Next month 100,000 units of Part 296A will be scheduled for production in 5 separate production runs. Assume that setup men receive $2.50 per hour. What will be the labor cost including setup?

2. Compute the material cost, assuming 3 per cent scrap.

3. Assume that next month will have 25 working days and that three 7½-hour shifts are to be operated each day. For this work there are available:

> 2 AB Cut-off Saws
> 1 South Bend Bench Lathe
> 4 Avery Single Spindle Drill Presses
> 1 Norton Centerless Grinder

Are there enough machines for this schedule of work?

4. Disregard machine capacity and assume a production schedule of 1,000,000 of these parts in some future month having 26 working days, each with three 7½-hour shifts. How many employees will be needed for this work? The answer will involve fractions, but these need not be confusing since the same employees will work on other items of production.

DISCUSSION CASE

The Boland Company, manufacturers of machine-tool parts, has relied upon its workmen to remember sequences of operations. Many workmen recorded these on small slips of paper. For about 15 years job orders had been produced in the shop, which was reasonably well equipped and which employed 210 workmen. Three foremen supervised the work. For some orders they had blueprints from customers, for other orders rough dimensional sketches, and for still others they received sample parts.

When inquiries were received by the manager, estimated prices were based on a broad background of toolroom and shop experience. Though actual costs were not often in agreement with estimates, the errors were sufficiently on the liberal side to return a modest net profit. When orders were obtained, the manager issued factory orders with only general information such as: "Make 6,000 trunnions like our old sample for the North Company." The foremen gave out the work with instructions on the number of pieces to machine. They also inspected the first few pieces completed.

Only a few parts were ordered frequently enough to warrant the use of inspection gages; other parts were checked by micrometers, surface plates, and height gages. The workmen not only memorized the sequences of operations and the nominal dimensions but also retained a general idea of dimensional tolerances that had been acceptable. That is to say, they recalled that in some instances certain dimensions had varied as much as ±0.006 inch without causing complaints from the customer.

At one time, the firm filled an order for 500 small pistons to be used in pumps. (See Figure 47.) The diameter of these pistons had to be held within ±0.0005 inch, but the distance from the center of the wrist pin hole to the end of the piston had to be at the nominal dimension +0 −0.001 inch. The original sequence of operations was:

1. Turn grooves, center-drill one end, and cut off +0.003 inch longer
2. Parallel straddle mill one end
3. Center-drill opposite end, and drill and ream wrist pin hole
4. Form straddle mill one end, parallel to hole
5. Locate on pin hole, and grind opposite end to +0 −0.001 inch
6. Center grind diameter to ±0.0005 inch

One worker machined the original pistons and made a few notes on the importance of using the wrist pin hole as a center for location. These pistons worked so well in the customer's pumps that after the lapse of a year he ordered 3,000 more.

By that time the worker who had handled the original order had left the company. His notes could not be found, but a sample piston

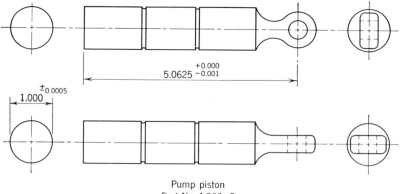

Pump piston
Part No. A 262-3

Fig. 47. Drawing of a pump piston.

hung on the sample board. A tag attached to it explained that extreme care should be exercised in the grinding operation. Since 30-day delivery had been promised, 5 men performed the various machine operations. The wrist pin hole was drilled and reamed last. The ends were ground just before the diameter was ground.

While the machining was in progress one foreman made some receiving gages. Upon checking the finished pistons, he found 20 per cent of them too long from the pin hole to the end. These were reground, using the pin hole for location, after which 63 per cent were too short and had to be scrapped. Only 37 per cent of the 3,000 pistons were shipped to the customer on time, with a promise of the remainder within 30 additional days.

The customer, of course, was displeased and resolved to place no more orders with Boland. The foremen grumbled about workmen being stupid and careless. The manager announced that nothing like that should happen again, but did not tell how to prevent it. He also complained that he had not had a vacation for many years because no one could estimate jobs while he was away.

Assume that you have been invited to discuss the problems of this company. List the causes for Boland's difficulties and recommend a course of remedial action.

12

Production Planning, a Basis for Financial Planning

In addition to plans and schedules for production, financial budgets must be prepared. Every manufacturing company must have a timetable of expenditures and receipts from which it can get a reasonably accurate picture of its cash position at any time during the operation period. Net working capital—cash—is the lifeblood of a company and must be adequate to meet its needs. If, for example, inventories eat up the whole net working capital, there will be no cash with which to meet payrolls and pay for raw materials. In most industries, the net working capital must also meet advertising bills and the cost of sales promotion. The need for a budget is, therefore, evident. All financial requirements of a company must be considered and planned in their relation to each other and in relation to the expected income, and this plan is embodied in the master budget.

The words schedule, budget, and plan are used interchangeably in this book. Each is a set of planned objectives to be used in continuous, critical comparison with actual accomplishment. It thus provides a quantitative measure of success and signals the necessity for corrective action.

The sales forecast, of course, provides an estimate of the income to be expected throughout any given period being planned. The forecast should not be used, however, to estimate the expenditures for direct labor cost, expenses, and raw materials, since both raw-material and finished goods inventories must be considered when the production and procurement budgets or plans are being established. Thus the master production schedule is the basis for most other budgets or plans.

The variations produced when budgets and inventories are balanced appear in the following simplified examples. It is assumed that

one of many products manufactured by a company is being planned
for production. Dealers' and retailers' stocks are known to be normal,
and the sales forecast indicates that 300,000 units of this one item will
be sold during the first quarter of the year. With a sales price of

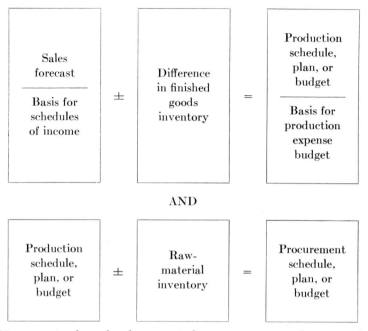

AND

$1.00 per unit, the sales forecast indicates an expected income from
this one item of $300,000 during the first quarter.

Experience has shown that orders from dealers are heavy at times
and light at others. A 30-day stock of finished goods is required to
meet these fluctuations. The finished goods inventory of this one
item is 180,000 units, and the production plan or schedule for the
first quarter will be:

$$
\begin{array}{rl}
      & 300,000 \quad \text{Sales forecast} \\
\text{less} & 180,000 \quad \text{Finished goods inventory} \\
\hline
      & 120,000 \\
\text{plus} & 100,000 \quad \text{Minimum inventory balance} \\
\hline
      & 220,000 \quad \text{Production schedule}
\end{array}
$$

Next comes planning for procurement. Here we find that a 2-
weeks' supply of raw materials for this one item has to be carried
in stores. Actually, however, there is a full month's supply of raw

material for this particular item. The procurement schedule, or budget, therefore, will be:

	220,000	Production schedule
less	100,000	Raw-material inventory
	120,000	
plus	50,000	2-week minimum balance
	170,000	Procurement schedule

Thus it is seen that the schedule of income will be based on 300,000 sales units. The production schedule and the manufacturing operating budget will be based on 220,000 units. The procurement budget will be based on the raw material required to produce 170,000 units.

In the foregoing example the net working capital position will improve, as far as this particular item is concerned, since both finished goods and raw-material inventories will be reduced. The opposite will prevail, however, in an example that is based on the same sales forecast and the same minimum balance requirements for raw-materials and finished goods inventories, but assumes that the finished goods inventory is depleted and that there are unfilled orders for 50,000 units. Under these conditions, the production plan or schedule for the first quarter will be:

	300,000	Sales forecast
plus	50,000	Back orders
plus	100,000	Minimum inventory balance
	450,000	Production schedule

Let us further assume that only a 1-week supply of raw materials is in stock. Then the procurement budget will be:

	450,000	Production schedule
less	25,000	Raw-material inventory
	425,000	
plus	50,000	2-week minimum balance
	475,000	Procurement schedule

In other words, an income schedule based on 300,000 sales units must be balanced against a production schedule and manufacturing, or operating, budget based on 450,000 units and a procurement budget for 475,000 units. This situation will require careful financial planning in order to maintain adequate working capital.

When the master production schedule has been prepared, take-offs are made of the direct labor hours or shifts, the machine shifts, the personnel, and the raw-material requirements. Using these various take-offs, procurement budgets, equipment and construction budgets, operating budgets, administrative budgets, sales budgets, and advertising budgets are developed, after which all are combined into a master financial budget. This last is extremely important, since it shows whether the sales volume is sufficient to break even or produce a profit. If a loss is indicated, the whole planning structure must be reviewed and modified.

The reason for having a number of budgets is that operations under each one must be assigned to some individual. Each of these individuals must be given the full responsibility for the results of his activity in their relation to his budget. Operating budgets are generally prepared for each manufacturing department, so that each operating foreman can be given clear and full responsibility for adhering rigidly to his budget or for deviating from it. Operating budgets are yardsticks that permit the company and its various departments to know how effectively each is operating expense-wise in relation to its planned objectives. Budgets also may reveal the need for corrective action in departments that might otherwise seem to be performing excellently. Thus a department meeting its production schedule may have an excess of indirect expense that seriously affects costs. On the other hand, a department may be operating at much less than its budgeted expense. Unless methods have been radically improved, this indicates that its production schedule is not being met—a suggestion that can be immediately verified or disproved by comparison of actual and scheduled production. If the reduction in expense was actually accomplished without sacrifice of any activity proper to the department, a new standard of performance may be in the making. If the results can be reproduced for a number of months, a new objective should be established by reducing the budget.

The budget for departmental operation is generally based on an expected level of direct activity during 3 or 6 months. It is assumed that if direct activity falls below this level, corrective action to reduce indirect expenses must be taken by the person responsible. The way in which the budget works is shown by the typical departmental budget statement that follows.

A first glance at the variance columns in this record may suggest that the underrun of $244, or 3.77 per cent, represents a real saving and therefore is desirable. Actually the record is mixed, with faults outweighing good points. The underrun on material handling is

Operating Budget

Department XXX   September, 1956

Controllable Expense

Account	Budget	Actual	Dollars Variance	Per Cent Variance
Foremen	$ 400	$ 400		
Assistant foremen	600	600		
Inspectors	400	460	+ 60	+15.00
Clerks	200	210	+ 10	+ 5.00
Material handlers	1,600	1,426	− 174	− 10.87
Rework	800	600	− 200	− 25.00
Scrap	500	800	+300	+60.00
Supplies	760	920	+160	+21.05
Overtime wages	1,200	800	− 400	− 33.33
	$6,460	$6,216	− $244	− 3.77%

good; it resulted from improved planning and can be carried on into the future. The overrun on supplies is a fault but not a grave one; it will not recur but will level out in the month of October. The overrun on scrap is more serious; it suggests that more rework should have been done or that the number of irreparably defective pieces was abnormally high. The underrun on overtime, which looks well in this record, takes on another meaning when the department's actual production is compared with its schedule. This shows that normal production was based on $1,200 worth of overtime work; the $400 seemingly saved caused a serious production shortage. The department would have done well to spend those $400 and turn out the material needed to meet orders.

Thus we see that the detailed operating budget, balanced against actual operating expenses, reveals both weaknesses and strong points in this department's record. With it as a guide, the foreman may refine or correct each phase of his work instead of relying upon overall impressions. There is also less likelihood of unknowingly perpetuating and increasing poor performance.

In some companies, department operating budgets include certain prorated accounts, such as general plant management, safety and fire protection, air conditioning, and heating, over which the foreman or supervisor has no control. One school of thought considers this to be bad practice. It maintains that foremen are not generally satisfied with the basis or distribution of these charges. They will be inclined to complain about them while a number of overruns in their controllable expenses receive no attention. The other school of thought holds that the foreman is a manager who should realize that his operations must meet these expenses as well as those over which he can exercise control. His position, therefore, is comparable to that of top management, which must conduct the company's operations so that they meet taxes, interest, and so on, as well as the day-to-day expenses of operation.

Companies that operate on a job-order basis cannot correlate budgets with production estimates of so many units for each sales item. They have a rough estimate of total dollar volume of sales, it is true, but this provides no satisfactory basis for department operating schedules. These companies generally use a flexible budget, in which expenses are allotted according to the varying percentages of capacity at which departments may operate. The percentage of capacity is determined by the standard hours of direct labor produced. The following example makes use of the latter figures:

Standard Hours	4,000 80%	4,500 90%	5,000 100%	5,500 110%	6,000 120%
Foremen	$ 500	$ 500	$ 500	$ 500	$ 500
Assistants			300	300	300
Inspectors	250	250	250	250	500
Clerks	200	200	200	200	200
Scrap	80	90	100	110	120
Cutting oils	128	144	160	176	192
Tools	480	540	600	660	720
	$1,638	$1,724	$2,111	$2,196	$2,532

As soon as the foreman gets an estimate of what his operating level will be, he starts to adjust his expenses so that they will not exceed the allowances for that percentage of the normal operating capacity. At the end of the month his actual percentage of capacity is computed from the standard hours produced, and his budget is selected to correspond with it. This budget is compared with his actual expenses.

Companies effectively using operating budgets find that, in addition to pointing up areas for improvement, the department budgets dis-

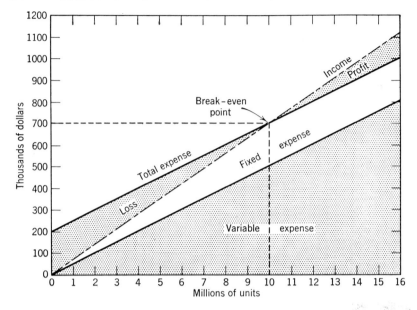

Fig. 48. A simple break-even chart.

cover outstanding individuals who can be promoted to more important management positions. This is particularly true where foremen are rotated periodically from one department to another. Comparisons among several individuals managing the same activity can then be made.

When all budgets have been completed the treasurer's office can use them for several financial analyses. One important analysis is the break-even chart. Such charts can indicate whether or not the forecast sales volume is sufficient to break even or return a profit. Because the cost of production is made up of some variable and some fixed charges, a certain volume of goods must be sold before the unit profit based on the variable cost pays for the fixed expense. Any volume over the break-even point is plus business, and the percentage of profit before taxes increases geometrically with this increased volume.

For a simplified example, let us assume that a company makes only one product and that careful financial analyses reveal a fixed expense of $200,000, a variable expense of $0.05 per sales unit, and a net selling price of $0.07 per sales unit. The difference of $0.02 between the variable expense and the selling price means that 10,000,000 units must be sold to meet the fixed expense. The break-even point, therefore, is 10,000,000 units.

In actual practice, where many products generally are produced by one company, this determination is not quite so simple. Actually some elements of cost will be fixed, some variable, and some semifixed. Figure 48 shows a simple break-even chart based on the foregoing simple data. The sum of the fixed and semifixed expense as shown in the figure would not actually be a zone between the solid line representing total expense and the parallel solid line representing

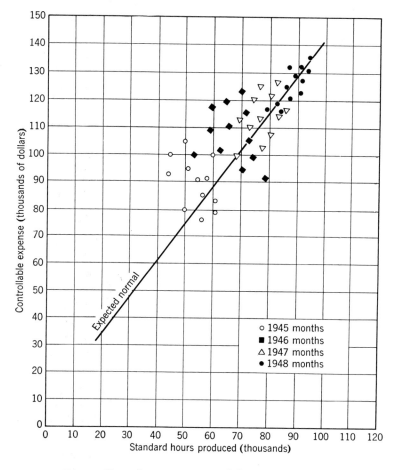

Fig. 49. Typical improvement with budgetary control.

variable expense because, when one calculates expansion from one level of activity to one somewhat higher, a supervisor or inspector cannot be fractionated. There will actually be a widening of the zone until the increased activity wholly absorbs the added supervisor and/or inspector.

Though the chart shown in Figure 48 is not truly accurate, it provides a rather good first approximation. Its purpose here is to present a simple picture. Many companies calculate actual expenses for several points on the chart and thereby obtain a more accurate picture of the levels where expenses may take sudden jumps, as, for example, where an additional shift is started.

No sudden improvement in expense control should be expected during the first few years of budgetary control. Figure 49 shows the typical gradual improvement to be expected.

SUMMARY

Financial budgets are necessary in the operation of a business. Their figures for income are based upon estimates of sales, whereas those for expenses are derived from schedules. Procurement budgets, equipment and construction budgets, operating budgets, administrative budgets, sales budgets, and advertising budgets must all be combined into a master financial budget. When total figures for income and expense are charted for various levels of activity, break-even points can be established, and thus the amount of profit or loss to be expected can be forecast.

Operating budgets are generally broken down into department or area budgets. This is done so that the responsibility for meeting each budget can be assigned to one individual in each department or area. Where production is at a reasonably constant level, fixed budgets are generally effective. Where production fluctuates, flexible budgets are more satisfactory. A few years of actual operation and adjustment of operating budgets are required before control from them can become effective.

All budgets, plans, or schedules are planned objectives used continuously for critical comparison of actual with planned or potential performance. Such budgets thus reveal the need for corrective action and suggest methods that give superior results.

QUESTIONS TO CHECK COMPREHENSION

1. What is used as a basis for estimating the income of a company?

2. How is the production budget or schedule determined? Show in an equation.

3. How is the procurement budget developed? Show in an equation.

4. What is a budget? How is it used?

5. If you were asked to establish operating budgets for a company producing on a job-order basis with wide fluctuations in activity, would you consider budgets of the fixed or the flexible type?

6. What purpose do break-even charts serve?

7. Would you expect operating budgets to become fully effective as soon as they are introduced?

8. Why is it important for companies to know what net working capital requirements will be in future operating periods?

9. The sales forecast for a certain production item is 1,000,000 units for the coming 3 months. A minimum stock of 200,000 units is required. The actual stock on hand at the beginning of the quarter is 500,000 units. What should the production schedule be?

PROBLEMS

A company with a top monthly production capacity of $8,000,000 in sales value has a net working capital of $4,000,000 at the beginning of the year. Its stock of finished goods is worth $2,000,000 and its raw material stock has a value of $500,000 at the beginning of the year. Fixed expenses are $1,000,000 per month and variable expenses are 60 per cent of sales values. The sales forecast and the production schedule are:

	Sales Forecast	Production Schedule in Terms of Sales Dollars
January	$ 3,000,000	$ 7,000,000
February	3,000,000	7,000,000
March	4,000,000	7,000,000
April	4,000,000	8,000,000
May	6,000,000	8,000,000
June	12,000,000	8,000,000
July	12,000,000	5,000,000
August	14,000,000	8,000,000
September	9,000,000	8,000,000
October	7,000,000	7,000,000
November	4,000,000	4,000,000
December	3,000,000	4,000,000
	$81,000,000	$81,000,000

1. Assume that each production unit has a sales value of one dollar and compute a monthly break-even sales value.

2. When will additional working capital be needed?

3. How much additional working capital will be needed?

4. When can a loan for this amount be repaid?

DISCUSSION CASE

The Walter Smith Plastics Company was an outgrowth of a war contract that Mr. Smith had obtained and filled to the complete satisfaction of the prime contractor and the armed services. When the war and the contract ended, he and most of his 30 employees took an extended vacation. A few of the employees obtained other jobs.

While Mr. Smith was away, the company from which he had received the wartime subcontract wrote to say that it needed several molded plastic parts. Blueprints of these parts were enclosed with the letter, with an invitation to bid on them.

Smith sent telegrams to his former employees telling them of the invitation and asking them if they would be willing to return to work.

A majority replied favorably. He, therefore, roughed out some estimates, placed his bid, and headed home.

Although Smith's relations with the prime contractor during wartime had been good, he was not content to be a subcontractor or supplier. He preferred to have a line of products of his own, and had even made up a number of molds for ash trays and other novelties. With the orders from his old wartime customer as a basis for operations and income, he felt able to embark on the venture of making his own products and offering them to dealers.

Production on contracts from his wartime customer showed Smith that his estimates had not included a reasonable allowance for defective pieces and overhead. His own product, however, returned attractive unit profits.

The lease on his factory building, which was expiring, specified that he must exercise his option to purchase the property or it would be put up for sale. Since Smith did not wish to go to the expense of moving his heavy equipment, he exercised his option and bought the property. This reduced his net working capital to 20 per cent of expected gross annual sales.

With the impending operating loss on contract items, he built up stocks of his own items to an estimated 3 months' supply of each. This further reduced his net working capital.

Because his deliveries on contracts had not been good, these contracts were not renewed at the end of his first year. Smith was faced with a drastically reduced sales volume and insufficient working capital to meet his factory payroll.

Mr. Smith has asked you to attend a meeting to discuss his problems. List what is wrong and suggest remedies:

13

Procurement

Purchasing is one of the most vital functions within industry. Basically, it procures the materials, parts, and supplies that keep the company going. Financially, its activities account, on the average, for about 40 per cent of the money expended in costs.

Although decentralization has proved itself effective in many types of organization and manufacturing operation, a great majority of companies maintain centralized purchasing departments. Thus they secure the benefits of quantity prices, uniform quality, and standardized buying policies. They also are able to assemble an array of technical knowledge and skills of suppliers that could not be maintained in small, decentralized departments.

Cooperation between a centralized purchasing department and decentralized production planning and control poses problems of communication. Purchasing must receive a steady flow of information about material requirements, inventory positions, and delays in delivery of raw materials. Buyers must study both long-range and short-term sales and production forecasts. Many raw materials requiring long process intervals in their preparation necessitate forward buying. These intervals must be allowed for when procurement schedules are planned.

The primary function of any purchasing department is to develop and maintain sources of supply. To learn each supplier's managerial ability or limitations with respect to current or expanded demands is in itself a complex and important task. In addition to this, alternative sources of supply must be encouraged and developed, both as stopgaps when certain suppliers fail and as means of securing improved material or reduced prices.

The purchasing department considers service and quality quite as much as price. Besides meeting their promises of delivery, suppliers must show an eagerness to cooperate in solving common problems and making technical improvements. They must also offer value, both intrinsic and in relation to price. For example, buyers will be quick to specify a cutting tool that has twice the life but costs less than twice as much as another cutting tool. Similarly, certain raw materials will give better production yields than others, or will result in more attractive goods. The alert purchasing department will discover these advantages and will specify materials that provide them. Well-organized purchasing departments maintain complete and detailed specifications covering all raw materials and finished articles that they are required to procure. Each supplier receives copies of specifications for the things he supplies. Since these specifications

---

No. 166–262

Issue No. 6
Date X/X/X

RAW-MATERIAL SPECIFICATION COVERING
MOLDING COMPOUND NU 67–C

Our Code Nu 67–C

Vendor Code PR 9824

Property	Requirement	Test
1. Granulation	Thru 12 mesh 5% max. Thru 140 mesh 10% max.	ASTM D–392–38
2. Bulk factor	2.7	ASTM D–392–38
3. Molded sp. gr.	1.40 max.	ASTM D–392–38
4. Molding shrinkage (inch per inch)	0.007 max.	ASTM D–551–41
5. Impact strength (Izod)	.24 foot-pound per inch of notch max.	ASTM D–48–43T
6. Tensile strength	6000 psi min.	ASTM D–48–43T
7. Flexural strength	8000 psi min.	ASTM D–48–43T
8. Dielectric strength (short-time)	300 volts per mil min.	ASTM D–48–43T
9. Water absorption (Max. weight gain %)	0.70%	ASTM D–48–43T

All values of limits indicated are inclusive.

Shipping and Packaging Instructions

This material shall be delivered in air-tight, sealed steel containers of 40- to 20-qt. capacity, conveying 50 lb. net or 25 lb. net, respectively. Containers shall be labeled in accordance to contents, net weight, production lot number, inspection control code, and name of vendor.

Fig. 50. Specimen raw-material specification.

Regardless of the type of production or the organizational arrangement in force, the production-control department and the purchasing department work in intimate cooperation.

Many companies learned a good lesson during World War II, when certain basic raw materials were scarce, or in so-called short supply. During the early part of the war these companies hoarded plentiful materials in the hope that they would somehow obtain the scarce materials to go with them and would thereupon be able to make their accustomed products. When scarce materials were not forthcoming, these companies found themselves with unbalanced and excessive inventories that would not turn over. This caused shortages of working capital and storage facilities when both were badly needed.

Today most planning and purchasing departments gear their plans and purchases to the component raw materials in shortest supply. The result has been healthy inventory situations. As an example, suppose that a company needs 100 tons of aluminum, 200 tons of steel, and 50 tons of brass to manufacture its monthly schedule of a product. Further assume that only 150 tons of steel are available. The company will be wise to order 150 tons of steel, 75 tons of aluminum, and 37.5 tons of brass. This will enable the company to meet only 75 per cent of its production schedule, but its money and space will not be tied up in 25 unused tons of aluminum and 12.5 tons of brass. These can be bought if and when the steel needed for further production is secured.

In job-order production, delivery dates generally are based on time needed to procure the necessary raw materials, but in continuous production a supply must always be on hand. If the supply is excessive, added working capital will be needed and will be a charge to inventory; added storage facilities will be required, and the company will run the danger of loss if commodity prices fall and thereby reduce the inventory value. If the supply is insufficient, on the other hand, production will be interrupted, costs will increase, and planning will break down. Companies that produce to stock must have some device that tells them when orders must be placed, and in what quantities, to insure continuous production.

Excluding such factors as quantity discounts, cost of storage space, and the cost of handling orders, the ideal maximum inventory to be carried for continuous production is determined by:

1. The time required for a supplier to complete an order and make delivery.

2. The minimum order, which is the smallest number of items the supplier can accept as an economical production run.

3. The rate of consumption by the purchaser.

When the purchaser's production is at a constant rate, this can be expressed in the following formula:

Ideal maximum inventory

$$= \left(\begin{array}{c} \text{Number of weeks to} \\ \text{produce order} \end{array} + K \right) \times \text{(Weekly consumption)}$$

| | Supplier Dependability | |
	Dependable	Unproven
When supplier is near	$K = 1$	$K = 2$
When supplier is within 500 miles	$K = 2$	$K = 3$
When supplier is within 1,000 miles	$K = 3$	$K = 4$
When supplier is within 2,000 miles	$K = 5$	$K = 6$

It must be understood that the foregoing formula establishes only a hypothetical figure that must be proved by actual performance of the various suppliers. The degree of dependability may vary greatly, and K factors must be developed for each item. When a supplier's performance improves or becomes unfavorable the K factor must be adjusted accordingly.

The minimum order is an important consideration. If less than a given quantity increases the unit cost more than 5 per cent, for example, it will be more economical to order the supplier's minimum quantity, paying for it from working capital or borrowing the money to do so at lower rate of interest.

In a practical application of this formula, we may assume that a supplier is 50 or 100 miles away and is dependable, thus receiving a K rating of 1. He needs 2 weeks to produce an order, which must not be for less than 1,000 units in order to be filled at his standard quoted price. Let us further assume that the purchaser will consume the raw material at a constant rate of 1,000 units per week. Under these conditions our formula gives:

(2 weeks to produce order + 1) × (1,000 units consumed per week)

$$= 3,000 \text{ units maximum inventory}$$

and ordering, receipts, consumption, and inventory work out as follows:

Week	1st	2nd	3rd	4th	5th
Order	2,000		2,000		2,000
Received			2,000		2,000
Consumed	1,000	1,000	1,000	1,000	1,000
Stock	3,000	2,000	3,000	2,000	3,000

It will be noted that the formula contains a 1-week safety factor. Sometimes, after long association, supplier and purchaser establish such perfect coordination that this safety factor may be reduced or omitted. Even then, however, accidents may happen, and there should be some contractual agreement to "protect for production."

The foregoing formula can be used only when weekly consumption is at a constant rate. Some manufacturing departments prefer to set constant monthly production levels, producing the whole schedule in a few days or a week and then turning equipment over to some other type of production. This requires a different plan for order control. Instead of maintaining *ideal inventories,* ordering must be based on the *order point* and must provide an inventory equal to the maximum quantity that can possibly be consumed in a week. This can be expressed in the following formula:

$$\text{Order point} = \left(\begin{array}{c} \text{Number of weeks} \\ \text{to produce order} \end{array} + K \right) \times \left(\begin{array}{c} \text{Maximum possible} \\ \text{weekly consumption} \end{array} \right)$$

For the sake of an example, we may again assume a supplier whose K rating is 1. This time, however, production is at an erratic rate, and the purchaser may elect to consume as many as 2,000 units in 1 week.

$$\left(\begin{array}{c} \text{2 Weeks to} \\ \text{produce order} \end{array} + 1 \right) \times \left(\begin{array}{c} \text{2,000 Possible units} \\ \text{consumed per week} \end{array} \right)$$

$$= 6,000 \text{ units} = \text{Order point}$$

Week	1st	2nd	3rd	4th	5th	6th	7th
Order		2,000	2,000	2,000	2,000		
Received				2,000	2,000	2,000	2,000
Consumed	0	2,000	2,000	0	500	1,500	2,000
Stock	6,500	4,500	2,500	4,500	6,000	6,500	6,500

With this arrangement of intermittent production the maximum economic inventory will frequently be exceeded. The supplier must be advised of such arrangements because he will probably have to arrange his production on a continuous basis to meet the quarterly requirements.

The foregoing indicates that it is important to plan and schedule production so that raw and purchased finished materials are consumed at a constant rate. Otherwise there can be no assurance that inventories will be at ideal maximum quantities or less. Of equal importance is the fact that the problems of the purchasing and stores organizations are many times multiplied when production is intermittent and irregular. Manufacturing problems are also increased because of preparation time at each resumption of production. Operator efficiency is reduced and waste generally increases until the operators have gone through a period of practice that is generally called "getting their hand in again."

It should be understood that these formulas are guides to give some idea of maximum inventories that should not be exceeded and to indicate when orders should be placed. If smaller inventories than those indicated by the formulas prove safe, they should be used and the formulas should be so adjusted. Common sense should also be exercised on small inexpensive items where the cost of a year's supply may be less than the cost of placing and receiving an order.

These treatments apply particularly to production to stock. Ordering materials for job-order production requires an altogether different treatment and is covered in Chapter 14.

SUMMARY

Purchasing is an important part of industrial activity because materials, parts, and supplies constitute a large part of the cost of manufacturing. Production planning and control depend upon purchasing to arrange for deliveries of the desired types of raw materials in specified quantities at the right times. The purchasing department must also maintain adequate and alternative sources of supply.

Where goods are manufactured to stock, the production-planning department generally prepares a blanket take-off of all materials needed for the period being planned. If the period is a quarter, 6 semimonthly or 13 weekly deliveries may be specified. From these lists and delivery requirements, the purchasing department arranges for the flow of raw materials into the manufacturing facility. In job-order production, purchase requisitions are prepared by the planning department to cover each customer's order as it is received. The purchasing department arranges for deliveries of these materials.

When component raw materials needed to manufacture an item are scarce, it is important that orders for the other component raw materials be geared to the one in shortest supply. Unless this is done inventories become unbalanced and excessive.

Ideal maximum inventories that should not be exceeded can be computed when the purchaser's production is at a constant rate, and proximity and dependability of the supplier are considered. When production is not at a reasonably constant rate, raw-material inventories are best maintained by the establishment of order points.

QUESTIONS TO CHECK COMPREHENSION

1. What are the primary responsibilities of a purchasing department?

2. Certain information is needed so that a correct raw material can be ordered. In what form is this information compiled, to forestall any doubt about the specific characteristics of the material?

3. If purchase requisitions are issued by the planning department, how will it know that the material actually has been ordered and received?

4. If six basic materials are required to produce an item, and one of them is in short supply, should the remaining five items be procured in full quantities, or in quantities proportionate to that of the one in short supply?

5. What are the arguments against decentralizing a purchasing department?

6. What other factors in addition to price must a buyer take into consideration?

7. In manufacturing to stock, is it necessary to prepare a purchase requisition for each material needed for the period being planned? How can this be simplified?

8. What are the disadvantages and risks associated with the maintenance of excess raw-material inventories?

9. When goods are manufactured to stock, what risks are involved in hand-to-mouth buying?

10. Why is cooperation between purchasing and production planning necessary?

11. Would you consider the average purchasing function to be as important as the average manufacturing function? Give the reasons for your answer.

12. Should a purchasing department maintain records of each supplier's quality level? If so, why?

13. How is the accounting department kept informed of what has been ordered and what has been received, so that it can pay invoices properly?

14. Who should follow up on deliveries from suppliers: manufacturing, production planning, or purchasing? Why?

PROBLEMS

1. A supplier of a certain item is located 1,000 miles from the purchaser. He has demonstrated his dependability. His process interval is such that he needs 2 weeks to produce an order. The smallest quantity he can economically produce is 2,000 units. The purchaser will consume 3,000 units per week at a continuous rate. What is the ideal maximum inventory of this item for this purchaser to carry?

2. If this purchaser produced intermittently in various quantities each week, would his inventory and ordering problems be simpler or more difficult?

DISCUSSION CASE

At the end of World War II, Pitston Inc. found itself with many excess raw-material items in its inventory. The value of this material had decreased to a point where a serious loss would have to be written off. The purchasing agent who reported to the treasurer of the company was blamed for this situation. He defended his position by pointing out that he had been encouraged to hoard as much material as possible to insure continued operation of the business. He also pointed out that some materials had been sold at a profit during the war.

The organizational arrangement, as shown in Figure 52, was simple but somewhat unusual. An analysis of costs showed that raw materials constituted 72 per cent, direct labor and factory expense 18 per cent, and selling and general expense 10 per cent.

A meeting was called to establish some arrangement to prevent any

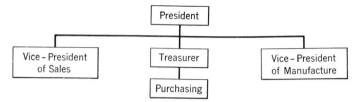

Fig. 52. Organization chart.

future excess raw-material inventories. The treasurer proposed a budget plan under which the purchasing agent would be allowed to place orders only to the value of 75 per cent of the cost value of production in any one month. The cost value of production would be calculated from the schedule at the beginning of each month. When the purchasing agent had placed orders for 75 per cent of this amount, he would be permitted to place additional orders that month only with the treasurer's approval.

The purchasing agent complained that this would give him only a 3 per cent leeway. He suggested that he would prefer to work to maximum and minimum stock limits, which were based on minimum risks of running out of materials on the one hand, and the building up of excess inventories on the other. He produced a stock list showing such maximum and minimum limits. Moreover, he demonstrated that, under this policy, actual purchases during the next 6 months would be considerably less than 75 per cent of production costs because he would exhaust present excess items in stock.

The treasurer overruled the purchasing agent. The president was inclined to accept the purchasing agent's plan, but he had placed the responsibility for correcting the situation on the shoulders of the treasurer. The meeting is in progress and you are a participant. State what is wrong and why, and suggest the action to be taken.

14

Stores and Raw-Material Stock Control

Under some organizational arrangements the purchasing department operates the receiving department as well as the raw-material stockrooms and storages. In other organizations a material-control section of the production-planning department operates these divisions. Principles of operation remain the same under either arrangement.

Planning demands that raw materials, piece parts, subassemblies, and finished products be identified and listed by number. In many identification systems, the numbers assigned to these various materials possess categorical meanings. Thus, the first three digits of an identification number may indicate the material composition such as:

010 steel	013 plastic
011 brass	014 glass
012 rubber	and so on

The next pair of digits may indicate the type of processing to which the material has been subjected:

010-10 steel billets	010-13 steel forgings
010-11 steel blooms	010-14 steel sheets
010-12 steel castings	and so on

The last three or four digits may designate the specific items. Thus, 010-14-0365 may be 52 x 52-inch extra deep-draw autobody sheet steel.

Identification numbers enable the storeroom force to put like parts or material together, but there also must be some device that tells where these things shall be stored and where they can be found. To locate a person we refer to his address—his city, street, and house number. Materials must also have addresses in the stockrooms. Visible card files generally show the stockroom locations by aisle number, bin number or floor-block number, bin section number, and shelf or possibly drawer number.

Where stockroom space is ample, definite locations are assigned to each part or material, and it is always stored there. Companies crowded for space and having various materials that arrive seasonally must store them in whatever space is available. Card index files, therefore, may show varying quantities of the same material stored in several different locations. When material is released from the stockroom, that stored at one point generally is exhausted before another storage unit is tapped.

Industry demands precise correlation between production planning and control of materials. In the days when each automobile chassis was built on a separate stand, materials often arrived late and mechanics "filled in" by assembling parts that were available. The conveyor line ruled out this stopgap method, for the man who performs one small operation on a moving chassis cannot shift to something else if he has no material. Work authorizations, therefore, are not issued until all materials to fill the schedule are on hand, ready to be transported from storage to the production lines.

The automobile industry was the first one to establish this policy of operating with everything planned and available, or of shutting down until even the smallest gap had been closed. The decision was not easy to make; its complications and implications were carefully studied and weighed. The deciding factor was a conviction that the policy would make faults of planning and control so obvious that they could be quickly corrected. If poor planning and control could be obscured by overtime work, or by performing operations out of their normal sequence, the basic faults might never be corrected. But when five or ten thousand men were told to go home at eleven o'clock in the morning because of a planning failure, every executive from the plant manager down was sure to be out on the production floor to learn the facts and find means of making sure that the failure would not recur.

Although few other industries work with quite the clockwork precision of an automobile factory, all can have their operations disrupted by poor planning or material controls. The author has seen situations in which a simple failure to have packaging material on hand caused whole departments to be inundated by unpacked products until exit aisles were blocked and employees had to climb over the piles to go home. It would have been much better to withhold work authorization until all was in readiness for production, or to shift to some other work for which materials were ready.

In operating a raw-material stockroom, records must be kept of all materials received and disbursed, and balances of materials on hand must be carefully checked. In addition, actual physical inventories are made periodically to correct clerical errors, and for accounting purposes.

To know what material is actually on hand is important, but it is equally essential to know how much of it has been ordered and how much is available for future planning. There are several methods of keeping such records, but the one that has proved most reliable is based upon double checking that promptly reveals clerical errors. This method also shows what action should be taken as soon as a transaction is posted.

For each item of raw and purchased finished material a record is kept that shows four quantities in four categories:

1. *On order*—material that has been ordered but not yet received
2. *On hand*—material actually on hand
3. *Reserved*—material allocated to specific orders or schedules
4. *Available*—material available for future planning

The first two categories tell us whether material is actually in the stockroom or is to be expected by a specified date. In either event it may be reserved for a specific order or schedule of work, thus becoming unavailable. Available material, either on hand or on order, has not been reserved for any specific commitment. This material, therefore, is free for assignment in future planning.

The term *available* often leads to confusion, for to most people it indicates that the material is physically on hand and ready for use. Here, however, it means that the material is *available for planning*. It may be on hand or it may be on order, but it has not been reserved for the production of any order. Although not grammatically correct the term *unreserved* would perhaps be less confusing.

$$\text{On hand} + \text{On order} = \text{Reserved} + \text{Available}$$

The sum of the material on order and that actually on hand must always equal the sum of material reserved and that available for future planning. A quick comparison of these figures can be made after every posting; if they fail to agree, an error has been made or some transaction, such as the placing of an order, has been overlooked. This system therefore warns those who operate it of steps that must be taken after any posting is made. Records themselves are generally kept on cards in readily accessible files of the visible drawer or visible rotary type. Data are posted from purchase requisitions, stock releases to production, receiving reports, copies of stock reservations for customers' orders, or schedules developed from forecasts.

Beginning with the receipt of a customer's order or the preparation of a schedule of items to be produced to stock, a list of component materials is prepared. Purchase orders are written for all raw materials that are needed. As purchase orders are prepared, the quantities of each item are posted in the *on order* column of the stock record. The quantities needed for the customer's order also are posted in the *reserved* column to show that they are reserved for production that has been planned and are not available for future planning.

As shipments of materials arrive and are cleared by receiving inspection, the quantities on receiving reports are subtracted from quantities in the *on order* column and added to the *on hand* column.

As materials are withdrawn from stock for production, the quantities are subtracted from both the *on hand* and *reserved* columns. These two postings complete the planning phase of stock control of these raw materials.

Sometimes a production schedule of stock items is reduced or a customer's order is canceled after raw materials for it have been received or a supplier's production has progressed so far that the purchase order cannot be canceled. When this happens, the materials involved are subtracted from the *reserved* column and added to the *available* column, showing that they can be used in future planning. The *available* column also lists quantities left over when purchases in round figures exceed planned or actual requirements. Minimal balances also are carried in the *available* column so that production of some things can begin before materials are received or ordered.

To see how such a record actually works, let us assume that a company uses $\frac{5}{16}$—18 cap screws both in items produced to stock and also in others to meet job orders. Experience has shown that a minimal balance of 100,000 screws should be maintained. On December 1, the stock card shows the minimal balance both on hand and available:

SCREWS, CAP $\frac{5}{16}$—18

On Order	On Hand	Reserved	Available
	100,000		100,000

On December 15, the planning department advises that 200,000 screws are required for January stock production. The clerk immediately lists 200,000 as reserved, issues a purchase requisition for the same number, and posts the following record:

On Order	On Hand	Reserved	Available
PR. 406 200,000 Dec. 15	100,000	Jan. Sched. 200,000	100,000

On December 20, a customer's order requiring 20,000 is received. The clerk immediately lists 20,000 as reserved and issues a purchase requisition for 20,000.

PR. 420 20,000 Dec. 20 ——— 220,000	100,000	Order 283 Jones Co. 20,000 ——— 220,000	100,000

On January 2, 150,000 screws are received, and the production department issues a stock requisition covering 20,000 on the Jones order and 100,000 to cover the first part of January production.

		+150,000	
Jan. 2 −150,000 ——— 70,000	Stock order 52	250,000 −120,000 ——— 130,000	Stock order 52 −120,000	100,000

On January 12, 70,000 screws are received, but 20,000 fail to pass inspection and are so indicated on the receiving report. The clerk posts the record and prepares shipping instructions for return of the defective screws to the supplier.

−50,000 ——— 20,000	+50,000 ——— 180,000	100,000	100,000

On the foregoing typical card, the transactions are explained and the amounts carried down for clarity of explanation. In actual practice, amounts are not carried down in each column, but the last figures in each column are checked for balance with each transaction. The advantage of this type of record is that it indicates instantaneously what action must be taken after each entry. Moreover, it effectively links planning with control of inventories.

Where the types of materials are few, some companies prefer to add columns for figures on raw material received, the balance due,

DATE	ORDERED	RECEIVED	BALANCE DUE	BOOKED	BALANCE AVAILABLE	USED	ON-HAND
6/1				60,000	940,600	20,000	1,000,600
6/2	100,000		100,000	150,000	932,600	18,000	982,600
6/3			100,000	140,000	923,400	19,200	963,400
6/4			100,000	130,000	913,900	19,500	943,900
6/5			100,000	170,000	853,800	20,100	923,800
6/8			100,000	159,900	845,300	18,600	905,200
6/9			100,000	159,900	826,000	19,300	885,900
6/10			100,000	180,000	786,000	19,300	866,600
6/11			100,000	310,000	637,100	19,500	847,100
6/12			100,000	360,000	526,900	20,200	826,900
6/15			100,000	380,000	526,800	20,100	806,800
6/16			100,000	420,000	467,200	19,800	787,200
6/17			100,000	400,000	467,200	19,600	767,600
6/18	50,000	50,000	50,000	400,000	446,800	19,800	747,800
6/19			50,000	380,000	498,700	19,100	778,700
6/22			50,000	369,700	438,700	20,300	758,400
6/23			50,000	425,000	363,200	20,200	738,200
6/24			50,000	404,800	363,300	20,100	718,100
6/25			50,000	385,000	363,300	19,800	698,300
6/26			50,000	403,000	325,700	19,600	678,700
6/29		50,000		450,000	258,500	20,200	658,500
6/30				430,700	258,500	19,300	689,200

GRADE *30 Pound Basis Kraft Outerliner*   *Pounds*

Fig. 53. A typical stock record.

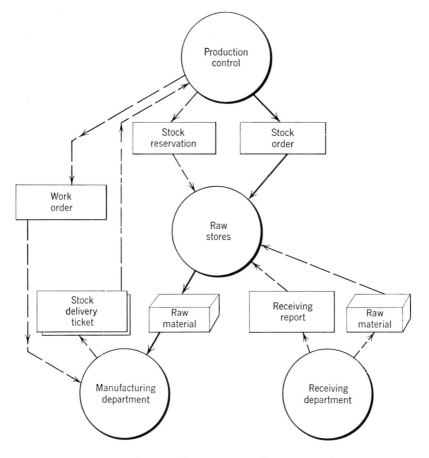

Fig. 54. The general arrangement of stores control.

and the quantity used. Figure 53 shows such a stock record card, which also can be readily checked for balance. The sum of *Received, Balance Due,* and *On Hand* must always equal the sum of the *Booked* and *Balance Available.* This record is posted at the end of each production day, using accumulated figures from purchase requisitions, receiving reports, customer order take-offs, and stock releases.

Tabulating forms can be devised to meet other needs. By using machines, cards recording purchase requisitions can be matched with cards for stock reservations to make sure that the planning has been completed. Cards punched to cover stock deliveries can be matched with others punched to cover stock orders to reveal whether or not performance has been completed.

Centralized stockrooms generally require excessive material handling. Many companies make a practice of delivering raw materials directly to storage space near that area in which the first operations will be performed. Figure 54 shows the general arrangement of raw-stores control as it is associated with production planning.

SUMMARY

Simple numerical codes are generally used to identify the materials brought into stockrooms. The locations in which these materials are stored must also be identified by stockroom number, bay number, aisle number, bin number, and section number.

All materials needed for a production run should be on hand before production starts. Lacking this, there must be assurance that materials will flow into the operation according to definite schedules.

Stockrooms must record receipts and disbursements, as well as figures for materials on hand, on order, reserved (for planned operations), and available (for future planning). Since the sum of on hand and on order must always equal the sum of the reserved and available, their agreement can be verified after each transaction. Such a record also indicates what action to take after each posting.

QUESTIONS TO CHECK COMPREHENSION

1. Is raw-material inventory control intimately associated with production planning?

2. How can raw materials be identified without referring to long commodity names?

3. Explain a typical arrangement for locating materials in a stockroom.

4. All components for an assembly are ready except one very small part. An expediter is expected to arrive with a trunkful of these small parts sometime tomorrow morning. Production starts at 7.00 A.M. Should the schedule be switched to some other assembly, or should the assembly be completed progressively on a conveyor line and the missing parts installed as soon as they arrive?

5. What would be accomplished if your company should establish a policy of shutting down any operation on which the planning had been faulty, sending workmen home with full pay for the day?

6. Would it be advisable to use perpetual-inventory figures from year to year without taking actual physical inventories? Why?

7. There are 50,000 units of a certain raw material on hand and 70,000 have been ordered. Customers' orders already received will consume 100,000 of them. How many are available to future planning?

8. Can a proper record of raw materials actually indicate what must be done next after a transaction has been posted?

PROBLEMS

1. A numerical identification system is needed for the classification of raw materials in a stockroom. Among the items stocked are:

Steel bars	Alcohol	Mica sheets
Steel tubes	Lacquer	Powdered soap
Sheet steel	Caustic soda	Steel screws
Brass castings	Cotton cloth	Liquid soap
Brass sheets	Cotton yarn	Steel castings
Plastic powder	Rayon cloth	Titanium dioxide
Plastic sheets	Rayon yarn	Turpentine
Plastic rods	Nylon cloth	Brass bolts

Devise a numbering system that will identify each of these items by type of material and its form.

2. At the beginning of July there are 500 yards of a special cloth on hand. Another 1,000 yards have been ordered on P.O. 2950. A customer's order, C.O. 3745, has been received for finished products that will require 800 yards, and 500 yards should be kept in stock as a minimal balance.

On July 3, another customer's order, C.O. 3751, is received that will require 1,400 yards of this material. A purchase order is placed for 1,200 yards.

On July 6, the manufacturing department draws 500 yards from stock.

On July 12, 1,000 yards of the cloth are received from a supplier on P.O. 2950.

Later the following transactions take place. They do not include placement of purchase orders, the need for which is to be inferred.

July 15 Manufacturing draws 1,000 yards
July 18 Customer's order requiring 1,800 yards is received
July 23 Customer's order requiring 2,000 yards is received
July 26 A delivery of 1,800 yards is received
July 29 Manufacturing draws 1,000 yards

Set up a balance-of-stock record for this cloth item and post entries for the foregoing transactions.

DISCUSSION CASE

In a large, multibuilding, multistoried manufacturing plant, all raw materials were stored in a centralized storage building designated as the storehouse. Twelve manufacturing units in seven multistoried buildings were served by this central storehouse. All stock records were maintained in the central storehouse. These records were reasonably accurate, but slow deliveries from the storehouse often delayed manufacturing operations. An industrial engineer in one of the production units suggested that considerable time and effort would be eliminated if raw materials were received and stored in the manufacturing areas. He produced blueprints showing that there was sufficient room in the manufacturing areas to store all raw materials. The storehouse building could then be used for the manufacture of a new product that would not quite fit into any of the other manufacturing areas. His analysis showed that raw materials would be more quickly available, with considerably less handling, under this proposed arrangement.

PRESENT METHOD	PROPOSED METHOD
① Unload from trailer.	① Unload from trailer.
Truck to receiving area.	Truck to manufacturing stock area.
② Unload truck.	② Unload truck.
▽ Temporary storage.	▽ Temporary storage.
③ Check quantity and prepare receiving report.	③ Check quantity and prepare receiving report.
☐ Check for quality and prepare inspection report.	☐ Check for quality and prepare inspection report.
④ Load on truck.	④ Load on truck.
Truck to stock location.	Truck to operation.
⑤ Unload truck.	⑤ Unload truck.
▽ In storage.	▽ Temporary storage.
⑥ Load truck.	
Truck to manufacturing receiving area.	
⑦ Unload truck.	
▽ Temporary storage.	
⑧ Load truck.	
Move to operation.	
⑨ Unload truck.	
▽ Temporary storage.	

SUMMARY			SUMMARY	
◯ Operations	9		◯ Operations	5
○ Transportations	4		○ Transportations	2
☐ Inspections	1		☐ Inspections	1
▽ Storages	4		▽ Storages	2
Elapsed time	12¾ hours		Elapsed time	5½ hours

Fig. 55.   Material-handling analysis.

Under the old arrangement, 12 truckers, 3 stockroom clerks, and 1 receiving clerk were needed. The industrial engineer proposed that some of the truckers be trained as stock clerks and 1 stock clerk be assigned to each of the 7 manufacturing buildings. Each clerk would also assume the work done by the receiving clerk. The remaining 8 truckers would be placed in a pool under the supervision of the man who had been the receiving clerk.

The stockroom personnel has complained that it cannot be responsible for the accuracy of inventories in the manufacturing areas.

You are attending a meeting called to discuss this proposal (see Figure 55). List the causes for its informal nonacceptance and the advantages and disadvantages as well as the benefits and hardships to the majority of persons who are involved.

15

Loading

When a customer orders goods, he wants to know when they will be delivered. The job-order producer must determine this anew for each separate order. Companies that manufacture to stock have an easier time; they may quote a date for stock on hand or work in process, or they may make forecasts based on records of fast and continuous production. Yet even such companies may have to quote on special orders from federal procurement agencies or may find that sales so far exceed forecasts as to present emergencies. Can such special orders or overschedules be fitted into the production picture? If so, when can they be delivered, and how can existing facilities be utilized best?

The first step in answering these questions is to list available equipment. For convenience, the machines capable of performing one type of work are placed in one group, which is given a *group number*. (See Figure 56.)

The number of machines in each group, multipled by the number of hours or shifts to be worked each day, gives the number of machine-hours or shifts available for loading. It should be understood that the availability of machine shifts or hours must be based on the number of shifts or hours per day actually being worked at the time of planning or on those scheduled for some definite future date. In other words, if there are 10 machines in the group, and they are operating on one 7.5-hour shift per day without any already scheduled increase, the machine availability per day is only 75 machine-hours or 10 machine shifts. Other planning for operators and supervision must be completed before there can be any additional availability for production planning in terms of either hours or additional shifts.

Take-off sheets similar to the one shown in Figure 57 are used to compute the hours or shifts required on each article considered for production. Gantt charts can be used to show graphically the relation of availability to machine load.

Number Available	Machine	Group No.
26	#0 B & S	100A
17	#2 B & S	100B
12	#4 B & S	100C
3	7/8" Cleve.	100D
6	1¼" Cleve.	100E
8	2" Cleve.	100F
9	2¼ Bar turret	100G
6	2½ " "	100H
7	3 " "	100J
5	3½ " "	100K
14	Hand screw	100L
15	Single sp. dr.	101A
6	Horiz. mill.	101B
30	Sensitive dr.	101C
4	Vert. mill.	101D
3	Radial dr.	101E
2	Gun dr. 119	101F
2	Broach #1	102A
3	" #2	102B
3	" #4	102C
4	Ex. grind. sm.	103A
6	" " med.	103B
3	Int. " sm.	103D
4	" " med.	103E

Fig. 56. A typical equipment list.

For the sake of clarity, Figure 58 shows the loading of some automatic screw machines by hours. Ordinarily it is simpler to load equipment by shifts. It will be seen that the hours available must first be calculated and listed for each machine group. As an example, the planning has been set to operate the 26 #0 Brown and Sharpe automatic screw machines during three 7.5-hour shifts per day for 6 days per week. Thus:

26 Machines × 3 Shifts × 7.5 Hours per day × 6 Days per week

$$= 3,510 \text{ Machine-hours available per week}$$

Orders 237, 406, and 408 require a total of 3,200 machine-hours. They can be loaded in the week ending March 6. This leaves 310

MACHINE GROUPS

100A	100B	100C	100D	100E	100G	100H	100J	100K	100L	101A	101B	101C	
101D	101E	101F	102A	102B	102C	103A	103B	103D	103E	103F	103G	103H	

Fig. 57. A take-off sheet.

MACHINE LOAD CHART

26-#0 B&S	Hours Available	Week Ending March 6	Week Ending March 13
		26 x 3 x 7.5 x 6 = 3,510 Hrs.	3,510 Hrs.
Automatic screw machines 100A	Hours Load	Order 237 - 2,500 Order 406 - 450 Order 408 - 250 Order 510 - 310	Order 510 - 290 Order 615 - 3,000 Order 620 - 220
17-#2 B&S	Hours Available	17 x 3 x 7.5 x 6 = 2,296 Hrs.	2,296 Hrs.
Automatic screw machines 100B	Hours Load	Order 247 - 1,000 Order 251 - 500 Order 321 - 500 Order 403 - 296	Order 403 - 304 Order 456 - 800 Order 463 - 760 Order 508 - 500 Order 606 - 32
12-#4 B&S	Hours Available	12 x 3 x 7.5 x 6 = 1,620 Hrs.	1,620 Hrs.
Automatic screw machines	Hours Load	Order 259 - 1,000 Order 283 - 500	

Fig. 58. Simple loading of automatic screw machines.

hours still available for order 510, thus completing the loading for the week. The remaining 290 hours demanded by order 510 are carried over to the week ending March 13.

There are certain disadvantages in recording machine loading as shown in Figure 58. Canceled orders may release certain machine-hours reserved. Some contracts on which bids are made will not be secured. It then becomes necessary to recompute and prepare new sheets. It is much more desirable to use movable indicators of shifts or hours reserved or scheduled, placing them on sheets or cards calibrated to represent shifts or hours available. Machine loading can be simplified by using Kardex files equipped with plastic riders to designate how much of the available capacity of each machine group has been loaded or allocated. (See Figure 59.)

Many practical men are inclined to object that machine loading involves too much work, that solutions to problems can be reached as well, and much more easily, by a quick mental balancing of data. That this contention is unsound is shown by the accompanying problem, which is typical of problems encountered in day-to-day production planning. As a test, this problem was presented to some 300 management students, many of them practicing production managers. Only three reached an approximately correct answer by inspection—and they agreed that graphic solution was simpler and more reliable.

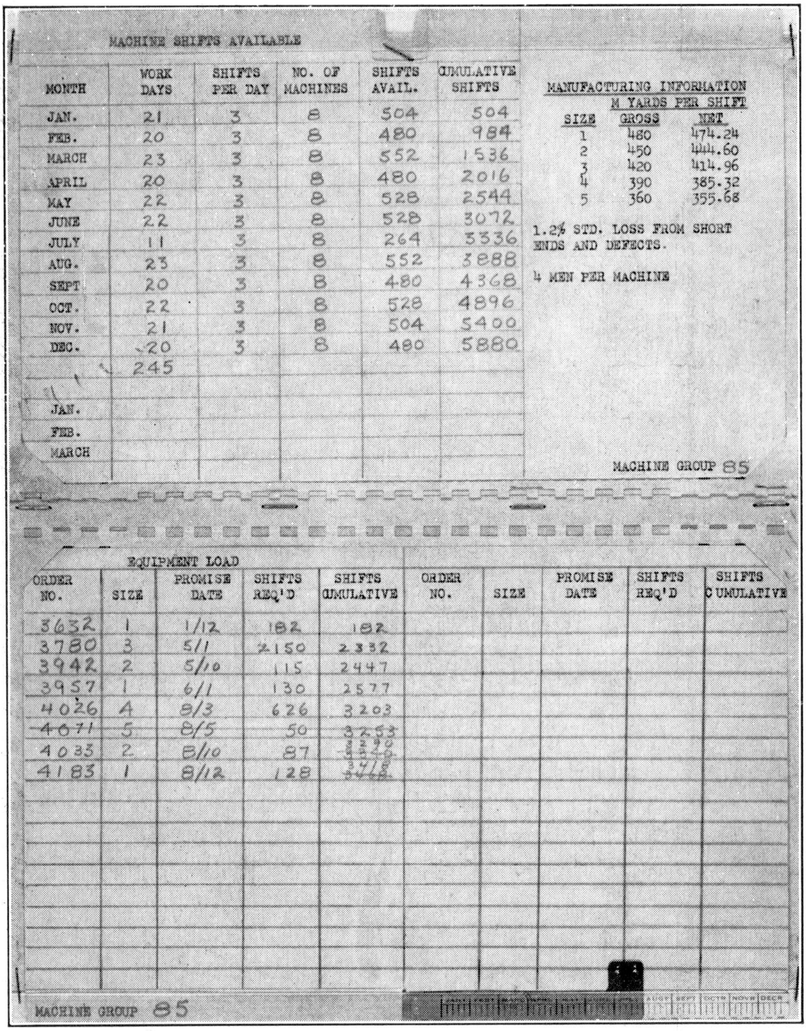

MACHINE SHIFTS AVAILABLE						
MONTH	WORK DAYS	SHIFTS PER DAY	NO. OF MACHINES	SHIFTS AVAIL.	CUMULATIVE SHIFTS	MANUFACTURING INFORMATION
JAN.	21	3	8	504	504	
FEB.	20	3	8	480	984	
MARCH	23	3	8	552	1536	
APRIL	20	3	8	480	2016	
MAY	22	3	8	528	2544	
JUNE	22	3	8	528	3072	
JULY	11	3	8	264	3336	
AUG.	23	3	8	552	3888	
SEPT	20	3	8	480	4368	
OCT.	22	3	8	528	4896	
NOV.	21	3	8	504	5400	
DEC.	20	3	8	480	5880	
	245					
JAN.						
FEB.						
MARCH						

Manufacturing information — M YARDS PER SHIFT

SIZE	GROSS	NET
1	480	474.24
2	450	444.60
3	420	414.96
4	390	385.32
5	360	355.68

1.2% STD. LOSS FROM SHORT ENDS AND DEFECTS.

4 MEN PER MACHINE

MACHINE GROUP 85

EQUIPMENT LOAD									
ORDER NO.	SIZE	PROMISE DATE	SHIFTS REQ'D	SHIFTS CUMULATIVE	ORDER NO.	SIZE	PROMISE DATE	SHIFTS REQ'D	SHIFTS CUMULATIVE
3632	1	1/12	182	182					
3780	3	5/1	2150	2332					
3942	2	5/10	115	2447					
3957	1	6/1	130	2577					
4026	4	8/3	626	3203					
4671	5	8/5	50	3253					
4035	2	8/10	87	3379					
4183	1	8/12	128	3448					

MACHINE GROUP 85

Fig. 59. Loading on a visible index card.

PROBLEM IN MACHINE LOADING

To be solved in fifteen minutes—first without graphic aids and then by means of a Gantt chart.

An order for machine #1405 has been received from a customer who wants delivery in 20 weeks. The master schedule shows the following:

Machine #1405 is composed of 6 subassemblies denoted 1405A, 1405B, 1405C, 1405D, 1405E, and 1405F, respectively.

Subassembly 1405D requires 3 shifts on a turret lathe and 2 shifts on planers. Metal is in stock. Assembled in toolroom in 2 shifts.

Subassembly 1405B requires 8 machine shifts on a punch press and 5 machine shifts on automatic screw machines. Raw stock will be in within 3 weeks. Assembled in toolroom in 1 shift.

Subassembly 1405C is purchased and must be assembled to 1405B. Assembly time is included in finished assembly time given below. It is due in 12 weeks.

Subassembly 1405D requires 15 machine shifts on planers and 3 shifts subassembly time in toolroom. Material is in stock.

Subassembly 1405E is purchased to be assembled with subassembly 1405D in toolroom. Subassembly time is included in subassembly of 1405D. Will arrive in 6 weeks.

1405F is cast and then occupies 5 machine shifts on planers. Foundry can produce casting in 4 weeks.

The final assembly takes 15 shifts including inspection and testing and cannot be taken off assembly line until passed. The assembly line is occupied for 12 weeks and cannot take on this job until work now in progress is completed.

Machine loading is as follows:

Equipment	No. of Machines	Present Load in Machine Shifts	Present Machine Shifts per Week
Turret lathes	4	140	48
Planers	8	800	144
Die presses	2	72	36
Auto screw machines	4	100	48

Assume that toolroom can take work at any time after 2 weeks. Can the machine be in the customer's hand in 20 weeks?

A simple Gantt chart can be used to solve this problem quickly and correctly. The chart shown in Figure 60 indicates both machine loading and progress of work on component parts. It was prepared from the problem data in fifteen minutes. In addition to answering the question of whether the specified delivery date can be met, it shows that punch presses and screw machines are not being used to full advantage. If the number of these machines cannot be reduced, the company's sales representatives should be urged to secure more work for them.

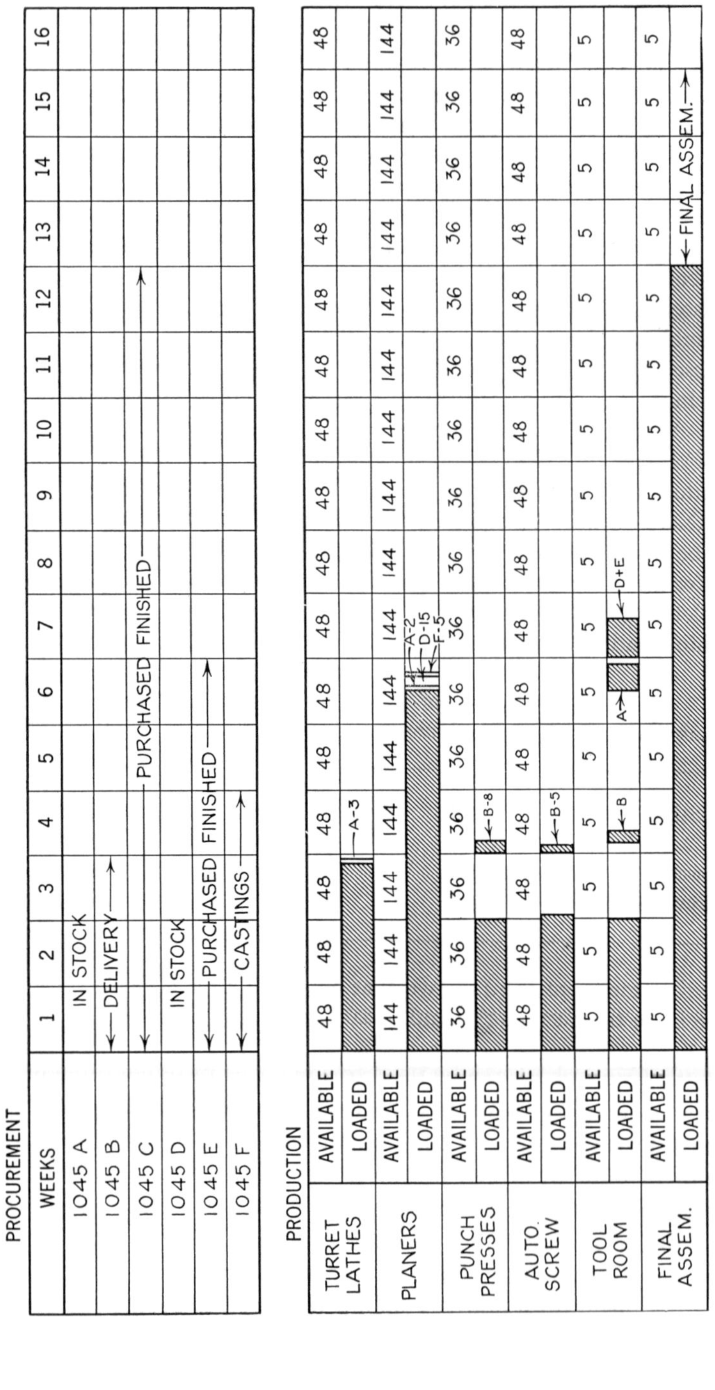

PROCUREMENT

WEEKS	1	2	3	4	5	6	7	8	9	10	11	12	13	14	15	16
1045 A	IN STOCK															
1045 B	← DELIVERY →															
1045 C				← PURCHASED FINISHED →												
1045 D	IN STOCK															
1045 E					← PURCHASED FINISHED →											
1045 F			← CASTINGS →													

PRODUCTION

		1	2	3	4	5	6	7	8	9	10	11	12	13	14	15	16
TURRET LATHES	AVAILABLE	48	48	48	48	48	48	48	48	48	48	48	48	48	48	48	48
	LOADED				A-3												
PLANERS	AVAILABLE	144	144	144	144	144	144	144	144	144	144	144	144	144	144	144	144
	LOADED						A-2 D-15 F-5										
PUNCH PRESSES	AVAILABLE	36	36	36	36	36	36	36	36	36	36	36	36	36	36	36	36
	LOADED		B-8														
AUTO. SCREW	AVAILABLE	48	48	48	48	48	48	48	48	48	48	48	48	48	48	48	48
	LOADED			B-5													
TOOL ROOM	AVAILABLE	5	5	5	5	5	5	5	5	5	5	5	5	5	5	5	5
	LOADED				B		A→		D+E								
FINAL ASSEM.	AVAILABLE	5	5	5	5	5	5	5	5	5	5	5	5	5	5	5	5
	LOADED													← FINAL ASSEM. →			

Fig. 60. A graphic solution to the loading problem.

Some persons who have sought to solve this problem made the serious error of assuming additional final assembly shifts that actually were not available. It must always be kept in mind that before a shift can be added, employees must be selected, hired, and trained. This cannot be done unless a continuing work load is assured. No company can afford to hire men and train them for only ten or twelve weeks of work, nor is it fair to engage them for such a short time and then terminate their employment.

The general failure to solve this problem shows that reliable promises of delivery cannot be made by inspecting a series of figures or by deciding what *should* be done. This is true even in the small job shop that works on two or three orders at a time. It is still more true in the large factory that has many jobs in simultaneous progress and many inquiries under consideration for quotation and scheduling of delivery dates. Under these conditions, a system of machine loading is the only alternative to chaos and broken promises.

There remains the problem of salesmen who become overoptimistic or overeager, promising delivery dates that cannot be met. This can be corrected by insisting that both quotations and carefully determined delivery dates be obtained from the manufacturing offices. Another method, for companies producing to stock, is to provide representatives with lists of materials on hand. The General Electric Company, for example, gives each of its power equipment dealers a list showing the number of motors, switch gears, transformers, etc., that are actually in stock. No promises of delivery are made unless the dealer finds that equipment is available for shipment. As a result, the company has built up an enviable reputation for frankness and reliable deliveries.

Manufacturing executives too often make hasty decisions to accept attractive orders without knowing the available capacity of their manufacturing facilities. The results are always the same. The nerves of production men become frayed trying to accomplish the impossible. The company earns a reputation for delayed deliveries, and, what is equally serious, the customer's planning is irreparably dislocated.

During World War II the armed services procurement agencies were quick to discover poor machine loading and production planning. In many cases these discoveries were made long before deliveries were due. If an officer called a company about the status of an order and the executive replied, "Sir, I can't tell you just how it is coming because we are all jammed up for a few days," the officer generally sensed a bad situation and sent some of his production planners to untangle it.

On the other hand, if a procurement officer asked a supplier the status of an order and was told it would be a week or perhaps twelve days late, it was evident that the supplier at least knew where production stood. Such suppliers were generally invited to bid on additional contracts. As it was with the armed services during war, so it is with civilian purchasers in peacetime. Both want reliability when deliveries are promised.

A simple method for determining when to schedule overtime work or start a partial additional shift is discussed in the chapter on "Level Production and Stable Employment." Not much uncertainty is involved in such problems because of known growth trends and production load data for orders in hand.

More complex problems in equipment loading can be solved by Operations Research and Mathematical Programming. Factors such as variable efficiencies of machines performing the same operations, delivery time-order, shift premiums, overtime premiums, night shift efficiency, overtime efficiency and others can be arrayed on programming matrices to obtain optimal solutions.

Some production loading problems often contain so many complex factors that electronic data-processing equipment is required for their solution. When such equipment is not available, the cost of manually programming may sometimes exceed the production savings gained unless some simpler approximation methods are used.[1]

The simple act of arraying a loading problem on a mathematical programming matrix provides a valuable insight into the problem. The data array will also indicate the appropriate method for solution. Choices of method range from simple index schemes to complex series of iterations. Even when the cost of a programming study exceeds the reduction of production costs, the knowledge gained can be used in many other similar problems and therefore has great value. Dislocations caused by deviations in sales trends and cancellation of orders require that loading and scheduling be recomputed. This is not too difficult once the method for programming has been established.

As we have already found, machine-load charts also call attention to equipment that is not fully utilized. A parts manufacturer may find, for example, that his grinders are used only about half of the time, while his radial drills are overloaded. If the grinders are needed to handle recurring rush orders, the manufacturer will urge his salesmen to secure more grinding work. If such rush orders seldom recur,

---

[1] Robert W. Metzger, *Elementary Mathematical Programming*, John Wiley & Sons, New York, 1958.

it may be wise to sell some of the grinders and use the money to buy additional drills. As a third possibility the manager may select orders that make the best possible use of his equipment. Thus he may reject an order for small parts that will use his screw-machine capacity. In its place, he accepts another order that requires only part of the screw-machine capacity but will keep grinders and many other machines and the assembly floor busy for a long period. Such selection means wise utilization of equipment, balanced work loads, and profits that come from full plant operation.

Thus the need for machine loading is apparent even in simple situations. In the usual complex situations it is indispensable. After scheduling has been discussed, machine loading will be further explored to relate it or even combine it with scheduling.

SUMMARY

In both manufacture-to-stock and job-order production, management must know when equipment will be available for work on each order or item. The first step in acquiring this information is to list the number of machines capable of performing similar operations. Knowing the number of machine shifts available to perform each type of operation and the number of shifts required for each type of operation in order to complete a schedule to stock or to produce customers' orders, the planning staff then can determine whether the load is greater or less than the capacity of equipment. Graphic representations of both load and availability can also show whether a schedule or customer's order can be completed within the required time.

Machine-load charts also reveal equipment that is not fully utilized. This enables management to take corrective measures, which may range from selling surplus machines to selecting orders that will result in balanced and profitable operation.

QUESTIONS TO CHECK COMPREHENSION

1. A supplier is known to provide acceptable quality at reasonable prices but has been notoriously late in deliveries. Will you place an order with

him for component parts used in your production if other suppliers who are or may be prompt offer comparable prices and quality?

2. A company has been operating on a one-shift basis. The manager accepts an order based on operating three shifts, starting tomorrow. Is he likely to fill this order on time? What are the implications of this situation?

3. A bid is invited for several machines. All machining and assembly times have been estimated for pricing. If you know the hours or shifts presently loaded on the equipment, do you consider that you could quote a reliable delivery date?

4. What are the three essentially bad results of failure to make delivery as promised?

5. How can machine-load charts reveal unbalanced equipment facilities?

6. Why and how do machine-load charts permit selectivity in accepting orders?

7. Did you solve the problem in this chapter in 15 minutes? What does your success or failure mean?

PROBLEM

1. An export order has been received for a machine designated as model 305. It consists of 4 major parts and includes several standard parts such as nuts, bolts, washers, and an electric motor, all of which are in stock. This order was accepted on the basis of the purchaser's letter of credit, which will expire after 10 weeks unless the machine is loaded aboard a ship ready for delivery.

Part 305–1 is an iron casting requiring 6 shifts in the foundry, 3 shifts on milling machines, and 6 shifts on drill presses.

Part 305–2 is a drop forging requiring 3 shifts in the forge, 4 shifts on lathes, 6 shifts on grinding machines, and 5 shifts on drill presses.

Part 305–3 is a brass casting requiring 10 shifts in the foundry, 5 shifts on milling machines, 6 shifts on drill presses, and 4 shifts on grinding machines.

Part 305–4 is purchased finished from an outside supplier and will require 6 weeks for delivery.

Part 305–1 must be fitted to part 305–4 in assembly and this will require 6 shifts. The final assembly will require 12 shifts. Testing will require 6 shifts and painting will require 1 shift.

The factory load is as follows:

	No. of Machines	Present Load in Machine Shifts	Available Machine Shifts per Week
Foundry	10	1080	180
Forge	4	490	72
Millers	6	650	108
Lathes	5	550	90
Drills	10	920	180
Grinders	4	290	72
Assembly	5 stations	630	90
Test	2 stations	220	36
Painting	2 booths	190	36

Prepare a load chart and determine whether the delivery date can be met.

DISCUSSION CASE

The Buster Company, manufacturers of producer goods, was actually run by its sales department. The chief executive of the company had started as a salesman. He had only a peripheral knowledge of manufacturing and its problems.

The manufacturing department kept excellent load charts. It also complained that both production planning and control were breaking down because of rash delivery promises made by the various salesmen. On many occasions the chief executive of the company had ruled that sales promises had to be accepted and ordered that production for them be sandwiched in with other orders even if some deliveries were late.

Early in 1948 the planning department prepared an analysis showing that for the past two years forecasts had required the full plant capacity. Overschedules resulting from rash promises would require another 20 per cent of plant capacity. This analysis was borne out by an analysis of backlog and cancellations. Plans were prepared for new equipment and a plant expansion. The chief executive rejected these plans.

In the summer of 1948 one salesman informed the manufacturing

tomers can wait for delivery. New orders are generally accepted with consideration of how they will fit into the planned arrangement of orders already on hand.

3. Where goods are produced to stock, it is unwise to establish production schedules without determining the quantities of various items in the inventories of dealers and retailers. Either of two situations may be found. Dealers and retailers who normally carry one or two month's supply of goods may have let their stocks run low. If this is the situation, there may be a sudden influx of large orders, partly to replace depleted stocks and partly to provide future stock in normal amounts; the manufacturer may find himself with a two-month back order. On the other hand, dealers and retailers may have stocked up heavily in anticipation of a price increase. In this case, orders may lag and the manufacturer may find that his production schedules are building up an excessive finished goods inventory.

Some manufacturers avoid such maladjustments by having their sales representatives report the inventory positions of dealers and retailers in their respective territories. Other companies require dealers to report their inventory positions each month. To secure accuracy in these inventories, some companies give price protection only to items appearing on the dealers' reports. In other words, if the price of those items declines, the dealer is given credit for the difference between the old, higher price and the new, lower one. Since items not reported are denied this advantage, dealers take care to list their full inventories.

4. The first internal factor to be considered in situations where goods are produced to stock is that stock itself. A company may ordinarily carry a finished goods inventory amounting to one month's supply of each item. If certain items have moved more slowly or more rapidly than expected, the result is an excessive or reduced inventory which must be balanced in future scheduling.

If an item has moved more rapidly than was expected, both from the manufacturer's stock and from the stocks of dealers and retailers, a new sales forecast is prepared in accordance with the change. This forecast may indicate that the actual finished goods inventory must be increased substantially to provide one month's supply of the item. This increased quantity, together with a quantity sufficient to restore the currently depleted finished goods inventory, must be provided in the production schedule.

Items that have moved more slowly than expected will likewise be studied. If this situation is caused by excessive dealer and retailer inventories, production plans will have to be adjusted for the reduced sales.

5. Process intervals vary greatly, and so does their importance. If the elapsed time needed to produce certain articles is long, planning and scheduling must be completed well in advance of the dates set for delivery. As an example, in the woodworking industries, the kiln-drying operation may add a month to the process interval. In many types of machine-tool production the actual time required for the machine cuts, heat treating, polishing, and painting may amount to several weeks. The process interval in textile mills also is likely to be a matter of weeks. In some food-packing operations, on the other hand, the process interval is less than one day. It is obvious, there-fore, that a food packer may give much less thought to this factor than the planner for a furniture factory or a cotton mill.

6. Availability of equipment is best determined from machine-load charts. This subject has been treated in Chapter 15.

7. Availability of personnel requires planners to seek first to pro-vide employment for people already on the payroll and to try to keep hardship at the minimum if layoffs are required. If new employees are being hired, the criteria become the number of workers seeking employment, their reliability, and their skills. In planning hirings, time must be allowed for indoctrination and specialized training, with-out which few workers are able to give good service.

8. Availability of material must be considered in terms of the ma-terial already on hand as well as that to be secured from suppliers. Both aspects of this subject have been treated in Chapter 14.

9. Manufacturing facilities also are a factor that must be broken down into several components. If work requiring additional person-nel is scheduled, planners must make sure that there is space for these new workers. They may need additional machines, but if they are to do table work, plant additions and new services may also be required. The same applies to assembly work, where equipment may not be required but where additional work space is necessary.

10. Many papers have been written about and many formulas have been given for the calculation of economic production lot quantities. These formulas are designed to determine the lost sizes for which the preparation cost equals the possession cost to carry finished goods or in-process stock. It is obvious that below an optimum lot size, prep-aration or setup cost increases the total cost and above this same lot size the carrying cost increases the total cost. The lot size in which both these costs are equal is, therefore, the quantity that can be produced at the optimum cost.

Some formulas are elaborated to compute the cost of floor space, obsolescence, working capital charges and other possession cost factors. The short formula most generally used is:

$$L = \sqrt{\frac{2AP}{SC}}$$

in which L = Economic lot size
A = Annual requirement in units
P = Preparation or setup cost per lot
S = Stock carrying charge as a percentage of unit cost
C = Unit cost

The percentage, S, to be used is calculated for the total operation or for classes of products in the operation. This percentage or these percentages are then used as standard factors in the formula. Calculation of lot quantities can be simplified by using nomographs.

Prudent production planners use this method to check the economics of producing lots of various sizes. Planners and production men familiar with both costs and production usually can sense an uneconomic lot quantity and verify their suspicions by mental calculations. Other factors obvious to production men are excluded from the formulas. To include these factors would make the formula burdensome and would even require separate formulas for each product. If, for example, raw materials are received in certain quantities such as 100-pound bags, 50-gallon drums, or 1,000-yard rolls of textile, it is often best to base the lot on multiples of these quantities that are nearest the rational lot size.

Some notion of the calculation of economic lot sizes can be gained by assuming the values that follow and applying them to the general formula:

Let A = 1,200 units per year
P = $50 per setup
S = 20% the cost for carrying stock
C = $2.00 the cost of one unit of production

Then:

$$L = \sqrt{\frac{2 \times 1200 \times \$50}{\$2.00 \times 0.20}} = 547.7 \text{ units}$$

Explored further, this set of data shows that there is a rather broad range of choice of lot size without deviating too far from the theoretical optimum total cost.

Lot Size	Annual Product Cost	Setup Cost	Carrying Cost	Total Cost
	AC +	$\dfrac{AP}{L}$ +	$\dfrac{(CL) + P_S}{2}$ =	$AC + \dfrac{AP}{L} + \dfrac{(CL) + P_S}{2}$
200	$2,400	$300.00	$ 45.00	$2,745.00
388	2,400	154.63	82.60	2,637.23
400	2,400	150.00	85.00	2,635.00
500	2,400	120.00	105.00	2,625.00
543	2,400	110.49	113.60	2,624.90
547.7	2,400	109.55	114.54	2,624.90
552	2,400	108.69	115.40	2,624.90
600	2,400	100.00	125.00	2,625.00
700	2,400	85.00	145.00	2,625.71
777	2,400	77.22	160.00	2,637.22
800	2,400	75.00	165.00	2,640.00
1,000	2,400	60.00	205.00	2,665.00
1,200	2,400	50.00	245.00	2,695.00

These data are charted in Figure 61, which shows a flat part in the curve from lot sizes 543 to 552. It is also evident that a choice of lot size as small as 388 or as large as 777 will increase the total cost per year only one half of one per cent above the optimum cost of $2,624.90.

Problems of two kinds confront production planners in setting the sizes of production lots. Problems of the first kind are those in which it seems desirable to produce more than the calculated lot size in one setup to consume even multiples of perishable raw materials. Then too, it is often desirable to increase the productive time of equipment that would be nonproductive during setup intervals.

Problems of the second kind are those in which production mixes are such that long production runs of one product will create unbalanced stock. Shipments for several different products on a single customer's order, therefore, may be delayed. When several component parts for an assembly are produced on the same equipment, unbalanced stocks of these components will create assembly dislocations.

To gain freedom in solving these problems, production engineers may first compute rational lot sizes, using the formula and the total annual cost associated with them. The next step is to compute the

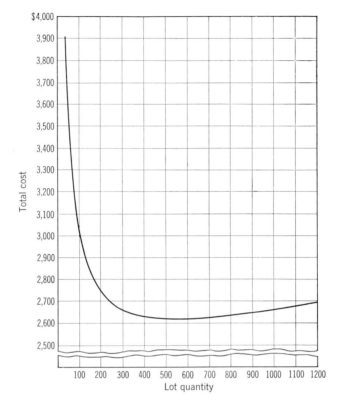

Fig. 61. Chart showing annual cost of various lot sizes.

total annual cost with realistic or desirable lot sizes, either larger or smaller than theoretical optimal. With these figures, a decision as to how many units to produce in one setup may be based upon the extra cost of producing realistic lots instead of rational lots.

Figure 62 is a master schedule prepared from a sales forecast; it shows the exact number of each item needed during the schedule period, which in this case is three months. It would be difficult, however, for department foremen to view this master schedule and arrange their work to synchronize with that of other departments. The master schedule, therefore, is broken down into departmental schedules like the one in Figure 63. These department schedules are phased so that work from one department will be completed in time for another department to start other work on the article without delay. Thus a foundry schedule will probably be phased 2 weeks

MONTHLY PRODUCTION SCHEDULE DETAIL SHEET
PRODUCTION CONTROL DEPARTMENT

Date Dec 3   Department 26   Group 12   Month In Effect January, 1957   Reported by Jackson

PRODUCT	UNIT	CODE NUMBER	PEAK STOCK	STOCK ON HAND	Monthly Schedule			ADJUSTMENT PREVIOUS MONTH		SCHEDULE REVISED	Schedules		TOTAL
					REGULAR	SPECIALS	TOTAL				OVER	OVER	
Cylinders 9"	1	6810	1000	750	750	0	750	250	−	1000	0	0	1000
Cylinders 12"	1	6811	250	250	250	0	250	−		250	0	0	250
Cylinders 18"	1	6812	1500	2500	500	0	500	−		500	0	0	500
Cylinders 24"	1	6813	2500	3000	1500	0	1500	0		1500	500	0	2000
Cylinders 30"	1	6814	350	150	350	0	350	150		500	0	0	500
Cylinders 36"	1	6815	500	250	500	0	500	0		500	250	0	750
Plates 1	1	7101	12,000	6000	12,000	10,000	22,000	4000	+	18,000	0	0	18,000
Plates 1 1/2	1	7102	9000	3000	9000	3000	12,000	0	−	12,000	3000	0	15,000
Plates 2	1	7103	30,000	12,000	30,000	5000	35,000	6000	−	41,000	7000	0	48,000
Plates 3	1	7104	6000	6000	6000	0	6000	0		6000	0	0	6000
Plates 4	1	7105	3000	3000	3000								

Fig. 62. A typical master schedule.

PRODUCTION PLANNING DEPT
FOREMAN John Jones

PRODUCTION SCHEDULE

DEPT. NO. 26
DATE 1-28-57 to 2-1-57

PRODUCT	MONDAY					TUESDAY					WEDNESDAY					THURSDAY					SATURDAY			Total Shifts
	Mach or Person	Shifts	Quan Sch	Prod	Del'd	Mach or Person	Shifts	Quan Sch	Prod	Del'd	Mach or Person	Shifts	Quan Sch	Prod	Del'd	Mach or Person	Shifts	Quan Sch	Prod	Del'd	Quan Sch	Prod	Del'd	
Cylinder 9"											Weld	1	250											1
Cylinder 12"																Weld	1	250						1
Cylinder 18"																								
Cylinder 24"						Weld	1	250																1
Cylinder 30"	Weld	1	250																					1
Cylinder 36"																						Welding		1
																								5
Cylinder 9"	Grind	1	400																					1
Cylinder 12"																								
Cylinder 18"											Grind	1	370											1
Cylinder 24"						Grind	1	350																1
Cylinder 30"																Grind	1	340						1
Cylinder 36"																						Grinding		1
																								5

Fig. 63. A simple department schedule.

ahead of a machining schedule, and a machining schedule will probably be phased 2 weeks ahead of an assembly schedule.

Production schedules must be established so that work on raw materials and purchased finished parts will not be supposed to begin before they are received. It is thus seen that the procurement schedule must be carefully integrated with the schedule for production.

Figure 64 shows a typical gap phasing of schedules for a casting assembly. It will be noted that a time gap is allowed between the receipt of raw material and the beginning of work. Other gaps intervene between completion of one class of work and the beginning of the next. These gaps are safety factors, designed to make sure that work on one order will not be completed before the entire lot has been delivered from the preceding operation. Thus it will never be necessary to break down a setup, take other work, and then reassemble the first setup again when the rest of the lot is delivered. There is no gap between painting and finishing because these operations have no significant setup time.

Where planning and performance have been refined, lap phasing of schedules is often used. Under this arrangement, as soon as some of the lot has been completed in one department, it is forwarded to

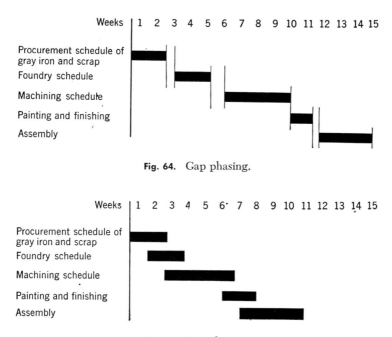

Fig. 64. Gap phasing.

Fig. 65. Lap phasing.

the next department. The remainder of the lot is forwarded as it is completed. Figure 65 shows lap phasing of the same production lot scheduled for gap phasing in Figure 64. It will be noted that lap phasing shortens the process interval from 15 weeks to 11.

Both the foregoing examples represent lot production under a class-of-work arrangement. Let us now consider the same item in continuous progressive production. The castings are poured on a conveyor that runs through the machining, painting, and assembly departments, a plan that reduces process interval to one or two days. Of greater significance here is the fact that only the beginning of the process will have to be scheduled, while production will have to be accounted for only at the end. There will be no scheduling of individual operations or follow-up between them.

Production scheduling in an automobile factory may be taken as typical of production to stock. Although production is to dealers' stock, rather than to a substantial finished goods inventory in the factory, it can serve as a simple example, because the picture is not complicated by the hundreds or thousands of other stock items that many other companies produce.

Figure 66 shows a condensed sales forecast for a car with three body models in two grades or price groups. As is now the rule, both standard and de luxe body shells are the same. Upholstery, painting, and accessories are used to convert the standard model into its more costly counterpart.

Some forward notice of intention will be given to suppliers. Definite orders will be placed for the daily arrival of 800 frames, 800 batteries, 800 motors, and 4,000 wheels during the month of January. Purchase of other items will also be arranged. Although the body shop is only a few blocks away, a schedule for bodies must be established.

For January the schedule for delivery of bodies in the white metal is:

Coupe	200 per day
Coach	400 per day
4-door	200 per day

The current color preference is:

Black	30 per cent
Maroon	10 per cent
Blue	40 per cent
Gray	20 per cent

January's daily schedule for the body shop is:

	Black	Maroon	Blue	Gray	Total
Coupe	60	20	80	40	200
Coach	120	40	160	80	400
4-door	60	20	80	40	200
					800

Note: After World War II, with demand exceeding the supply and production limitations caused by material shortages, automoblie manufacturers actually produced on a customer-order basis rather than a dealer-stock basis. Figure 67 shows how General Motors operated under these conditions. Here again is evidence of the adaptability of American industry.

The actual assembly-line schedule would be quite simple if all the black standard coupes could be scheduled together, then the black de luxe coupes, and so on through the schedule. Actually, however, dealers' orders will call for both standard and de luxe models; for coupes, coaches, and 4-door cars, all in a variety of colors. Further variations will be introduced by overdrive, conventional transmissions, heaters, radios, and so on. The men on the loading platforms must

	De Luxe			Standard			
	Coupe	*Coach*	*4-door*	*Coupe*	*Coach*	*4-door*	*Total*
Jan.	2,000	4,000	2,000	3,000	6,000	3,000	20,000
Feb.	2,000	4,000	2,000	3,000	6,000	3,000	20,000
Mar.	2,500	5,000	2,500	3,750	7,500	3,750	25,000
April	2,500	5,000	2,500	3,750	7,500	3,750	25,000
May	2,750	5,500	2,750	4,250	8,500	4,250	28,000
June	3,000	6,000	3,000	4,500	9,000	4,500	30,000
July	3,000	6,000	3,000	4,500	9,000	4,500	30,000
Aug.	3,000	6,000	3,000	4,500	9,000	4,500	30,000
Sept.	2,750	5,500	2,750	4,250	8,500	4,250	28,000
Oct.	2,500	5,000	2,500	3,750	7,500	3,750	25,000
Nov.	2,000	4,000	2,000	3,000	6,000	3,000	20,000
Dec.	2,000	4,000	2,000	3,000	6,000	3,000	20,000

Fig. 66. A condensed automobile sales forecast.

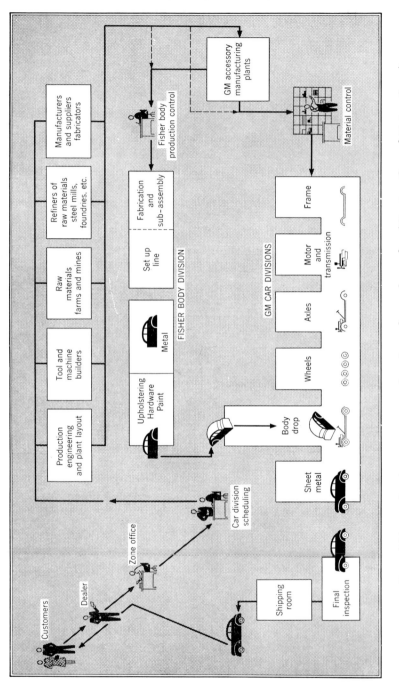

Fig. 67. General Motors planning arrangement when demand exceeds supply. (Courtesy General Motors Corp.)

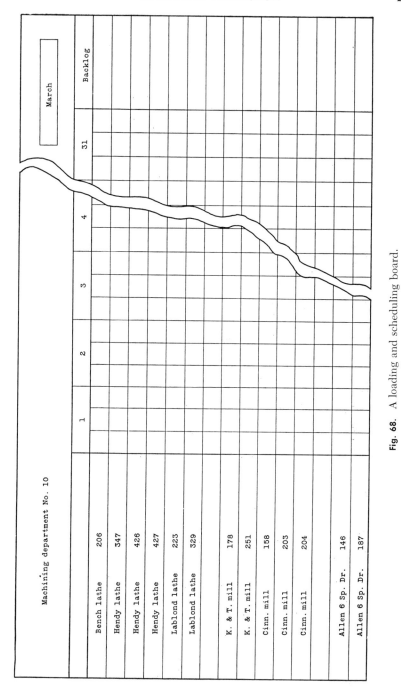

Fig. 68. A loading and scheduling board.

have some cars with each of these variations so that they can load out dealers' orders, in freight cars and on trucks, and also can accommodate drive-away customers.

The final line-assembly schedules will be complicated by these variations, all of which must be considered in planning. Even in our relatively simple example, 192 car variations must be provided in the production of 800 cars per day. Add a few more body models, optional tires with white side walls, and so on, and it will be seen that the scheduling of automobile production requires a keen eye for detail and sensitive adjustment to it.

Reduced to its simplest form, any arrangement of loading and scheduling will generally be most effective in actual operation. Flexibility is an essential requirement, for adjustments are sure to be necessary in even the best-made plans. Planning boards were used many years ago by Frederick W. Taylor and are being revived in a simple device now popular in industry. It consists of a combined loading and scheduling board on which small tickets indicate the schedule in terms of when certain items are to be run, while blank spaces on the board reveal available equipment. (See Figure 68.)

For each machine there is a row of spaces to hold small tickets or cards covering every shift to be operated during the month. Cards list the part number and the operation to be performed, together with the quantity to be produced during the shift. As machine-hours are calculated for inquiries or actual orders the number of pieces that can be produced on a shift is posted on cards until there are enough cards to cover the requirement. The cards are then placed in position on the board, each card canceling the availability of specific machines during the shift covered by it.

As an example, 2,000 pieces of part 2695 are required on order 4582. Eight hundred pieces can be produced in operation 1, milled on machine 158. Tickets are made out accordingly and are placed on the board for the third day of March. (See Figure 69.)

This operation will use the capacity of this machine for 2½ shifts. The next order, No. 4926, requires a number of shifts; on each one 600 pieces of part 3032 can be milled in operation 2. Three hundred pieces are, therefore, scheduled on the third shift of March 3, and the remainder on March 4 and 5. Sometimes two items are posted on one ticket as shown in Figure 69, but greater flexibility is achieved by making a ticket for each item. Tickets to cover a shift's output are placed one behind another on the space for the shift being loaded or scheduled.

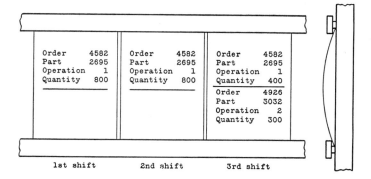

Fig. 69. Loading and scheduling for one day.

Spaces on the right-hand side of the board hold tickets covering the backlog of work for subsequent months. Tickets for work completed are removed on the sixteenth of each month, and the board is loaded for the first 15 days of the following month.

The flexibility of such boards is a major advantage. If an inquiry or order is canceled, all tickets representing it can be removed from the board and other tickets can be moved into the empty spaces. If some orders become more urgently needed than others, tickets can be shifted to give the urgent orders preference. For scheduling purposes, dispatchers can refer to the board and have necessary stock and tools for an order at each machine in readiness for the proper operation. When a machine operator has completed his work on one part, he can refer to the board and get the routing information and the blueprint for the next part to be machined.

Such arrangements can be used in production to stock as well as job-order production. Figure 70 shows a modern loading and scheduling board.

In any combination of loading and scheduling, simplicity of control should be a primary objective. A good general rule to follow is to control by the factor presenting the smallest number, be it machines, items, or workers. If the number of different items is greater than the number of machines on which they are produced, it will be simplest to control by machines. If a few items are produced on many similar machines, control by items will be simpler. If many items are produced on a large number of machines by a few workers, control should be based upon the workers.

Mathematical programming can be used to advantage by a manufacturer who has several items to produce through a period of

Fig. 70. A typical loading and scheduling board. (Courtesy S. Curtis and Son, Inc., Sandy Hook, Conn.)

several months. Production of items in advance of delivery dates involves storage and possession costs. Production scheduled for completion on shipping dates often involves premium overtime work. A simple matrix method can be used to determine optimum loading and scheduling of such production items.[1]

SUMMARY

Two external factors governing the scheduling of both types of production are consumer demand and customer delivery dates. In production to stock, dealers' and retailers' inventories also are important factors. In both stock and job-order production, the internal factors include process intervals, availability of equipment, personnel and material, manufacturing facilities, and economical production runs.

[1] S. Vajda, *Readings in Linear Programming*, John Wiley and Sons, New York, 1958.

In stock production, the finished goods inventory is another internal factor.

In production to stock, master schedules are first prepared from sales forecasts adjusted to balance finished goods inventories. These master schedules are broken down into department schedules. In job-order production, department schedules are generally established while the operation take-offs are being made.

Where the flow of material from one department to the next is not constant and uniform, gap phasing of interdepartmental schedules is generally used. Where planning operation and control are effective, lap phasing can be used.

By using ticket boards, loading and scheduling can often be combined. Such arrangements are simple and flexible.

QUESTIONS TO CHECK COMPREHENSION

1. In November a manufacturer announced a price increase to take effect on January 1. The normal sales of a certain item had been 1,000,000 per month. November and December sales went to 4,000,000, bringing the monthly average for the year to 1,166,666 units. Finished goods inventories were normal. Production schedules, therefore, were increased to 3,500,000 units for the first quarter of the following year, but sales for the quarter declined to 1,000,000 units. What consideration had been neglected?

2. The process interval on a particular item normally is 20 weeks, since foremen prefer to start work only when entire production lots have been delivered to them. During emergencies, however, parts of lots have sometimes been scheduled on a send-ahead basis. These partial lots have had a process interval of 8 weeks. What type of production schedule phasing should be considered?

3. The preparation or setup cost for a particular product is $1,000. A 1-month supply should be carried in finished goods stock, and its value is $10,000. How many times a year should production of this item be scheduled?

4. You are given the choice of planning production schedules for class-of-work manufacture or planning schedules for progressive manufacture. Which will you choose? Why?

5. In planning production for an automobile final line assembly, you have scheduled production of standard models during the first 5 hours of the day and that of de luxe models during the remainder. What activity will be dislocated? Why?

6. What three external factors govern production scheduling?

7. What seven internal factors govern production scheduling?

8. In manufacturing to stock, the finished goods stock allows some cushion for scheduling production. What serves as a similar cushion in job-order production?

9. A master schedule for production in a manufacturing plant has been prepared for the first quarter of the year. If a copy of it is given to each production foreman, will this be sufficient for the scheduling of each department? Give the reasons for your answer.

10. Can loading and scheduling be combined?

11. What are the advantages of planning boards?

12. Planning can be done by workers, items, or machines. What factor is considered when selecting one of these three methods?

PROBLEMS

1. The month of September, which begins on Thursday, will contain 22 working days excluding Saturdays. Six turret lathes with three shifts per day are available for work on five customers' orders and one stock item requiring 132 shifts which can be produced at any time during the month. Customer order 349 requiring 60 shifts has been promised for September 7, C.O. 365 requiring 96 shifts for September 30, C.O. 358 requiring 60 shifts for September 20, C.O. 352 requiring 48 shifts for September 13, and C.O. 360 requiring 12 shifts for September 15. Prepare a department schedule for this work and indicate whether or not Saturday work will be required.

2. Assume that you are the department foreman. How will you assign this work to the six machines to keep the number of setups at a minimum and still meet delivery dates?

3. A textile company operates two 600-loom weaving mills 8 hours per day on a single shift basis. Multiple shifts have been avoided because the union contract requires a 25 per cent premium for work on a second shift and 30 per cent on a third. Overtime pay is at time and one-half for time in excess of 8 hours per day, or for any work week of more than 40 hours, and for holidays, Saturdays, and Sundays. The contract also specifies that all employees shall share equally in overtime.

Direct labor cost per loom hour is $3.40. Indirect operating cost per loom hour is $1.60. Fixed expense for possession of one inoperative mill is $5,000 per week. Loom efficiencies are as follows:

Mill A	Mill B
20 looms @ 100%	10 looms @ 110%
40 looms @ 95%	100 looms @ 100%
100 looms @ 90%	180 looms @ 95%
140 looms @ 85%	200 looms @ 90%
100 looms @ 80%	110 looms @ 85%
100 looms @ 75%	

The production load per week for the next 12 months is 42,900 loom hours at 100% efficiency. The cost to move a loom from one mill to another is $60.00. Establish an optimal operating plan assuming that if any looms are moved the cost for moving them will be recovered within a year.

DISCUSSION CASE

In one manufacturing division of a company there were 4 operating foremen, 1 industrial engineer, 1 production-planning engineer, and 1 quality-control engineer, all reporting to a divisional superintendent. Communications were excellent and so was cooperation.

Before any production schedules were issued, the production-planning engineer always made a physical check of the various raw materials needed for the production. The quality-control engineer also examined the schedule to determine the quality characteristics of the needed raw materials. If any variations were to be expected in process behavior he advised both the production planner and the appropriate foreman.

Production was made to stock, which was maintained between predetermined maximum and minimum limits. Since a variety of items were shipped together on customers' orders, a balanced supply of finished goods had to be kept on hand for shipment.

This manufacturing division had established an excellent record for control of its raw-material and finished goods inventories. It also had enviable records for level employment and cost control. Everyone in the division took great personal pride in these records.

When an opening for the position of divisional superintendent occurred in another division of the company, one of the foremen of this division was promoted to it. A workman who had demonstrated initiative and technical knowledge was promoted to foreman, in spite of the fact that he had always worked alone on jobs and so had not developed skill in teamwork.

After a few introductory weeks, the new foreman was given full responsibility. The divisional superintendent explained that, while there were not too many strict boundaries of domain within the organization, the planning engineer was fully responsible for production plans and for adjustments to them. Operating foremen were held strictly accountable for control of production and costs. The foreman was given a schedule for the coming week and a tentative schedule for the subsequent 6 weeks. He noted that a machine unit having a high overhead expense and complicated change-over was scheduled to produce a heavy-running item (A) for 4 days followed by a 1-day run of another item (B). This schedule was repeated each week for 7 weeks. He concluded that running item A for 28 days followed by 7 days of item B would save 12 setups in 7 weeks. This would reduce costs and help justify his promotion. He decided to ignore the schedule of 1-day production of item B during the coming week.

At the end of the week the production planner noted that item B was short. He discussed this with the foreman and rescheduled the item at double the quantity for the next week, but the foreman again ignored the schedule.

During those 2 weeks the demand for item B was unusually heavy and the finished goods stock was exhausted. More than 100 orders calling for item B had to be back-ordered.

One of the divisional superintendent's most sensitive controls was a report on back orders. These normally never exceeded 10 in any 1 week and none ever remained unfilled for more than 3 days. The superintendent asked the production planner for an explanation. When schedules showed that the planning had been correct the new foreman was called in. He explained his hope of making a new cost record, admitted his error, and offered to come in over the week end and change the machine over for item B so that production could start on Monday morning.

List the causes for what was wrong and recommend remedial action.

17
Recording and Reporting

Both records and reports are essential in planning and controlling production. They also provide management with data on which to base decisions vital to every company.

Since reports generally are prepared from records, the records must be considered first. Any system of records worth the name must meet three requirements. First, it must preserve essential facts in orderly

Fig. 71. A Wheeldex direct posting cabinet. (Courtesy Wheeldex Manufacturing Co., Inc.)

Fig. 72. A circular workplace. (Courtesy Wheeldex Manufacturing Co., Inc.)

array, so that they can be consulted with the minimum of effort. Second, it must eliminate data that are not significant as well as those whose value has vanished with the passing years. This does not, of course, apply to records preserved for *purely* historical purposes. American industry has been lax in recording and telling its own story and might well do more in this field. Such history, however, is beyond the province of this book, and the records required for it might well be termed archives. Our concern is with records that form a tool for scheduling and controlling production. Third, it must be so designed that postings can be made quickly and simply, for records requiring undue effort are a drain upon time and manpower. They force production to support the files instead of making the files a means to more efficient production.

Like all other phases of modern business, recording has been mechanized. This is evidenced by Figure 71, which shows a Wheeldex direct-posting cabinet that holds 10,000 4 by 6 inch cards. The mechanism of this cabinet is motor-driven and fingertip control. It permits

Fig. 73. Robot Kardex record files. (Courtesy Remington Rand, Inc.)

Fig. 74. A Remington Rand Kardex record room containing information covering millions of items. (Courtesy Remington Rand, Inc.)

rotation forward or in reverse, yet automatically provides a firmly stabilized writing surface so that entries can be made on cards while they remain in the file. Figure 72 shows a section of an almost semi-circular arrangement of Wheeldex units in which a comfortable posture chair rotates from a central pivot. Thus one person has complete and instantaneous control of 60,000 or more cards, depending on their size. By placing two such arrangements together, one person can attend 120,000 or more items. If the activity as well as the number of items is great, two operators can be accommodated in such an arrangement. Two posture chairs rotating from the central pivot are then provided.

Figure 73 illustrates posting and reference ease with the Robot-Kardex in which file slides are electrically delivered to the use position in four seconds. Figure 74 shows a record room, in which records containing millions of entries are easily available for reference, preparation of reports, and statistical treatment.

The Holerith system of punched cards can also be used for recording data. The cards are collated by machine and used to prepare many types of reports from the same data. Collators and tabulators and other machines operate automatically.

Modern dynamic systems of control require recording, computing, and reporting to be performed at lightning speeds. This performance is necessary because of the vast volume of data to be processed and because the several steps in programmed control are interdependent and cannot long wait for each other. Manual posting of, computing, and reference to data in such systems would be so slow and complex as to make them ineffective as well as inaccurate.

Figure 75 shows the UNIVAC Solid-State Computer. From right to left we see the High-Speed Card Reader that reads, verifies, and sorts 450 cards per minute and next the Read-Punch Unit that reads, punches, and verifies 150 cards per minute. Next is the Central Processor that stores 50,000 digits of information and can compute while other operations such as reading, punching, and printing are taking place and finally the High-Speed Printer that prints 600 lines per minute on continuous multicopy forms.

The UNIVAC is not limited to control operations. It is also used by banks, insurance companies, railroads, utilities and engineering firms to list only a few. UNIVAC can be used also to solve complex problems in mathematical programming, operations research, and decision making that would otherwise remain unsolved.

In the past, locating and processing specific records required searching through large volumes of information. Manual searching and processing were so expensive and took so much time that unprocessed and unrecorded information was generally allowed to accumulate for a week or more before it was processed. Even after the introduction of punched-card accounting, which greatly simplified the processing of information, cards generally accumulated for about three days before they were processed and recorded. This delay often forced executives to base decisions upon information which was not up to date and, therefore, was likely to be incorrect.

The IBM 305 provides a rapid means of locating and processing specific records without searching through large volumes of information. It offers electronic access, in less than a second, to as many as 20 million digits of information stored in its magnetic memory. A digit is one character, groups of which constitute words or numbers.

The ability to process information through RAMAC 305 without regard to sequence gives the system its name—a Random Access Method of Accounting and Control. Figure 76 shows the IBM

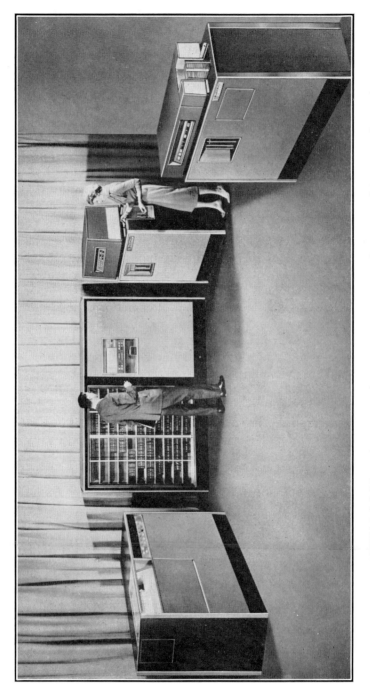

Fig. 75. UNIVAC Solid-State Computer. (Courtesy Remington Rand, Division of Sperry Rand Corp.)

Fig. 76. The IBM RAMAC 305 (Random Access Method of Accounting and Control). (Courtesy International Business Machines Corp.)

RAMAC 305 a complete data processing system built around a disk memory unit which consists of 50 magnetic metal disks as shown in Figure 77. The RAMAC 305 is designed to provide continuous, or "in-line," accounting for all types of businesses. Data are recorded on or read from each side of the disks (see Figure 78) in random order by a rapidly-moving access arm which is shown in Figure 77. Disks have storage capacities of 5 and 10 million digits and may be used either singly or in any combination of two to provide storage capacities of 5, 10, 15, and 20 million digits.

Electronic data processing equipment can hold basic information in its memory system, as well as information that records the current status of items. New information can be introduced, after which the equipment calculates the action to be taken and up-dates the status. For example, memory units can hold records of the raw materials required per unit of output, the number of units of raw materials on hand, on order, allocated for other requirements, the economic order quantity, procurement lead intervals, and other data. Then when information for a new order or forecast requirement is presented to the system, it performs the proper calculations, specifies the raw materials to be reordered, and brings the stock status up to date in readiness for the next operation.

Customers' orders for finished goods fed to the electronic data processing systems cause them to tell if sufficient quantities of the items are on hand, extend the quantities at selling prices, compute

Fig. 77. The IBM RAMAC 305 disk memory unit. (Courtesy International Business Machines Corp.)

discounts, prepare shipping orders and invoices, and bring the stock status up to date. The application of electronic data processing to production forecasting, planning, and control operations are almost unlimited.

The most exciting development in information recording and storage is TPR, thermoplastic recording, invented by Dr. William Glenn of the General Electric Research Laboratory. The information storage capability of TPR is almost incredible. In principle TPR could record the twenty-four volumes of the *Encyclopaedia Britannica* on a reel the size of a spool of thread and it would take only a minute to record each volume. (See Figure 79.) In addition, the information can be erased easily and the tape will record both images and sequential information.

To give some notion of the capability of TPR to concentrate information in storage, Figure 80 shows the "checkerboard" pattern recorded on thermoplastic tape by the General Electric Engineering Laboratory which is approximately $\frac{3}{1000}$th of an inch in length and width. With the binary digit system, where the light and dark squares could represent "0" and "1," it is thus possible to record at the rate of forty million "bits" of information per square inch of thermoplastic. In February 1960 General Electric Company officials stated that TPR is still in the development stage. The reader will, of course, at once see the vast potential for application of TPR in both civilian and military activities.

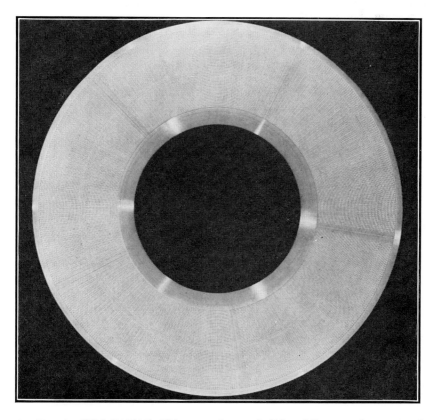

Fig. 78. An IBM RAMAC 305 magnetic metal disk. (Courtesy International Business Machines Corp.)

Fig. 79. Dr. William Glenn holding a reel of tape on which all 24 volumes of the *Encyclopaedia Britannica* can be recorded. (Courtesy General Electric Co.)

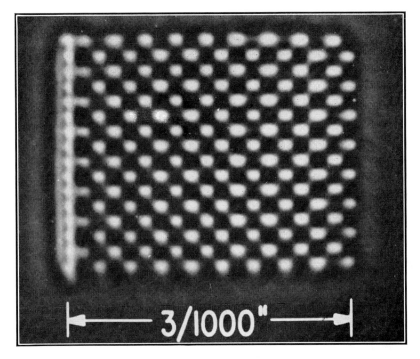

Fig. 80. Showing the capability of TPR to concentrate recorded information. (Courtesy General Electric Co.)

The team of engineers and executives charged with the responsibility for forecasting, planning, and control of production will require records of three basic types in sixteen secondary categories:

A. Records of basic information
  1. Blueprints
  2. Bills of material
  3. Time values for fundamental operations
  4. Production routings

B. Records showing what is available
  1. Raw materials
  2. Work-in-process
  3. Semiprocessed stock
  4. Finished stock
  5. Machinery and equipment
  6. Tools, jigs, fixtures, and inspection gages
  7. Available personnel

raw materials delivered to operating departments should be accounted for by them or by the stores department. To keep stores records balanced, many companies consider all raw materials to be consumed and a part of work-in-process as soon as they have been delivered to the operating departments.

3. Semiprocessed Stock. Many industrial operations consist of primary processes in which weaving, machining, paint making, etc., are performed, and secondary processes that include cutting to size, packaging, assembly, filling into cans, and so on. In recording these operations, the primary process materials are generally considered as semiprocessed stock, since it would be difficult to identify them in terms of the production items that they will ultimately become. That is to say, an inventory containing several thousands of yards of bleached cloth may later be used in the production of sheets, pillow cases, or other products. Some of it may even be sold as bulk yardage. Since the ultimate use of this cloth cannot be predicted, it is recorded separately as semiprocessed stock that later will be allocated to orders.

A similar situation exists in the manufacture of internal-combustion engines. Balanced quantities of component parts must be produced for use in final assembly. Some additional parts may be produced for parts and service sales. Figure 82 shows a typical Kardex record of such parts. It will be noted that this record contains a control feature. After production and consumption have been posted, plastic slides are moved on the visible portion of the card to show the balance of stock that remains. Vertical lines on the stock status area show boundaries between which action should be taken if the slide shows more or less than a normal stock. In the example illustrated, the stock of 3,059 (crank shaft center bearing shim) is low and its production should be expedited.

4. Finished Stock. Inventories of finished goods constantly change, since they are depleted by sales and replenished by production. Records posted for production and shipments must be balanced every day if planning and control are to be effective.

5. Machinery and Equipment. Accurate records of machines and other equipment are needed for the plant assets and depreciation accounts and to show what is available for production planning. Pieces generally are identified by numbered brass tags attached to them. These numbers are employed in compiling the accounts and may also

6	12	17	23	29	35	41	47	52	58	64	70	77	82	93	105	140	175	210
6	12	18	24	30	36	42	48	54	60	66	72	84	96	108	144	180	216
6	12	18	25	31	37	43	49	55	62	68	74	86	99	111	148	185	222

DATE

RE ORDER QUANTITY

3001	Cylinder Head
3002	Cylinder Head Gasket
3003	Cylinder Head Cap Screw
3008	Cylinder Head Front Cover
3012	Cylinder Cover Felt
3017	Time Gear Cover Gasket
3018	Time Gear Cover Plate
3020	Piston
3021	Piston .003" Oversize
3022	Piston .010" Oversize
3024	Piston .020" Oversize
3025	Piston Pin
3026	Piston Pin .003" Oversize
	Piston Ring
3040	Crank Shaft
3041	Crank Shaft Gear
3042	Crank Shaft Rear Bearing Cap
3043	Crank Shaft Front Bearing Cap
3044	Crank Shaft Front Bearing Upper
3045	Crank Shaft Front Bearing Lower
3046	Crank Shaft Front Bearing Shim
3048	Crank Shaft Center Bearing Cap
3049	Crank Shaft Center Bearing Upper
3051	Crank Shaft Bolt
3052	Crank Shaft Liner
3053	Crank Shaft Pin
3055	Crank Shaft Cap Stud
3059	Crank Shaft Center Bearing Shim
3061	Cam Shaft
3063	Cam Shaft Front Bearing
3064	Cam Shaft Center Bearing
3065	Cam Shaft Rear Bearing
3066	Cam Shaft Bearing Ring
3069	Time Gear - Large
3070	Time Gear - Small
3071	Cam Shaft Dowel Pin
3072	Cam Shaft Lock Nut
3075	Valve - Standard
3076	Valve Bushing
3077	Valve Spring
3080	Push Rod
3082	Exhaust Manifold
3084	Inlet Pipe
3085	Breather Pipe
3086	Inlet Pipe
3087	Cam Shaft
3089	Water Pump Body Bushing
3090	Fly wheel Splash Guard
3091	Time Gear Cover Plate

KARDEX CONTROL OF INVENTORY RECORD

SP KD 4245

Fig. 82. A Kardex file with control limits and plastic slides to show actual stock positions. (Courtesy Remington Rand, Inc.)

be used in planning. As we have seen, however, modern practice generally uses numbered machine groups for loading and scheduling.

6. Tools, Jigs, Fixtures, and Inspection Gages. In the machine-tool industry all special equipment such as cutting tools, drill jigs, milling-machine vises, special fixtures, and inspection gages must be identified and cross-referenced, so that they can be ordered out for any operations in which they are needed. These items are generally stored in tool cribs containing ready reference records with which to locate tools when needed and to charge them out when they are delivered to operations. Many of these items must have periodic inspections, and these also are listed on the records.

7. Available Personnel. People and their skills are of primary importance in planning production. Records must, of course, be kept for payroll purposes, and can be extended for use by production planners to assure that the necessary skills are available when needed.

C. HISTORICAL RECORDS

1. Production. These records can be included in the finished stock report. Operating supervisors also generally maintain records of performance by machines and operators.

2. Waste and Rejects. Quality and inspection records should be designed so that these shrinkages can become the basis for allowances in future planning and scheduling.

3. Machine Performance. These records provide a means of determining standard capacities from the proved capabilities of machines. Schedules for individual machines or machine groups are based upon these records.

4. Sales. The sales record can also be included in the finished stock report. It will be used in establishing sales forecasts.

5. Absenteeism. Data on absenteeism may be included in personnel records. They provide a basis for allowances when total personnel requirements are computed in scheduling.

Reports generally summarize data contained in records. A variety of graphic and statistical methods is available to present such sum-

Fig. 83. An illustration of immediate reference with Kardex files. (Courtesy Remington Rand, Inc.)

maries for consideration by management. Moving averages are sensitive indicators of growth and decline. Direct comparisons of values for a certain day and the corresponding day a year before and the current month and year to date and the corresponding periods last year are important to managers. Ratios are often employed in reporting because they permit comparison of two sets of factors simultaneously.

The frequency of reports should be given careful consideration. Records themselves are often adequate for dynamic control of production. Figure 83 shows the ease of record reference using summary data in Remington Rand Kardex files. In other situations the exception principle may be applied in reporting. As an example, it would be absurd to send a plant manager a daily inventory of some 10,000 items in stock. Instead, he may receive a weekly list of shortages and items in oversupply. Noting these exceptions, he will assume that all other items are stocked in proper quantities.

It should be kept in mind that, if records are accurate and complete, data and information are in memory positions ready to be summarized in report form when they are needed.

Some simple high-light reports can be prepared daily with very little time and effort. This process will be discussed, with examples, in the latter part of Chapter 18.

Production planners should critically examine both records and reports to determine their effectiveness. Answers to the following questions will generally indicate whether records and reports meet this requirement.

1. Do they form the basis for executive decisions and acts?

2. Does the time required for their maintenance make them too late to be of any use?

3. Does someone else maintain a duplicate or similar record? If so, can the two be combined, or can one be eliminated?

4. Are particular records necessary for planning and control? If not, and if they are necessary for some other purpose, should some other division maintain them?

5. Are data ambiguous? Are classifications specific and in the desired terms? Can the data be misinterpreted?

6. Are records actually used, or has the need for them ceased?

In engineering departments, records and reports are of critical importance not only in engineering development but also in providing current information to operating and cost departments. The methods for bringing new blueprints and bills of material to production departments are explained in Chapter 11. Within engineering organizations, engineering change notices authorize design and tolerance revisions. They describe the changes and tell why and when they are to be made. Numbers of engineering change notices are generally recorded on blueprints so that successive changes of design can be traced through old blueprints and change notices associated with them. Files of blueprints and engineering change notices thus provide records of what, when, and why changes were made.

SUMMARY

Records and reports are necessary in the forecasting, planning, and control of production. The mechanics of records should include simplicity and ease of posting and reference. Many reports can be prepared from records either currently or at some later date if they are needed.

Production planning utilizes records of basic information, records of inventories, and historical records. Reports may be prepared as summaries of these records. Records also provide the data for statistical studies required by management as a basis for its decisions.

Records and reports should be examined to determine whether they serve their purpose or involve duplication. Records that have become obsolete should be discontinued.

QUESTIONS TO CHECK COMPREHENSION

1. Should records be designed first and procedures and operations adapted to them later?

2. Discuss the mechanics of records in relation to ease and simplicity in use.

3. What basic records are generally used by industrial engineers?

4. Certain records show what is available for work. What are they?

5. Why are certain historical records important to planners?

6. What is the difference between a record and a report?

7. What factors test the effectiveness of records and reports?

8. A report of production by items is issued quarterly, one month later than the quarter on which it reports. Can it be of any use in planning current production? Give the reason for your answer.

9. Is it often possible to work from the records themselves without summarizing them in reports?

10. Can some records be designed to indicate what should be done as well as to serve as a posting and reference medium?

11. Why are production planners interested in records of tools, jigs, fixtures, and inspection gages?

12. Do records of absenteeism serve any purpose in scheduding production? How?

PROBLEM

1. A team comprising representatives from the purchasing, cost, personnel, and payroll departments, plus you as production-planning engineer, has been formed to simplify records and reports. Prepare a table showing common interests in the essential records and reports needed by these different divisions of your company.

DISCUSSION CASE

Mr. Bigger, the manager of a small manufacturing plant, requested many detailed reports—so many and in so much detail that he seldom found time to study them. He did this because incomplete records had once caused the company to lose a lawsuit over a patent infringement.

The company's current records were excellent. The principal burden of preparing reports fell upon Mr. Wilson, the production-planning engineer, who gave more than half his time to them. He knew that much of his work was being wasted, and he had repeatedly urged that this or that report be eliminated. Mr. Bigger emphatically rejected these proposals.

Suspecting that reports were never read, Wilson prepared one report in skeleton form but did not issue it for several months. He then asked that this report be eliminated, but Bigger insisted that it was needed. Wilson countered with the statement that it simply could not be so important, since Bigger had not seen one for months. Wilson thereupon told Mr. Bigger that he really did not know the difference between a record and a report. Wilson also explained that the production records were so well kept that information could be assembled for reports covering any phase of the business if they were actually needed.

Mr. Bigger challenged this statement and asked Wilson to prove it by supplying certain summary data covering production. Mr. Wilson led Mr. Bigger to some visible reference cabinet files and quickly took off the figures needed for the summary report. Mr. Bigger was impressed with the completeness of the records and with the ease of reference to them. He related his experience with the lawsuit and admitted that he had asked for too many reports. A meeting was called to discuss the whole subject of records and reports. You have been invited to attend this meeting and offer your recommendations.

18

Evaluating Results
and Controlling

Equipment load charts determine whether there is sufficient capacity to accommodate a customer's order or the requirements indicated by forecasts. Production schedules are actual plans to produce definite items at definite periods of time. Since there will always be some difference between the forecast and what is actually sold, and between schedules and what is actually produced, there must be some provision for follow-up. There also must be provision for follow-through and adjustment.

A. DISPATCHING

Some of the older methods of dispatching, such as the one employed by Franklin Motors at Syracuse, were highly systematized. Pneumatic tubes at work stations were connected with a central dispatching room. When a job was completed a ticket was sent via tube to the dispatching room, and instructions for the next job were promptly forwarded to the work station. Records of performance in comparison with schedules were maintained in the central dispatching room.

Such systems were evidently too cumbersome, for they are no longer used. Where work must move from one department to another, it is now general practice to have department clerks prepare move tickets in duplicate. One copy is attached to the material and another is generally sent to the production-control office. The ticket authorizes material handlers to forward the material to the next department. The copy indicates completion of a number of pieces or units in a department. It is used by the production-control department to

DATE	QUANTITY	UNIT	ARTICLE	DR. DEPT.	CR. DEPT.

NOTICE:-ONLY ONE ARTICLE ON A TICKET   NUMBER

DESCRIPTION OF MATERIAL:-

INTER-DEPARTMENTAL DELIVERIES

PREVIOUS VALUE	VALUE AT STAND.	QUANTITY	VALUES		
			MATERIAL	LABOR	BURDEN

Form 29-27-2500-11-41

Fig. 84. A typical move ticket.

compare actual production with the corresponding production schedules. Figure 84 shows a typical move ticket.

Some companies use tickets having stubs for operations to be performed. As each operation is completed, the appropriate stub is torn from the master ticket and forwarded to the production-control department. In one plant using such tickets, the author found three sides of a large room equipped with numbered hooks. As operations were completed, the several stubs for each order were hung on a hook. Mounting stepladders, several young women placed the stubs on appropriate hooks. Other young women were busy making entries in registers. An inquiry about stubs for order 2647 brought out the fact that no hook bore that number. It was necessary, therefore, to refer to a register to find that stubs for order 2647 were on hook 385. The register also showed that 5,000 units had been completed in operation 3. Hook 385 had stubs for operations 1 and 2, but the stub for 3 was in a pile waiting to be hung. Further questioning revealed the fact that the stubs were also used by the accounting department to check incentive wage credits. The system was established because at one time someone had cheated by marking more units than had actually been produced in an operation. The controller, therefore, had given orders that all stubs had to be matched up and checked for production quantities. Discussion with the controller revealed that some $6,000 per year was being spent to hang stubs on hooks in order to prevent a possible loss of $50 per year through dishonesty. Moreover, such dishonesty could be quickly detected when the stubs were posted in the register. The hooks and stepladders thereupon were removed, and the young women who had worked on them were assigned to useful work.

Any system should be carefully devised and critically examined, not once, but periodically. Otherwise, its faults are likely to grow until it dominates people instead of being operated by them for the benefit of their company. Thus, there are plants in which goods must be moved because of a system, whereas actually the system should be modified so that the transfer is recorded and the move eliminated.

A well-planned dispatching system forwards stores requisitions to the raw-stores department for delivery to the correct manufacturing department in time for the first operations to be performed. Move tickets should be prepared as soon as a sufficient quantity has been produced in one operation to be sent to the next department for another operation. Copies of these tickets permit the production-control department to keep a running record of work-in-process.

B. FOLLOW-UP

Most production-control departments employ expediters who are sometimes called stock chasers, but their work and qualifications deserve a better title. Henry Kaiser's expediters have only two rules for action:

1. Never be hard-boiled.
2. Never take no for an answer.

The finished goods inventory control and expediting functions of production control are like a servomechanism for controlling a machine operation or a temperature. (See Figure 85.)

To accomplish any objective, some action must be taken. The results of the action must be evaluated. Adjustments must be made so that the completed and the future action will conform to the objective. In production, the objective may also change so that adjustments must be made for a changing objective as well as a variation between performance and plan. The scheme shown in Figure 86 is generally used for dispatching and follow-up of production.

In many plants the inventory section is housed in the same office with scheduling and loading. Shortage lists, therefore, can be pre-

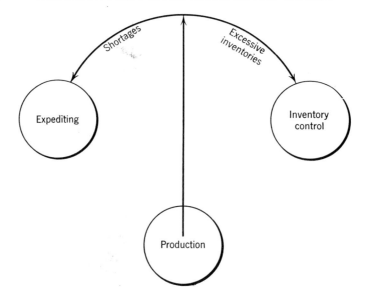

Fig. 85. A servomechanism analogy.

pared easily by comparing the inventory position with schedules. In small companies, and in large ones that decentralize production control, one man may perform all the functions of loading, scheduling, inventory, dispatching, and expediting for a group of products or processes. Such concentration eliminates errors introduced when one person takes up where another has left off. Moreover, the person who performs all these functions generally has a full knowledge of the whole situation. On the other hand, too much reliance is placed upon one man who, in the normal course of events, may resign, fall ill, or even die. It is wise to provide him with an understudy who is trained to carry on his work in an emergency.

Many companies have devised both simple and effective means of comparing results with schedules. Figure 87 shows a simple daily schedule sheet given the department foreman two or three days in advance. The foreman checks his actual production against the schedule and explains any deviation from it. One advantage of this sheet is that it gives the production-control organization a comparison between schedule and actual production, quickly, and in compact form.

Figure 88 shows a similar check-up sheet based on a weekly schedule. Foremen generally prefer weekly sheets because they allow a

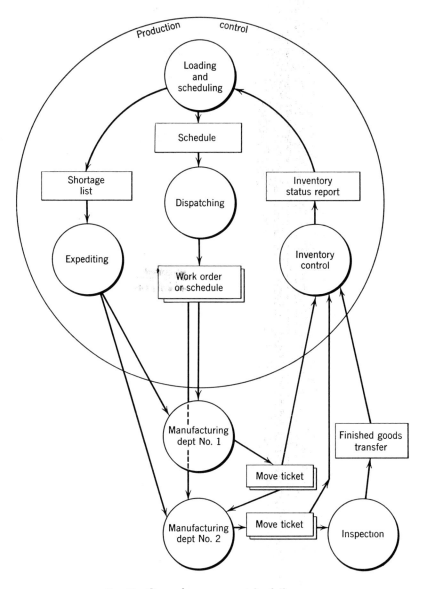

Fig. 86. General arrangement for follow-up.

PRODUCTION SCHEDULE

DEPT __6 Mill and Frame__   DATE _____May 16_____

____2____ SHIFTS   ____8____ HOURS EACH

The following is the indication of the order of preference wanted for jobs in your department. Insofar as possible this order should be maintained, availability and machine set-ups being first considered. Return duplicate copy of this schedule to Schedule Department with necessary comments under "Job Complete" and "Remarks" columns, before five o'clock each day

Part Number	Quantity	Description	Del. to Dept.	Job Complete (x)	Remarks
36052	408	Tips	12	X	I7 OVER
73481	2,235	Plates	8	X	
92137	360	Base	14	X	
77498	400	Angles	14	X	
77499	100	Plates	14	X	
77500	200	Stringers	14	X	
77501	200	Headers	14		IO SHORT WILL REPAIR
77502	100	Cross-piece	14	X	
21437	300	Base	10	X	+6 FROM 5/14 REPAIRED
21438	300	Sub-frame	12		8 SHORT *
21439	2,400	Gussets	8	X	
63072	3,000	Housings	14		** I800 COMPLETE
*	8 PIECES	SHORT FROM DEPT 3		PLEASE	LOCATE
	AND RESCHEDULE	BEFORE	END	OF RUN	
* *	WILL RUN	ON 3 EXTRA	MACHINES	5/17	
			John R Jones		

Fig. 87. A department production schedule.

little more freedom and array the work of a whole week on one sheet. It is especially suitable where production is so well controlled that the production-control office need only post and review results.

When many companion parts are to be machined in advance of an assembly schedule, a Gantt chart can be used to reveal which parts

PRODUCTION PLANNING DEPT.
FOREMAN John Jones

DEPT. NO. 6

PRODUCTION SCHEDULE

PRODUCT	9 MONDAY Mach. or Person	Shifts	Quan. Sch.	Prod.	Del'd	10 TUESDAY Mach. or Person	Shifts	Quan. Sch.	Prod.	Del'd	11 WEDNESDAY Mach. or Person	Shifts	Quan. Sch.	Prod.	Del'd	12 THURSDAY Mach. or Person	Shifts	Quan. Sch.	Prod.	Del'd	14 SATURDAY Quan. Sch.	Prod.	Del'd	Total Shifts
BL-05	26	1	600	804		26	1	600	842		26	1	600	774	1,920	26	1	600	455					5
BL-20	18	1	5,000	5,300		18	1	5,000	3,284		18	1	4,000	5,290	13,874	18		Repair				Repair		3
AR-10	16	2	900	775	648	16	2	900	937	1,296	16	2	900	711	753	16	2	800	645	774				6
AR-20																								2
AR-30																								2
BR-10	12	2	2,600	3,108	504	12	2	2,600	3,031		12	2	2,600	3,044	2,100	12	2	2,600	2,125	3,024				4
BR-20					1,524					3,024														6
BR-30	20	2	1,100	725	480	20	2	1,100	1,074	600	20	2	1,100	976	600	20	2	1,100	701					10
RF-05	8	2	375	404	1,200	8	2	375	377		8	2	375	382	240	8	2	375	376	480				10
RF-10	9	2	225	225		9	2	225	284	300	9	2	225	274	240	9	2	225	156	300				10
RF-20	10	2	300	310		10	2	300	289	500	10	2	300	320		10	2	300	295					10

Machine shifts 68

Man shifts 138

Fig. 88. A simple weekly schedule.

Production Control Dept.

Date:

IDLE MACHINE DAILY REPORT

Department:

Group:

Reasons for Idleness

Time of Idleness
Express in ½ hour periods
Draw a Horizontal Line

Name of Machine	Mach. No.	Operation	Shift	1	2	3	4	5	6	7	8	Sym-bols	Remarks
1			1										
			2										
			3										
2			1										
			2										
			3										
3			1										
			2										
			3										
			1										
7			3										
8			1										
			2										
			3										
9			1										
			2										
			3										
10			1										
			2										
			3										

MAIL TO PRODUCTION CONTROL DEPARTMENT EACH MORNING   Reported by: _____

Symbol: A – Breakdown (Temporary) B – Down for repairs C – Job Change D – Sent to Machine Shop E – Lack of Material F – Lack of Operator G – No Schedule

Fig. 90. An idle machine report form.

class-of-work type of production. When production is on a continuous, progressive basis, dispatching and expediting are simplified but planning and control of the products must be given exacting attention. Moreover, if progressive continuous production has been decided upon, it should not be changed. An example from the record of World War II shows the necessity for this:

A company obtained a contract for an item that required the production of one unit per minute. A three-month period was allowed for tooling and setting up the equipment for operations that included machining, assembly, painting, and packing on a conveyor line.

When the arrangement of equipment was about half completed, executives decided to begin operation of the completed portion of it and to store semifinished parts until the rest of the equipment was in operation. This course led them into difficulties in three ways:

1. Although some raw material was on hand, planning had been based on a steady flow starting six weeks later. After four weeks of operation, there was too little raw material to continue the starting operations and the whole personnel planning was dislocated.

2. Since cost estimates had not allowed for handling and storage of semifinished parts, those estimates were exceeded.

3. The planning had been arranged with minimal gaging of dimensions, because, with a short process interval, minor tolerance revisions could be made if final assembly showed them to be needed. When arrangement of equipment was completed, it was found that mating parts commonly were at the extremes of their tolerances. This caused such difficulty in assembly that male components had to be remachined.

As an overall result, three weeks were lost instead of six weeks being gained. Costs rose considerably above the contract price. Employees were demoralized. Fortunately, the contract had a long run. When the original policy and planning were restored, the scheduled production of one item per minute was achieved and losses were canceled.

C. RATIO-DELAY ANALYSIS

Once production executives awakened to the great opportunities offered by statistical quality control they soon learned that small samples could also be used to determine the effectiveness of operations. This method, called ratio-delay analysis, was developed by

L. H. C. Tippett of the British Cotton Industries Association, and to him industry is indebted for an important evaluation tool.[1]

As has been explained in Chapter 4 on manufacturing planning, industrial engineers long ago learned to study carefully the time necessary to perform the elements of operations. When these operations were combined in long and complex processes, final outputs generally fell far short of expectations. Detailed analysis of what was happening in the whole process at any instant was difficult if not impossible because many of the operations were carried on in large areas, parts of which were beyond the vision of a single observer.

Ratio-delay analysis provides a simple, workable, and accurate means of evaluating the effectiveness of complex processes. The method uses small samples to permit statistical inferences of operating effectiveness, just as small samples tell of quality performance as production continues. For a short time (say ten minutes), an observer simply walks through the area in which the process is operating, observing delays and their causes. These short-period observations are repeated at random intervals until the cumulative average ratio of delays becomes reasonably constant, or until enough observations have been made to establish statistical control limits.

Observations ordinarily are classified as avoidable delays, unavoidable delays, and productive time, but other more detailed classifications can be used. When an analysis has been completed, the production executive can state with confidence that his process effectiveness is a certain ratio or percentage of what can be expected as ideal. He first seeks to improve that ratio by eliminating avoidable delays; others, currently called unavoidable, are attacked by modification of equipment and preventive maintenance. Finally, delays that are completely unavoidable are accepted and expectations are reduced to make allowances for them. This in itself is substantial progress.

Ratio-delay analysis can thus be used not only to evaluate but also to improve operations. It also makes it possible to predict profit or loss from an operation or a process as well as to calculate the production economics involved when process modifications are contemplated.

Chester L. Brisley, Wolverine Tube Division, Calumet and Hecla Consolidated Copper Incorporated, Detroit, Michigan, has described the ratio-delay technique in a simple understandable exposition.[2]

[1] L. H. C. Tippett, *Technological Applications of Statistics*, John Wiley & Sons, New York, 1950, and *Methods of Statistics*, John Wiley & Sons, New York, 1952.

[2] C. L. Brisley, "How You Can Put Work Sampling to Work," *Factory Management and Maintenance*, Volume 110, Number 7, July, 1952.

D. CONTROL LIMITS

In production to stock there must be some control of the stock of finished goods, with both a lower and an upper limit that the inventory should not normally exceed. As a matter of company policy, these limits should be established only after careful consideration of the working capital required and the service demanded by customers.

It would be difficult and time-consuming for a policy group to set stock limits for each product made by a company. The policy is, therefore, generalized to specify the number of weeks of stock to be carried in finished goods inventory, with upper and lower limits also expressed in terms of weeks. As an example, the general policy may call for a normal three weeks' stock, with variations that do not run below two weeks' supply or more than four weeks'. If the normal sales of a certain item are 10,000 units per week, this policy calls for a normal stock of 30,000 units. The policy also says that stock shall not be less than 20,000 units or more than 40,000.

There are, of course, many variations. Thus one company may specify that not more than two weeks' supply of any item shall be carried in finished goods stock, with no lower limit. This policy may have been established to conserve working capital, with a calculated risk of loss by late filling of orders. Another company may have built a reputation for prompt customer service. To preserve this reputation, it maintains three weeks' stock as a minimum, with twice that as a maximum.

Companies that have several categories of products, made to stock, generally find that some groups of products move faster than others. Sales of some product groups are less likely to bring unusual demands at unexpected times than other groups. These companies, therefore, usually establish different finished goods stock limits for their various families of products, based upon past experience.

When companies produce to plans based on sales forecasts, there will be times when actual sales exceed or lag behind estimates. If the sales estimates have been accurate, too much importance will not be attached to a few isolated periods when finished goods stocks exceed the maximum requirements by a few weeks. The planner will, however, bring these cases to the attention of the forecaster. A review of dealers' stocks may show that although sales are late they will eventually come through. When stock falls below the minimum requirements, production schedules are generally increased so that customer service will not be impaired.

Even when the sales estimate has been reasonably accurate, it will require occasional adjustment, and the plan or schedule will also have to be adjusted. Figure 91 shows the planning of one product and adjustments made during the year. It will be noted that sales were heavy during August, September, and October. Despite the fact that annual sales exceeded the original forecast by 18.65 per cent, the continual attention and adjustment to it showed that this particular item had to be produced during the vacation period with volunteer help in order to maintain stock and keep back orders from accumulating for a number of months.

This item was planned and produced in conjunction with a number of other items in order to maintain level employment. It was, however, necessary to operate 6 days per week during a number of months to accomplish this.

Because there had formerly been some wide fluctuations in demand for this item, the ideal inventory had been set at a 3 weeks' supply, or 9,000 dozen, with the understanding that this figure would be exceeded when stock was being built up to anticipate a vacation shutdown. The planned stock limits were not more than 5 weeks, or 15,000 dozen, and not less than 2 weeks or 6,000 dozen. Sales exceeding normal expectations reduced the actual inventory to less than 1 week's supply. The exceptionally high turnover was advantageous in the conservation of working capital.

Examination of Figure 91 reveals that, in spite of errors, forecasting, planning, and control produced highly satisfactory results that could not otherwise have been achieved. Serious back-order situations impairing customer service were avoided. Any deviations from the plan were in control to assure stability of employment. Working capital was used to excellent advantage. It is thus seen that consumers, producers, and investors were all well served.

E. THE 85–15 CONCEPT OF CONTROL

Companies that manufacture many different products or many varieties of the same basic products are confronted with highly complex problems of control. Yet for many years the same attention was given to all products regardless of their sales volume and the size of production lots. As a result, control often cost more than the value of many low-volume items. Raw-material and work-in-process inventories were generally excessive when low- and high-volume items received identical attention.

Recommendations to discontinue low-volume items, often called cats and dogs, generally met with objections from management. The reason given was that such action would significantly reduce total production, resulting in increased burden costs per dollar of sales.

Somewhere in the march of industrial progress it was realized that there should be a relationship between the volume of sales of various items and the control attention given them. Analysis of companies manufacturing as many as 500 items also revealed that approximately 15 per cent of these items generally accounted for some 85 per cent of the total value of production. (See Figure 92.)

The 85–15 notion of control directs attention to and implementation of high-volume production items. Narrowed stock limits for high-volume items and wide ones for low-volume items can often reduce working capital requirements and improve manufacturing costs.

This generalization indicates the need for arrangements in which the approximate 15 per cent of the high-volume items are given closer control attention and better facilities than the remaining approximate 85 per cent of the items of low volume and value. One solution to this problem is the formation of a small-lot department or shop, but this cannot always be done without excessive expenditures for addi-

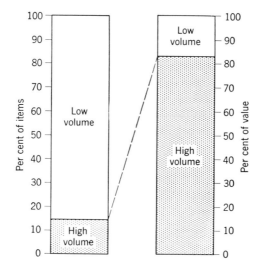

Fig. 92. General distribution and value of high- and low-volume items.

tional production facilities. Another solution gives more critical control attention to high-volume items and less to those of low volume.

To understand the advantages of the second solution, assume that a company manufactures 1,000 different items and controls finished goods stocks between limits of 3 and 5 weeks' supply. Assume also that the value of a week's supply or sales of all items is $1,000,000. Under this arrangement the average stock of finished goods for 4 weeks' supply will be worth $4,000,000.

Analysis of the 1,000 items manufactured by this company shows that 150 of them account for 85 per cent of the total value of production and 850 account for only 15 per cent. Then assume that the company decides to modify its stock limits for finished goods to not less than 2 and not more than 3 weeks' supply of the 150 high-volume items, and to not less than 2 and not more than 6 weeks' supply of the 850 low-volume items. The average value of finished goods stock will then be:

$2\frac{1}{2}$ Weeks' supply of high-volume items @ $850,000 per week = $2,125,000

4 Weeks' supply of low-volume items @ $150,000 per week   =   600,000

$\overline{\hspace{3cm}}$

Total average value of finished goods stock = $2,725,000

This total of $2,725,000 means a reduction of $1,275,000, or almost 32 per cent, in the net working capital required for stocks of finished goods.

The company may, however, elect to forego this reduction in working capital and instead gain more freedom to control the production of the low-volume items within wider limits, thus permitting larger lot sizes to be produced at one time. In this particular case, with the original working capital, the average finished goods stock of low-volume items can be increased to a $12\frac{1}{2}$ weeks' supply. Control limits can then be not less than an 8 weeks' or more than 16 weeks' supply of these items. The choice of plan will be based, of course, upon a comparative study of the economics of both plans.

Similar treatment can be applied to stocks of raw materials. Those used in high-volume production can be closely controlled and scheduled to arrive so that their value is maintained at the lowest practicable figure. Stocks of raw materials for low-volume production items can be maintained in larger quantities without adding significantly to the total value of raw materials on hand. Further, raw material stocks can be sizably reduced with a proportionate reduction of working capital.

The value of work-in-process inventories frequently exceeds the value of raw material stocks. Since the amount of work-in-process is a function of process intervals, engineers give close attention to facilities that will reduce process intervals and develop streamlined production for high-volume items. Low-volume items are produced discontinuously with longer process intervals unless they can be introduced into the same facilities used for high-volume items without disturbing production rates of the high-volume items.

F. SENSITIVE CONTROL INDICATORS

Production and financial executives require some yardsticks with which to measure the effectiveness of planning and control. A daily comparison of production and schedules provides this, and so does monthly comparison of production with schedules and sales forecasts.

Production executives are especially interested in labor effectiveness and planning effectiveness. The former can be determined on an annual basis as a ratio of the cost of sales to total factory payroll hours.

$$\text{Personnel effectiveness} = \frac{\text{Cost of annual sales}}{\text{Total payroll hours}}$$

This ratio is sometimes based on the ratio of annual sales to total factory payroll, but this does not allow for fluctuations in selling prices and wage and salary rates.

Planning effectiveness in companies producing to stock can be measured by the somewhat empirical formula:

Per cent of planning effectiveness

$$= 100 - \frac{\left(\begin{bmatrix}\text{Number of items} \\ \text{on back order}\end{bmatrix} + \begin{bmatrix}\text{Number of items over} \\ \text{stock maximum}\end{bmatrix}\right) 100}{\text{Number of items planned}}$$

In job-order planning the following formula may serve for measurement:

$$\text{Per cent of planning effectiveness} = \frac{\text{Number of deliveries on time} \times 100}{\text{Total deliveries}}$$

Financial executives will be concerned with many ratios and percentages. In connection with production planning and control, they will be primarily concerned with inventory turnover. This ratio is generally determined by the formula:

$$\text{Inventory turnover} = \frac{\text{Cost of annual sales}}{\text{Average inventory}}$$

The average inventory is usually computed from the sum of the inventory value at the end of each month, divided by 12. Ratios of inventory to annual sales should be computed for raw materials, work-in-process, and finished goods.

Because yearly figures are too infrequent for sensitive control, many companies compute these ratios on a 12-month moving average basis so that the data can be reviewed more frequently. Statistical treatment of these data, of course, can reveal any significant trends.

The factory manager must be in a position to have some daily measurement of results. A simple report crossing his desk each day will generally show total activity and can be easily prepared.

A simple daily report that can be prepared in 30 minutes or less:

	Today	This Month to Date	This Day Last Year	Last Year Month to Date
PERSONNEL				
A. Employees on roll	2,300		2,001	
B. Absentees	20		6	
C. Number working	2,280		1,995	
D. Number of grievances	0	3	2	6
E. Lost-time injuries	0	2	1	3
PRODUCTION				
F. Hours worked	11,750	120,360	8,765	89,420
G. Standard hours produced	14,650	154,302	10,606	119,087
H. Per cent effectiveness	124.7	128.2	121.0	123.0
J. Overtime hours	0	1,642	83	2,421
ORDERS				
K. Orders on hand	3,247		762	
L. Received	7,495	80,342	6,328	68,497
M. Shipped	6,438	91,265	5,827	71,235
N. Back orders	26		137	
MATERIALS				
P. Number of shortages	16		68	
Q. Number of items excess	8		136	

Before 10 o'clock in the morning the payroll department can call the factory manager's secretary and supply items *A, B, C, F, G,* and *J* in the daily report. The personnel department can supply item *D,* and *E* will come from the factory nurse. The secretary herself can compute *H,* the order department will furnish *K* and *L,* the shipping department *M* and *N,* and the raw-stores stockroom supervisor will provide *P* and *Q.* The report itself is so simple to prepare that it can be on the factory manager's desk by 10:30.

SUMMARY

Operation or production follows planning. Evaluation of results and adjustment for control follow operation. Dispatching, expediting, and follow-up are the shirt-sleeve functions of production control. With inventory control, they bring balance to the whole production objective.

Adjustment and control begin after actual production performance has been compared with the schedules. The basis for planning may change, and actual sales may be either more or less than the estimates. These departures require continual adjustments of plans.

As a control measure, stock limits for finished goods can generally be established in terms of the maximum and the minimum number of weeks' supply to be carried. This is true in manufacture to stock where actual sales must be continuously compared with the sales estimates. Actual finished goods inventories are normally controlled by stock limits, but inventories frequently must be built to anticipate rush periods or vacation shutdowns. Such inventories are carefully compared with those planned.

The 85–15 notion of control can generally direct attention to and implementation of high-volume production items. Narrower stock limits for high-volume items and wider ones for low-volume items can often reduce working capital requirements and manufacturing costs.

Overcontrols used by manufacturing and financial executives include ratios or percentages covering personnel effectiveness, planning effectiveness, and inventory turnover. Factory managers generally require some daily indications of control showing comparison of operations to day, month to date, this day last year, and last year month to date.

QUESTIONS TO CHECK COMPREHENSION

1. What two factors require adjustment of production plans?

2. Is dispatching more difficult where production is on a class-of-work basis than it is in continuous, progressive production?

3. What other function of control counterbalances expediting?

4. How does an expediter learn what items require his attention?

5. Can simple daily and weekly schedules be arranged to permit reporting of production results?

6. Are graphic representations of production situations helpful in follow-up work?

7. In what terms are the upper and lower limits of finished goods stock generally set?

8. What formulas can be used to determine the effectiveness of planning?

9. What formula can be used to determine the effectiveness of inventory control?

10. How can a company manufacturing a large number of products improve its costs by modifying its stock limits for high- and low-volume items?

PROBLEMS

1. An analysis of 1,800 products made by a manufacturer of household products shows that 300 of them account for $2,100,000 of monthly sales. Total annual sales are $30,000,000. Finished goods stocks of both high- and low-volume items are maintained within limits of not more than 8 and not less than 4 weeks' sales volume. Low-volume items are produced in the same facilities used to produce high-volume items. This practice has created excessive setup or preparation costs to the extent that this factor of cost for low-volume items is $85,000 per year.

The company decides to revise its stock limits to not more than 4 and not less than 3 weeks' supply of high-volume items. Stock limits for low-volume items are changed to not more than 12 and not less than 6 weeks' supply. Assume that stocks of finished goods are controlled, on the average, to the mid-point of both old and new limits. Calculate the reduction in working capital for finished goods and estimate the approximate savings as a result of reduced setup time.

2. The manager of a factory (preferably one with which you are familiar) requests a comprehensive but not cumbersome daily report that will keep him posted on the important factors related to production. Prepare a form for this information, and explain from what sources the data are to be obtained. Explain why each figure is essential in relation to the specific operation that you have chosen.

DISCUSSION CASE

The Ranell Company produced automatic machines and also manufactured all parts used in assembling them. Production planning was elaborate and detailed. Production orders together with production routings and blueprints were issued to the machining departments. Assembly parts lists, blueprints, production routings, and schedules were issued to the assembly departments.

Although forecasts were prepared each quarter and schedules were based on these forecasts, production departed widely from schedules. Despite this great variance, actual production usually was approximately equal to sales. Customer service was good.

The men responsible for evaluating results and controlling production hesitated to demand strict conformance to schedules because the final results always, or, at least, generally, came out right. Whenever they discussed schedule shortages or overages with the production foreman, they were advised that everything would be taken care of.

What actually took place in operations was this: A machining department foreman would receive a schedule for parts. He would call an assembly department foreman and say, "Joe, I have a schedule of 8,000 of part 26,572 for machine 26. Four are used per machine. That would make 2,000 machines for the second quarter. That looks like too many to me." Joe would answer, "Charlie, they aren't even close. If we make 800 No. 26 machines, we will be lucky and they will do well to sell 600." The machine department foreman would then do some quick figuring. "Tell you what I'll do, Joe. I'll machine 3,200. You make a note and if it looks like we are wrong, give me a call and I'll fix up some more." A month or two later, Joe would call Charlie and tell him everything was all right and not to machine any more of part 26,572.

The foremen had been doing this kind of second guessing for years and they had become expert at it. This was why production ran so close to actual sales. As a result, the forecasting skills of those who were responsible for forecasting had never been fully developed.

The production plan adjusted itself as work progressed, but foremen never took the purchasing department into their confidence when they ignored schedules. The procurement plan was based on original production schedules plus or minus stock balances. As a result, excessive raw-material stocks often accumulated, though there were also some shortages when foremen decided to overproduce their schedules.

After several years of this type of disorganization, the manager of the company prepared some conclusive statistics showing that something was wrong. He called a conference of production, purchasing, and planning executives.

Assume that you are participating in this conference. List the causes for what is wrong and determine what actions are necessary to correct each fault.

19

Organization

Organizational structure of a company is an important factor in determining the type of production planning and control appropriate to its operations. This chapter, however, does not attempt to discuss the many ramifications of industrial organization. Instead, its purpose is to show interrelationships that exist between planning and control and other functions in an industrial organization. The chapter also draws some inferences from general organization arrangements for application to production planning and control organizational structures.

Every organization must have a purpose. The purpose of even a small department of a company must be clearly defined, lest the

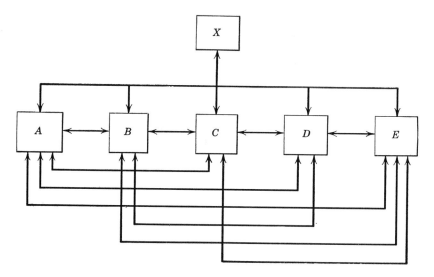

Fig. 93. Relationships in an organizational span of five.

functions spread outside the pattern of its framework. Pre-emption of functions outside a department's intended scope leads to contentious friction and, what is more dangerous, a weakening of attention to the organization's own original functions. It must, therefore, have a planned structure suitable to its purpose. The structural planning and design of an industrial organization must include a logical consideration of its spans and levels.

Figure 93 represents the relationships requiring coordination in a span of 5 functional executives reporting to 1 executive. In this span of 5 there are 41 relationships, as follows:

Direct relationships

X with each =	5	
		5

Group relationships

X with any 2 =	10	
X with any 3 =	10	
X with any 4 =	5	
X with all 5 =	1	
		26

Cross relationships

$AB, AC, AD, AE, BC, BD, BE, CD, CE, DE$ = 10

Total direct, group, and cross relationships   41

Although they would not be consistent with good organization, there could be 13 more relationships within this group of 6 men: ABC, ABD, ABE, ACD, ACE, ADE, BCD, BCE, CDE, $ABCE$, $ABDE$, $BCDE$, and $ABCDE$.

Fortunately, 41 "normal" relationships do not require simultaneous attention. If each of the direct and group relationships consumed an hour per week, little time would be left for attention to other matters for which the top executive is responsible. Moreover, relationships exist between executive X, his equals in the organization, and men who are above him. If each of these relationships also consumed an hour per week, X would never have enough time to meet their demands. The second-level men would fare somewhat better, yet an hour for each of their relationships would add up to an impossible drain on their time.

Some high-level executives believe that they can activate and control a span of 20 other executives who report to them. This, however, involves more than a million relationships, which increase roughly in the order of 2^{n-1}, n equaling the number of persons involved. If such arrangements are actually effective, they must rest upon some informal organizational structure that does not appear on the formal chart. This informal structure keeps relationships down to a number that can be handled by 1 man.

An executive on any level should have a span of functions in his responsibility which are generally closely related. The span must not be too broad or the interrelationships will increase beyond his capacity to manage them. The chiefs of the functions report directly to him.

At top levels, where functions often are varied in their nature, a span of 5 generally is satisfactory. Thus a president may have the chief executives of sales, manufacturing, research and engineering, finance, and personnel reporting to him. At lower levels, where functions commonly are more closely related, a span of 8 to 10 becomes practical. Thus the vice-president in charge of sales may have 8 to 10 district managers reporting to him. At still lower levels, spans of 20 are often satisfactory. As an example, a supervisory group leader can usually direct the activity of 20 workers if they all do the same type of work and encounter the same type of problems.

The number of levels in an industrial organization depends upon the size of the business and the degree to which control is centralized. As the number of levels increases, there is a loss in mobility and flexibility. Information passes more slowly up and down the line. Controls are less sensitive. Executive action becomes more cumbersome. It is therefore evident that a fine balance must exist between the breadth of the spans and the depth of the levels.

The small business generally has a simple organizational structure with 3 or 4 levels, a span of 5 to 7 at the upper levels and a span of 15 to 20 at the lower level. (See Figure 94.)

Some large business activities have as many as 16 organization levels. In addition, the line and staff functions are centralized. Both these factors contribute to a loss of flexibility and effectiveness. The execution of an order to start an action is sluggish in its movement through so many levels. Similarly, an order to stop or change an action is equally sluggish. The analogy is suggested of a man standing on a dock pulling on a line attached to a heavy barge in the water. He may pull with all his strength for 15 minutes. Nothing happens. Then suddenly the barge starts to move. Once it does start to move he may have to pull with all his strength for many minutes in the opposite direction before the barge will again come to rest. There is no sensitivity of response with respect to when it will start or stop. Where it stops has no exact relation to where it was intended to stop.

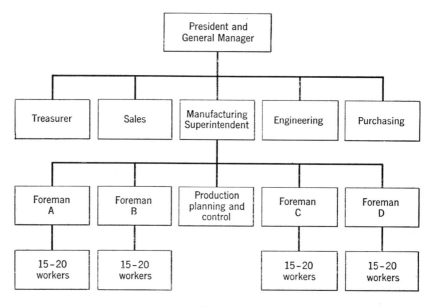

Fig. 94. A simple organization chart.

Such a lack of control in the execution of intentions with either barges or industrial activity is risky as well as unsatisfactory.

There also are countless instances of small companies that have operated effectively while their operational and organizational arrangements remained small and simple. As soon as sales volume tripled or quadrupled there was great confusion and ineffectiveness unless the organization structure was replanned and modified prior to and in anticipation of the expansion. This replanning should always be done with an impersonal consideration for the arrangements of the functions to be performed. In many instances the new organization is the result of sentimental parceling out of functions to people who just happen to be on hand at the time. In addition to the planning it is equally important to train the present people as well as the new people who will operate under the new organizational arrangement.

Because the small organization is so effective it should be studied and certain of its effective components applied to large activities. When some portion of production in a large centralized operation is physically decentralized, effectiveness generally increases almost amazingly. This is particularly true when the organizational arrangement of the decentralized operation is simplified and made to function without too much interference from the parent organization.

Production planning and control as well as many other functions are arranged in line organization under the decentralized plant superintendent or manager, and not as a staff under a production manager.

Some companies have learned a profitable lesson from the results of some physical decentralization and have applied the same organization principles to the remaining centralized operations. The whole secret is taking a large complex problem and breaking it down into a number of smaller, simplified problems. There are natural lines of separations in any large business. Machining can be operated with an entirely separate organization from the assembly, and both can be under the same roof. Some companies prefer to make the separation product-wise. One organization may be responsible for refrigerators, another for gas ranges, and still another for washing machines. Each organization operates independently of the other organizations. None is confounded with complex interactions beyond the comprehension of one or a small group of executives. Each can enjoy the company-wide administrative benefits and still be autonomous in its operational or applicative functions.

Figure 95 shows a typical decentralized organization in which the applicative functions, in the manufacture of three categories of products, are independent and autonomous. It makes little difference whether these three activities are under one roof or in three separate plants in as many communities or states.

Figure 96 shows the same activity with production planning and control as a separate staff function. When the complexity of so many interrelations is considered with only the production-planning and control functions shown, the confusion is magnified as many other staff service functions are added to it.

Some idea of how complex centralization of operations could become, both physically and in organizational structure, can be had by referring to Figure 17, which presents a composite picture of the factories of American Can Company.

From the organization of an entire business or plant, we now turn to that of the department of production planning and control. It, too, must have clearly defined objectives, and its sections must have responsibilities that are clearly and specifically spelled out. This does not imply, however, that all the functions involved in production planning and control will be concentrated in the department bearing that title. As we have already found, many groups make their contribution to planning and control. The sales department, for example, may and should be responsible for preparing and adjusting the sales forecast. The manufacturing department probably is charged with

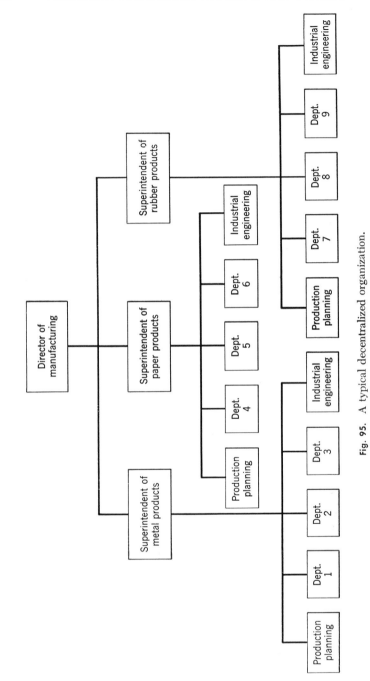

Fig. 95. A typical decentralized organization.

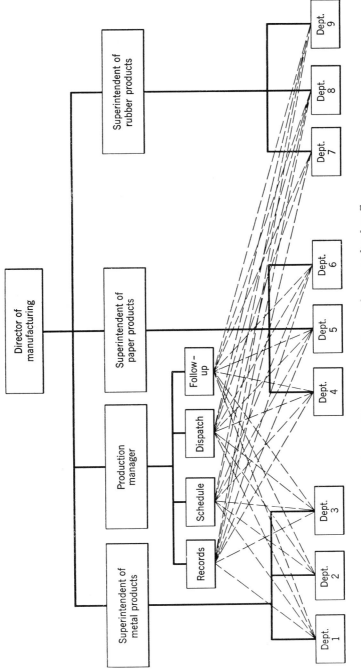

Fig. 96. The same operations with a centralized staff.

the task of taking physical inventories of work-in-process. The production-control department may check the work-in-process inventory and compile summaries. The shipping department may be responsible for finished goods inventories. The production-planning and -control department is a service organization that unites and coordinates these contributions and so secures a smooth, uniform flow of materials into, through, and out of the manufacturing facility—a flow that provides finished products ready for the customer at the right time.

Production-planning and -control departments often are divided into three sections. The material-control section issues purchase requisitions at the right time, so that materials will be on hand when they are needed. The section must limit stocks on hand according to company policy, so that inventories become neither so small as to create production delays nor so large as to seriously reduce the net working capital. In many plants, this section is required to price stock withdrawals and maintain prices of materials remaining in stock. In addition to maintaining perpetual book inventories, the section is also required to take periodical physical inventories.

The control section of the production-planning and -control department follows the planning through. It also consults with the sales department when actual sales are running ahead of or behind the forecast. If the sales department approves, the production plan may then be adjusted to maintain stocks within the predetermined limits.

The planning section of the production-planning and -control department translates sales estimates into master and department schedules that make the best possible use of both equipment and personnel. It also prepares alternative plans of action for use if they are required by changes in demand or by emergencies, and prepares take-offs of material, equipment, and personnel requirements from sales forecasts and/or customers' orders. Finally, the planning section prepares load charts or records that show whether delivery dates can be met and tell in advance whether equipment is being over- or underloaded.

The whole activity is subject to audit by the treasurer and sales and manufacturing executives who are not primarily concerned with the details of its operation. They are concerned, however, with the various ratios that provide continuous indications of effectiveness.

Production forecasting, planning, and control are thus cooperative activities shared by several departments instead of being confined within one. A knowledge of the functions to be performed will indicate their position on the formal organization chart. Many companies perform the many functions of planning and control without having given much consideration to their terminology. Where these activities are successful, the objectives are clear and responsibilities are set forth in simple language. Where the company is small, one man may be capable of handling all the direct functions of the production-planning and -control department together with some or all of the normally indirect functions such as sales estimating and manufacturing planning. In larger companies, several people may be required to cover one part of the whole arrangement, such as expediting. As companies become larger, careful consideration should be given to the decentralization of planning and control.

SUMMARY

The purpose of organization for production control, like that of all industrial organization, should be given appropriate consideration. The depth of the levels and the spans of control should also receive careful consideration. Decentralization of organizations can generally limit the complexity of production-planning and -control problems.

Although not all functions relating to production forecasting, planning, and control will be concentrated in one department, the objectives of each part of the activity must be explained and responsibilities must be clearly defined. The industrial-engineering department generally provides the basic production-routing information used in planning. The sales department has the major role in sales forecasting. The production-planning function is unique in that it is pivotal in cooperating with many departments. The desired result is a smooth, uniform flow of materials through the operations, with goods ready for delivery on time. Control follows through on planning, while inventories are maintained at the proper levels.

All these functions are generally found in large and small companies. The large companies, of course, may have whole departments attending one function, whereas one man may attend all the functions in a small company.

QUESTIONS TO CHECK COMPREHENSION

1. What are the disadvantages of too broad a span in an industrial organization?

2. What are the disadvantages of too many levels in an industrial organization?

3. Describe some advantages of decentralized operation and control.

4. Many companies have formal organization charts. Are informal organizational arrangements also common?

5. Why is the whole arrangement for production forecasting, planning, and control not confined within one department?

6. Individuals and departments have certain functions to perform. What must be clearly specified to make their work effective?

7. Could we set up an organization chart for production planning and control that would meet the needs of all companies?

PROBLEMS

1. Obtain an organization chart of E. I. du Pont de Nemours & Co. and discuss the depth of organization levels and the control arrangements.

2. Obtain an organization chart of Sears, Roebuck and Co. and discuss its spans of control.

Note: The organization structures of these two companies are very different. Both companies are eminently successful.

DISCUSSION CASE

The firm of Jackson and Sons has manufactured leather products for fifty years. The founder, Arnold Jackson, had intended the business to remain small. He wanted to limit its size so that he and his two sons, Arnold Jr. and Charles, could exercise full control and divide the profits.

In 1930 Arnold 3rd and Charles Jr. entered the company to learn the business. In 1935 their grandfather, the founder, died. Arnold 3rd, who had been made factory superintendent, and his father, who was treasurer, preferred to maintain the grandfather's policy of small business. Charles, who was president and sales manager, and his son Charles Jr., who handled orders and personnel, wanted to expand the business.

After many arguments, a new factory was built. The plan was to produce all job lots in the old factory and to manufacture a new line of items to stock in the new one.

Charles Jr.'s experience had been limited to job orders, to which he had given his personal attention in the old factory. Now, he and Arnold 3rd divided their time and attention, spending forenoons at the old plant and afternoons at the new one, several miles away. There were 15 foremen and 500 workmen in the old factory, and 10 foremen and 180 workmen in the new.

It soon became evident that the profit potential of the new plant was greater than that of the old one, and it, therefore, received more attention. This caused laxity and confusion in the old plant, which lost several long-standing customers by making extremely late deliveries. Employees of the old plant also became dissatisfied and finally struck. Since the health of Charles Jr. had been impaired by overwork, Arnold 3rd took over the duties of his cousin but found that he was unable to plan production satisfactorily. His skill in personnel work was excellent, however, and he quickly settled the strike. Realizing his limitations, he went to his Uncle Charles (the president) and urged that the company be reorganized, that men outside the family be taken in as officers, that the two plants be operated independently, and that two production-planning engineers be employed at once.

Assume that you are participating in a conference to settle this matter. List what is wrong and suggest remedial action.

20

Cooperation with the Accounting Department

As has been said in the discussion of material control (Chapter 14), there is a strong cofunctional relationship between planning, purchasing, and accounting. There is another close relationship in the establishment of operational budgets. Preparation of production routings also provides an opportunity for cooperation with cost accounting and planning. Throughout the whole course of production forecasting, planning, and control, therefore, there is interdependence between these functions and those of the accounting department.

The cost accounting department is concerned with product costs and their components as well as with pricing of inventories. The production-planning engineer needs a knowledge and appreciation of the elements of costs if he is to cooperate intelligently with this de-

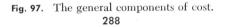

Quantity × Price	Time × Labor rate				
Direct material	Direct labor	Factory expense	General expense	Selling expense	Profit

Prime cost ————→|
Factory cost ————————→|
Manufacturing cost ————————————→|
Total cost ————————————————→|
Selling price ————————————————————→|

Fig. 97. The general components of cost.

288

partment. Figure 97 shows the general components of cost with which the planning engineer must be familiar.

Direct material cost is the product of quantity and price; it generally includes the cost of raw or purchased finished material used in manufacturing the product, even though part of this material becomes waste. As an example, if a part is made from a piece of steel, the whole piece of steel is considered direct material even though some of it goes into turnings and chips.

As was said in the discussion of procurement, materials constitute at least 40 per cent of the cost in all manufacturing industry. It is, therefore, important for the production-control organization, or any other that may be responsible for raw-material stores, to report accurately the amount of material used for a given quantity of production. Frequently these materials are priced as they are issued. Under this plan, the accuracy of figures for actual costs depends upon the accuracy with which both price and quantity appear in stores reports.

Other materials, like sandpaper and soap, which are essential to the process but do not become a part of the finished goods, are considered as expense materials and are accounted for under factory expense.

Direct labor is the actual labor employed in operations required to make a product. Indirect labor, such as supervision, inspection, and material handling, also are accounted for under factory expense. The production-control organization must arrange for accurate reporting of the units produced. Such reports are used by production control for comparison of actual with scheduled production, and by cost accounting in the computation of direct labor costs.

Factory expense includes indirect labor, indirect materials, heat, light, and all other items for which money is spent by or for the manufacturing departments. It does not include general office expenses or those of administrative executives and their staffs; these comprise general expense.

Selling expense includes the salaries, commissions, and expenses of salesmen, all cost of home and district sales offices, and expenditures for advertising.

Profit is the difference between the sum of all these elements of cost and the selling price. In modern, quantity-production industry, margins of profit are generally so narrow that all elements of cost must be carefully controlled. Without such control, the difference between the total cost and the selling price is likely to become negative and so constitute a loss.

Most plans for stockroom inventory control provide for records of materials received, on hand, and issued. As these materials are received and issued, quantities are also priced on both records and transfer forms. Though all this requires considerable clerical work, it is an essential part of the accounting procedure.

Before establishing any plan for inventory control, those who are responsible should consult finance executives to learn what method of determining inventory costs conforms best to the financial policy of the company. The extent of price fluctuations and the number of weeks' supply to be carried in inventories will largely determine the method for pricing inventories and withdrawals. Since different methods will produce significantly different current operating costs and different values for materials remaining in inventories, it is necessary to select the one that offers greatest simplicity and least risk.

The four pricing methods most commonly used are standard-cost, average-unit-cost, first-in-first-out, and last-in-first-out.

Each of these will be briefly discussed in order to show its advantages, its limitations, and its applicability to different situations.

A. THE STANDARD-COST METHOD

Standard costs are established by periodically revising costs of materials according to prices which are expected to be quoted for delivery during a specified period. These revisions will not be made at rigidly specified times but will keep pace with changes in the market. If there are no wide fluctuations in price over a long period, the standard costs need not be changed. If fluctuations are great and rapid, it will be necessary to establish new standard costs with corresponding frequency. Under this arrangement, costs can be determined with reasonable accuracy even before stock withdrawals and production. This has many advantages over computing costs after production has been completed.

The standard-cost method provides for control, since it permits only the correct quantities of the specified materials to be used. If too much material is used or if high-priced material is substituted, a comparison of the actual with the standard cost will reveal the unfavorable variance.

Records of actual prices paid for materials also must be kept. At the end of accounting periods some adjustments must be made on the company's books to offset any variations from standard costs in the actual inventory value. This adjustment is generally made by determining the difference between invoiced cost and standard cost and charging this difference to purchase variance.

The standard-cost method is especially advantageous when fluctuations in commodity prices are not wide and inventory turnover is high. It also transfers some clerical work from the stockroom to the accounting department, where it is generally done mechanically with the minimum of clerical error.

B. THE AVERAGE-UNIT-COST METHOD

In this, stock withdrawals of each class of material are priced at the average unit cost of all material in this particular class that is in stock at the actual time of withdrawal. This cost is calculated by dividing the balance value by the balance quantity. As an example, assume that the stock record for a particular fabric item is:

Quantity	Price	Value
10,000 yards @ $1.11 per yard =		$ 11,100
50,000 yards @ 1.20 per yard =		60,000
30,000 yards @ 1.05 per yard =		31,500
Totals: 90,000 yards		$102,600

The average unit price, therefore, is $1.14 per yard.

If 20,000 yards are withdrawn, the withdrawal will be priced at $1.14 per yard, giving a value of $22,800. Both the quantity and the value of the withdrawal will be deducted from the stock balance, and the new balance will be 70,000 yards at a value of $79,800.

Considerable clerical work is needed to place an accurate value on each withdrawal, and this work is sometimes done in the stockroom. Moreover, this method merely records facts and transactions that have been accomplished, providing no estimate of costs in advance of production. It has no control feature in the sense of setting objective or standard costs that are to be achieved.

The average-unit-cost method is generally used in job-order production, where customers' orders must be priced equitably on the basis of the average cost of the material used in filling each order. It is specially applicable where process intervals are long and raw-material inventory turnovers are low.

C. THE FIRST-IN-FIRST-OUT METHOD

This method constantly charges out the material that has been in stock longest, much as a grocer moves his oldest stock to the front when new stock is placed on his shelves. As withdrawals are made from stock, they are priced on the basis of the oldest lot until it is exhausted. Then the price of the next oldest lot is used, and so on. If lots received were the same as quantities withdrawn, it would be simple to cancel each one out at its price. Actually, a number of withdrawals may be needed to exhaust one lot, or one withdrawal will have to be charged at one price and other parts at other prices, thus increasing clerical work; on the other hand, current manufacturing is charged actual costs, and raw-material inventories are carried at values close to their current market prices.

This method is used when manufacturing costs must reflect the actual sequence of price fluctuations for raw materials, and to keep inventory costs closely in line with current commodity prices. The method can also be used when raw materials account for a relatively small part of the total production cost.

Perishable or semiperishable raw materials, such as rubber and some chemicals, are actually rotated on a first-in-first-out basis to prevent deterioration. Other materials do not demand this and can be issued without regard for the date when they are received. These variations need not affect accounting under this or other methods of pricing withdrawals.

D. THE LAST-IN-FIRST-OUT METHOD

This method is the reverse of the first-in-first-out method, and its clerical requirements are about the same. It is particularly advantageous for companies producing such items as textile and petroleum products, for which raw materials belong to a single general class. It permits stock to be carried on the books at old prices, so that inventory values do not change greatly from one accounting period to the next. Current fluctuations in the prices of raw materials are more realistically reflected in the current cost of sales. This method equalizes profits to a considerable degree by bolstering them when prices are falling and limiting them when prices rise.

When the raw-material component is the major factor in total cost, and when it also is sensitive to the market price of one basic commodity, some companies employ the raw-material inventory as a cushion and treat it much as they treat fixed assets. They reason that it is as much a fixed asset as the machinery used to convert it.

As an example, consider the publisher of a small newspaper who uses 50 tons of paper per week and pays prices that fluctuate between $135 and $210 per ton. His current costs may vary as much as $3,750 per week because of these fluctuations. The publisher may wish to have the market price of paper sensitively reflected in his figures for cost so that a price increase or price decrease in his advertising rates can be effected when either is justified and not a number of months earlier or later.

Being a cautious man, this publisher also carries an inventory of 10 weeks' supply of paper. This protects him against strikes, floods, transportation embargoes, and other mishaps that may temporarily cut off his supplies.

The 10-week supply, or 500 tons, was purchased at $180 per ton. Carried as a cushion inventory, the paper has an asset value of $90,000. The publisher considers it an asset, just like his pressroom equipment. When the price of paper increases to $200 per ton, the publisher will not have an inflated inventory value but will allow the price increase to appear in his current operating costs. Later the price of paper goes back to $180. This also does not change the inventory value, though the decrease will promptly appear in current operating costs.

Most production-planning engineers are aware that a company is not free to switch arbitrarily from one method of pricing inventories to another. After one method has been tested and adopted, the Bureau of Internal Revenue must give its approval before the accounting procedure may be changed.

Cost accountants will also find that, by establishing control centers in close relation to cost and burden centers, they can learn with considerable accuracy the cost of any product. Older arrangements using general burden rates generally conceal loss items by averaging them with the real profit items.

Factory expense can be minimized and controlled by intelligent planning and scheduling of production. If too many small-lot runs are scheduled, the setup or preparation expense may increase out of reasonable proportion to the actual direct costs to produce them.

When consideration is given to controlling pricing and recording of stock withdrawals to accurate, objective, and actual costs, and to controlled factory expense by proper planning and scheduling, it becomes evident that the production-planning department and the accounting department have important cofunctional relations.

Production engineers will need to know about electronic data-processing systems and accounting procedures, for many companies already are adopting EDP systems. The capabilities and capacities of modern EDP equipment have been so greatly extended that they can handle combinations of information for material control, costing, scheduling, forecasting and invoicing, all in integrated operations. With this integration of information handling there must be close cooperation and understanding between production engineers and accounting personnel.

SUMMARY

Since production planning and accounting must cooperate closely, planning engineers should have a working knowledge of accounting.

Establishment of operating budgets follows the translation of sales forecasts into operating schedules. Financial planning, in turn, is based on sales estimates and production schedules.

Raw-material inventories and stock withdrawals are generally priced by one of four methods: the average-unit-cost, the standard-cost, first-in-first-out, and last-in-first-out. It is important that stockroom clerks understand the method used and the reasons for calculations that it requires.

QUESTIONS TO CHECK COMPREHENSION

1. Why is it important for the planning engineer to have a working knowledge of the cost-accounting procedure used by his company?

2. A production routing contains some inaccurate information with respect to the times required to perform a number of operations. How will this affect the work of the planning engineer? How will it affect the work of the cost accountant?

3. A company produces a large variety of items containing a wide variety of raw materials. Its inventory turnover is high. Raw-material prices are not subject to wide fluctuations. What method of pricing inventories will best meet this company's needs?

4. A company produces cotton textiles. Its process interval is long, yet competition forces it to reflect current prices of cotton in its selling prices. What method of pricing inventories is appropriate?

5. Is the Bureau of Internal Revenue concerned when a company wishes to change its method of pricing inventories? May a company change its method at will, without the Bureau's approval?

6. What components of cost should be understood by production planners?

7. What are the characteristics of the four most generally used pricing methods? What factors must be carefully considered in selecting the method for a given type of operation?

8. Which pricing method provides for cost control? How is this accomplished?

9. If a standard-cost method is used, how are the differences between actual costs and standard costs reconciled?

10. Can the method of distributing burden or overhead conceal certain items that are unprofitable? How?

PROBLEM

The chief cost accountant and you (as production-planning engineer) have been asked to work together to solve a serious cost-accounting problem in your company's operations. Labor costs of products have been secured by asking foremen to estimate the time required to perform operations. Material costs have been estimated on the basis of the actual material contained in finished products plus a flat 10 per cent allowance for process waste and scrap. A general factory burden rate of 150 per cent has been used to determine factory costs.

Time values for each operation performed have been exceptionally accurate for production-planning purposes. A time study engineer modifies these values as processes are changed. You have material input values for given product output requirements, as well as records of scrap. Over a period of years you have established production scheduling centers in which different products are produced. Each of these centers has its own supervision and service employees. For purposes of stock control you have kept records of all stock withdrawals against specific work authorizations for the various items produced.

The general accounting department is adequately equipped with the most modern calculators and machines for the punched card method of accounting. This equipment is used only from 9:00 A.M. to 5:00 P.M.

Prepare a proposal that will simplify production planning as well as assure more accurate costs.

DISCUSSION CASE

Early in December the budget director of the Potts Company requested the production plan for the purpose of establishing operating budgets for the coming year. The production plan had not been prepared, but the sales estimate had just been completed. It was sent to the budget director in response to his request.

When fixed departmental budgets were issued during the last week of the year, the department supervisors complained that allowances were insufficient. They were told that expenses would have to be scaled down to these figures if a profit was to be made.

Because there were many back orders at the end of the year, most departments had to add second shifts. During February, with the second shifts in operation, the supervisors were told that expenses were still too high and must be reduced. The second-shift foremen were placed on operations, as were other indirect workers. With too few supervision and service employees, the production situation became confused and operating effectiveness declined.

The company's chief executive called a conference. The treasurer's reports showed that actual income was considerably in excess of the budgeted income. The president reported that the back-order situation was still bad and would continue so until the second shifts became more productive. The production superintendent presented figures to show that budgets allowed too little money for efficient operation of these shifts. The budget director, however, countered with figures showing that production was 40 per cent higher than that given him in the production plan.

The production-planning executive presented production schedules for the first quarter; they were actually about 40 per cent higher than figures quoted by the budget director, who complained about being given incorrect information. It finally developed that the sales estimates, not the production-plan figures, had been used as the basis for the budgets. The rounded figures were approximately as follows:

Sales estimate	12,000,000
Back order	3,000,000
Stock balance required	1,000,000
Production plan	15,000,000

As a participant in this conference, tell what is wrong and why and suggest remedies.

21

Cooperation with Quality Control

The production planner always has two unpredictables with which to contend. Even though he has placed purchase requisitions for the right raw material to be delivered at the right time, there is always a chance that the raw material will be unsuitable for production when it arrives. His production schedules may also correctly provide the needed quantities only to have some portion of them lost because the product fails to meet quality standards. He therefore needs to know the quality levels of inbound raw materials and the quality capabilities of processes within his company's operations.

Until shortly before World War II, these two factors gravely reduced the accuracy of production planning. Then statistical quality control was introduced by Dr. Walter A. Shewhart, a scientist at the Bell Telephone Laboratories. Under his stimulating leadership, and because of the demand for increased production during wartime, industry rapidly adopted this new and invaluable technique.

Quality control, reduced to its simplest terms, is the control of quality during the manufacturing process. It detects the causes for variations in the characteristics of products and indicates adjustments by which these variations may be controlled. Quality control is economic in its purpose, objective in its procedure, dynamic in its operation, and helpful in its treatment of operating difficulties. Since variations in raw materials have marked effects on the quality of in-process materials, quality control includes statistical sampling and testing before acceptance. It also includes the examination of quality characteristics in finished products, as an overcheck on the in-process controls and as a means of assuring satisfactory outgoing quality.

Both quality control and inspection are used to assure quality. Inspection is a sorting process that classifies materials, parts, or products as acceptable or unacceptable. As control becomes effective, the need for inspection decreases.

To measure every piece of incoming material, or to run chemical or physical tests on every drum of chemicals and every bolt of cloth received, would require a receiving inspection force almost as large as the manufacturing force itself. Inventories would have to be increased to allow time for detailed inspection and testing. It is here that scientific statistical sampling can be used to prevent acceptance of unsatisfactory materials quickly and at minimum cost. Although savings in cost are very important, the speed with which results are obtained often means the success or failure of the production plan. If, for example, a raw material is received today and found to be defective tomorrow, the purchasing department will have a week or more in which to obtain a replacement. If this is impossible, the planner will at least have time to devise an alternative plan for production.

The most popular sampling plans are based on the Dodge-Romig Tables for single and double sampling.[1] All these plans are designed for simplicity, speed, and economy. The sample size is a function of the lot size under consideration. The ratio of sample size to lot size diminishes with increasing lot sizes, yet it constantly maintains a stipulated protection.

As an example showing how these plans work, let us assume that a certain part is to be used in an assembly operation. If not more than 2 per cent of these parts are defective, assembly will not be delayed or stopped, since the defective parts can be cast aside by the assemblers. The supplier's price and the producer's estimate of costs have been based on this percentage.

Let us further assume that 40,000 pieces of this part are received in a single shipment. Inspection records show that the supplier's process average defective has been 0.5 per cent. Referring to Figure 98, which reproduces Table SA-2.0 of the Dodge-Romig Tables, we find that the lot is acceptable if 125 pieces picked at random from the lot contain no more than 4 defectives. If 5 or more defective pieces are found, the lot must be rejected. The actual count is 6. To keep from disrupting production, the supplier is urged to sort out the defectives promptly and resubmit the lot for what then will be certain acceptance.

The Statistical Research Group at Columbia University developed a sequential sampling plan used by several divisions of the armed services during World War II. Under this plan, additional samples

[1] H. F. Dodge and H. G. Romig, *Sampling Inspection Tables*, John Wiley & Sons, New York, 1944.

SINGLE SAMPLING LOT INSPECTION TABLES—BASED ON STATED VALUES OF "AVERAGE OUTGOING QUALITY LIMIT"

TABLE SA-2.0

AVERAGE OUTGOING QUALITY LIMIT = 2.0%

Process Average, %	0–.04			.05–.40			.41–.80			.81–1.20			1.21–1.60			1.61–2.00		
Lot Size	n	c	$p_t\%$	n	c	$p_t\%$	n	c	$p_t\%$	n	c	$p_t\%$	n	c	$p_t\%$	n	c	$p_t\%$
1–15	All	0	....	All	0	....	All	0	....	All	0	....	All	0	....	All	0	....
16–50	14	0	13.6	14	0	13.6	14	0	13.6	14	0	13.6	14	0	13.6	14	0	13.6
51–100	16	0	12.4	16	0	12.4	16	0	12.4	16	0	12.4	16	0	12.4	16	0	12.4
101–200	17	0	12.2	17	0	12.2	17	0	12.2	17	0	12.2	35	1	10.5	35	1	10.5
201–300	17	0	12.3	17	0	12.3	17	0	12.3	37	1	10.2	37	1	10.2	37	1	10.2
301–400	18	0	11.8	18	0	11.8	38	1	10.0	38	1	10.0	38	1	10.0	60	2	8.5
401–500	18	0	11.9	18	0	11.9	39	1	9.8	39	1	9.8	60	2	8.6	60	2	8.6
501–600	18	0	11.9	18	0	11.9	39	1	9.8	39	1	9.8	60	2	8.6	60	2	8.6
601–800	18	0	11.9	40	1	9.6	40	1	9.6	65	2	8.0	65	2	8.0	85	3	7.5
801–1000	18	0	12.0	40	1	9.6	40	1	9.6	65	2	8.1	65	2	8.1	90	3	7.4
1,001–2,000	18	0	12.0	41	1	9.4	65	2	8.2	65	2	8.2	95	3	7.0	120	4	6.5
2,001–3,000	18	0	12.0	41	1	9.4	65	2	8.2	95	3	7.0	120	4	6.5	180	6	5.8
3,001–4,000	18	0	12.0	42	1	9.3	65	2	8.2	95	3	7.0	155	5	6.0	210	7	5.5
4,001–5,000	18	0	12.0	42	1	9.3	70	2	7.5	125	4	6.4	155	5	6.0	245	8	5.3
5,001–7,000	18	0	12.0	42	1	9.3	95	3	7.0	125	4	6.4	185	6	5.6	280	9	5.1
7,001–10,000	42	1	9.3	70	2	7.5	95	3	7.0	155	5	6.0	220	7	5.4	350	11	4.8
10,001–20,000	42	1	9.3	70	2	7.6	95	3	7.0	190	6	5.6	290	9	4.9	460	14	4.4
20,001–50,000	42	1	9.3	70	2	7.6	125	4	6.4	220	7	5.4	395	12	4.5	720	21	3.9
50,001–100,000	42	1	9.3	95	3	7.0	160	5	5.9	290	9	4.9	505	15	4.2	955	27	3.7

Fig. 98. A sampling inspection table. (Reproduced by permission of Bell Telephone Laboratories, Inc., from *Sampling Inspection Tables,* by H. F. Dodge and H. G. Romig, John Wiley & Sons, New York, 1944.)

must be tested as long as the number of defectives falls between the acceptance and rejection numbers. In the seventh or eighth trial the acceptance and rejection numbers become consecutive, thus forcing a decision.

The following example of sequential sampling is taken from Appendix X, Standard Sampling Inspection Tables for Inspection by Attributes.[1]

[1] E. H. MacNiece, *Reading Course in Executive Technique,* Book 4, Sec. 5, "Organizing for Quality and Waste Control," Funk & Wagnalls, New York, 1948.

Sample	Sample Size	Combined Sample Size	Acceptance Number (Cumulative)	Rejected Number (Cumulative)
First	50	50	0	4
Second	50	100	2	6
Third	50	150	3	8
Fourth	50	200	5	10
Fifth	50	250	7	12
Sixth	50	300	9	14
Seventh	50	350	11	16
Eighth	50	400	15	16

If in the first 50 pieces tested no defectives are found, the lot is accepted. If 4 or more defectives are found, the reject number is reached and the lot is rejected. If there are 1, 2, or 3 defectives, a second sample of 50 must be tested. If the cumulated defectives in the 100 pieces of the combined first and second samples are 2 or less, the lot is accepted. If the defectives are 6 or more, the lot is rejected. If there are 3, 4, or 5 defectives, a third sample must be tested, and so on until the proper action is indicated.

An advantage claimed for sequential sampling is that exceptionally good lots will be accepted more quickly and exceptionally bad lots rejected more quickly than is possible with Dodge-Romig Tables. If the quality level is at some intermediate value, however, the Navy Department recognizes this situation and uses either single or double sampling, depending upon the supplier's past performance and the most economical treatment consistent with the desired assurance of quality.

The U.S. Department of Defense has prepared modified versions of Dodge and Romig's Single and Double Sampling Tables, and the Sequential Sampling Tables of the Columbia University Statistical Research Group, and included all three modifications in MIL-STD-105A.[1] MIL-STD-105A has been adopted by many industrial companies because it is required in acceptance inspection of commodities supplied to the armed services, because it offers a choice of any of the three inspection schemes, and because it is simple to use.

In the reorganization of a business a number of years ago, one of

[1] Department of Defense, Military Standard 105A, "Sampling Procedures and Tables for Inspection by Attributes," U.S. Government Printing Office, Washington, D. C., 1950.

the first considerations was the establishment of an adequate arrangement for production planning. Operations were typically primary, or machining, and secondary, or assembly. Raw-stores and finished goods inventory controls proved to be effective soon after their introduction. The assembly department consistently failed to meet its schedule, and finished-parts stores inventories failed to balance. An analysis showed that many of the finished parts were nonconforming. To reinspect all the parts in stock would have been expensive and, moreover, would have slowed up the whole program. Because no statistical sampling plans were available at that time, the problem was solved by an ingenious method. Small random samples of each part were selected in 5 groups. If the variation in the cumulative average of the per cent defective of the fifth group did not range more than ±5 per cent from the cumulative average of the first 4 samples, the average of the 5 samples was considered to be the per cent defective for the particular part in question. If the variation was greater than ±5 per cent, additional small samples were inspected until the variation did not exceed ±5 per cent.

The whole production planning was revised to allow for the defectives as estimated by this empirical method of sampling. Though the final results were far from perfect, the production planning was converted from a basis of certain failure to one that saved the life of the reorganization. Fortunately such crude treatments need not be resorted to today. Sampling plans proved by millions of trial applications are available for industrial use.

In the discussion of manufacturing planning, we found that industrial engineers could include material shrinkage allowances in their estimates of gross material requirements. This was once done by rather rough guessing. Today quality-control engineers have accumulated useful background information from the study of process capabilities. For example, if a dimension is to be held within a tolerance of ±0.001, the quality-control engineer knows that about 20 per cent of the pieces produced on an old-type milling machine will not meet specification, though the figure for a modern machine will be approximately 1 per cent. If a specific machine is under consideration for production, the engineer therefore can predict its process capability within narrow limits of accuracy. For a cloth of given specifications, the percentage of defective material will be considerably reduced if modern looms are used instead of older ones. In coating and spreading operations, process capabilities determine the yields from given quantities of raw materials. Suppose, for example, that an old paper machine must be used to produce sheets having a basis weight of 30 pounds ±0.5 pound.   Because of limitations in process capability, it may be necessary to run on the high side so that sheets will not fall below the minimum of 29.5 pounds.   The pulp consumption therefore will be considerably greater than that computed on a theoretical basis without regard for the process capability of the machine to be used.

Figure 99 shows the process capabilities of three coating machines that are to be used in producing a single item.   The coating compound is expensive, but a minimum of 2.6 ounces must be used on every square yard.   Figure 100 shows that on machine A the average weight of compound will be 2.74 ounces per square yard.   With machine B it will be 2.83 ounces, and with machine C, 2.95 ounces.

This simple analysis of process capabilities discloses five other facts of vital importance to the planner:

1. Raw-material requirements will vary, depending upon which machine is used for production of different items or the same items at different times.

2. Products requiring the most expensive coating material should be produced on machine A; the next most expensive on B, and the least expensive on C.

3. If the same objective average weights are used on all three machines, a large percentage of production from machines B and C will not conform to specifications.

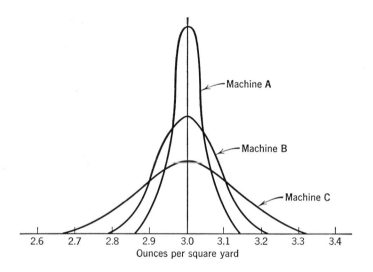

Fig. 99.   Process capabilities of three coating machines.

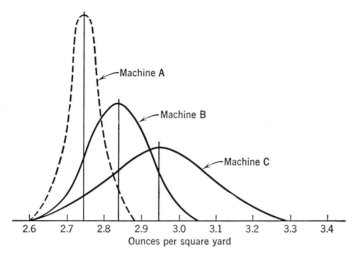

Ounces per square yard

Fig. 100. The three machines producing to the same minimum coating weight.

4. Machines *B* and *C* should be examined to determine whether they can be repaired or modified to equal the performance of *A*.

5. If repair or modification will not produce the desired results, production costs should be reviewed with care. They may show that machines *B* and *C* should be replaced with new ones.

The manufacturing planner and the production planner will be wise to work in close cooperation with the quality-control engineers, first, to learn what inputs of materials are required for given outputs, and second, to discover the need for new equipment when the old will not perform well or profitably.

The whole purpose of quality control is to maintain product dimensions and other characteristics within specifications during the manufacturing process rather than to report failure after things have been made. Where control is effectively used in a continuing sequence of *manufacture, test, adjust,* the production planner's work can proceed in a straightforward manner. He will, however, wish to maintain effective lines of communication with the people in quality control. Even in the best-run factories there will be times when certain processes get out of control, and the production planner will need to know the extent of each difficulty. If certain quantities are irreparably lost to production, or if the nonconformance to specifications requires rework, he must adjust his plans accordingly.

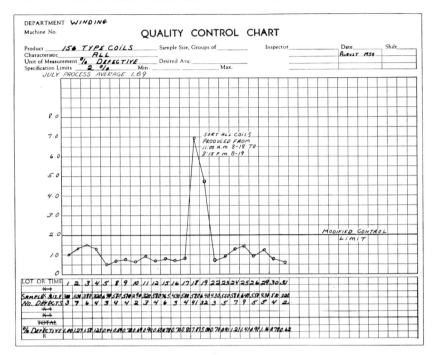

Fig. 101. A typical per cent defective chart.

Figure 101 shows a typical per cent defective quality-control chart. As long as the percentage of defectives remains below 2, there is no difficulty in subsequent assembly operations. Planned costs and outputs also are achieved. Excellent control was maintained until the eighteenth of the month, but most of the work produced on the eighteenth and nineteenth day had to be sorted on a 100 per cent testing basis. Production planning had a 5-day lead, and there was no disruption of the planning other than to replan for the defectives scheduled for repair. If the high rate of defectives had continued for 3 days more, however, the production planner would have had to substitute some alternative planning.

In the manufacture of many types of consumer goods the control of weights and measures is essential to the control of costs and quantities of material used. As an example, filling 1-pound cans of coffee requires control of weight. If the ordinary process of filling maintains a weight of 1 pound ± 5 per cent, the company may set its weighing machinery to fill at 476 grams, a pound being 453.6. This guarantees that requirements of the Food and Drug Administration will not be violated. Individual weights will vary between 454 and 499 grams. The average outgoing weight will be 476 grams, or 1 pound + 5 per cent.

Control charts may reveal factors the elimination of which will permit maintenance of control within ±1 per cent. The objective weight can then be set at 458 grams. Aside from establishing a competitive advantage by eliminating overages, quality control focuses attention upon subsequent production so that weights and measures are maintained with essential accuracy.

To be effective in its own sphere, and to stabilize production planning, quality control must concentrate its attention upon processes while they are in operation. It is essential that samples be examined before any defectives are removed. This permits an appraisal of process quality levels so that corrective action can be taken when it is needed.

Quality control is vitally important in the process industries because sorting is economically unsound. Most testing is destructive. To apply destructive tests on a 100 per cent basis would destroy all the product. Such a method might be of academic interest but would be economically fatal. As an example, the best test for a shot gun shell is to shoot it. After you have shot it nothing is left except the test results.

A chief inspector in a machine shop recently complained that, though fine for the process industries, statistical quality control could not be applied in a machine shop. There were several tote pans of machined parts near a machine, each pan containing about four thousand parts. The inspector was asked if he would be willing to release a particular pan without one hundred per cent inspection if not more than ten pieces out of 305 were found to be outside specifications limits. After some deliberation he replied that this would result in a probable two per cent culling in assembly and that this was not unusual even when every piece had been inspected. Yes, he would be willing to release a pan on that basis.

Periodic sampling at the machine was then suggested, with the understanding that 100 per cent inspection would be resorted to only when charts showed the process to be out of control. Small samples appealed to the inspector because they would cut inspection costs to a minimum. Control was even more appealing, since it would permit adjustments as the process continued.[1]

Many new high-speed automatic production processes have been introduced since 1940, and they have forced a change in the thinking

[1] E. H. MacNiece, "Statistical Control vs. 100 Per Cent Inspection," *Standardization*, June, 1949.

of management. In the past, conscientious efforts were made to produce large quantities of goods and then to achieve quality assurance by sorting the good from the bad. As we have said, this was both costly and unreliable. Persons responsible for production planning could never be sure of net production until too late for any reasonable degree of control. Production costs were uncertain. Finally, if inspection and attendant sorting were not much more accurate than the processes of manufacture, many defective articles went to dealers and consumers.

Variations are inevitable in any industrial process. Economics, moreover, dictates that variations should be accepted within limits that are consistent with a product's intended use. An examination of quality determinations from controlled processes will generally show a normal frequency distribution like that of Figure 99.

Individual measurements and test results are not well adapted to the purposes of analysis and control. Charted averages and ranges of subgroups of 3, 4, or 5 measurements or test results are extremely sensitive indicators. As an example, assume the following periodic measurements of viscosity:

$$
\begin{aligned}
\text{Sample } 1 &= 135.0 \text{ seconds} \\
\text{Sample } 2 &= 134.9 \text{ seconds} \\
\text{Sample } 3 &= 135.0 \text{ seconds} \\
\text{Sample } 4 &= 136.8 \text{ seconds} \\
\text{Sample } 5 &= 136.7 \text{ seconds} \\
\end{aligned}
$$

$$5\,)\overline{678.4}$$

$$135.7 = \text{average seconds}$$
$$1.9 = \text{range (difference between largest and smallest value)}$$

The foregoing average and range values appear as the first points on the chart forming Figure 102. This chart also plots 25 other averages and ranges, which establish control limits of 133.3 to 137.1 seconds for averages and 6.9 seconds for ranges.

During subsequent production, variations in averages or ranges that lie within the control limits may be confidently attributed to chance combinations of variables inherent in processes and equipment employed. Trends that transcend these limits reveal the introduction of variables abnormal to the controlled process and also indicate their causes, so that remedial action can be taken. As an example, the chart in Figure 102 shows 5 consecutive increases in viscosity from lot 148

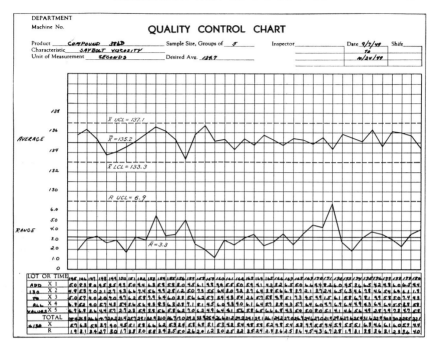

Fig. 102. An average and range chart.

to lot 153. If corrective action had not been taken with lot 154, the process would have wandered outside its own control.

When values for quality characteristics are charted and adjustments made to maintain their control, and, when per cent defective charts reveal process quality levels that demand only occasional sorting based on calculated risks, their assurance of high levels in outgoing quality is excellent. With assurance of both process and outgoing quality, planning and control of production become simple and reliable.

Instrument Control. No matter what system is used to control quality, measurements and tests must be made by production and inspection personnel. Measurements and tests require instruments, and these must be periodically checked for accuracy.

In the metalworking industries many jigs, fixtures, and gages must be given routine examinations using accurate subprimary standards for comparison and correction. Storage must be provided for jigs, fixtures, and gages, and records must be maintained to indicate when they need to be checked and when they will be needed in production.

In the chemical industries many instruments are used and they, too, must be checked periodically. Instruments that measure temperatures, for example, may automatically indicate, record, and control, but their accuracy must be compared with some subprimary thermometer, the accuracy of which has been checked with a standard or primary instrument. In addition, potentiometric checks are made electrically as an overcheck on the physical method of verification.

The actual checking of instruments is generally done by skilled technicians. Records of the condition of instruments are usually maintained by the inspection department or the toolroom personnel, but close liaison between production planners and those who keep these records is necessary to insure that tools, jigs, fixtures, and gages are accurate and ready when they are needed for production.

Since the cost and care required for accurate measurements are great, specifications for them should be realistic both in terms of what can be done with available skills and equipment and what is actually needed in product performance and appearance. Specifications are often wishfully set within narrower limits than are necessary or than can be attained. When visiting a European metal-working factory I was interested, among other things, in organization levels and the titles of the men who worked in them. I asked a workman what his job was called. The man replied that he was an inspector. Asked if he was the chief inspector, the man pointed to another individual and replied that he was the chief inspector. Asked what differentiated him from the chief inspector the man replied, "The chief inspector has the extreme allowable limit gages."

A more detailed study of the operation disclosed that workmen were given gages with extremely narrow limits, inspectors had gages with wider tolerances, and the chief inspector had a special set of gages with wide-open limits. So far as I could see, no parts were rejected for dimensions outside the established limits; they simply went from one man to another until the chief inspector passed them. This was an amusing game but quite unrealistic, as well as wasteful of time and money.

SUMMARY

Quality control uses statistical methods to overcome the two great unpredictables of planning. It indicates when losses impend because of nonconformance to standards of quality. It gives prompt notice when incoming raw materials do not meet specifications. Basing its computations on supplier and process capabilities, quality control also provides reliable estimates of material and product losses.

Statistical sampling of raw materials now provides reliable information quickly yet uses relatively small samples to represent large lots. The time interval required for receiving inspection is reduced so that raw materials promptly become available for production.

In processing, quality control avoids the production of large quantities of goods that would later prove to be unacceptable. The sequence of *manufacture-test-adjust,* frequently repeated, provides good control and assurance of quality. It minimizes losses from material overages by exercising effective control over weights and measures. Quality control also simplifies planning and scheduling by keeping returned goods at the minimum and so reducing the problems of replacement.

In all systems for controlling quality, instruments used to measure quality characteristics must be checked periodically to insure their accuracy. Specifications for quality characteristics should be realistic.

QUESTIONS TO CHECK COMPREHENSION

1. How will nonconforming raw materials affect production schedules?

2. How will production outside of specification limits affect schedules?

3. Define quality control, and tell how it differs from inspection.

4. Can small samples treated statistically provide a reliable basis for acceptance or rejection of raw materials?

5. How can free communication between the quality-control engineer and the planning engineer help the latter to plan production?

6. What are process capabilities? How do they affect production planning?

7. Can per cent defective charts provide any helpful information to production planners?

8. Can destructive tests be used except with statistically small samples?

9. What advantages are achieved by periodic testing of samples from production?

10. Can charts be used in the control of product characteristics such as weight, pH, dimensions, resistance, etc.?

PROBLEMS

1. Assume that you have been employed as production manager of a company that has often failed to meet production schedules. Rejected product has been in the neighborhood of 22 per cent. Since many different products are produced on the same machines, small lots have to be rescheduled to compensate for rejections.

Your studies show that workmen are well trained and highly skilled. Equipment is modern and in good repair. The majority of nonconforming products can be traced to outside limit raw materials. Of the major raw materials used, 6 lots of 10,000 units each are in stock. If more than 2 per cent of these units are defective, production difficulties are sure to occur. From each lot 460 units have been examined with the following results:

Lot	Defectives
1	26
2	14
3	12
4	15
5	13
6	16

Assuming that your contract with the supplier stipulates that not more than 2 per cent of each lot shall be defective, which lots will you accept for production and which will you reject?

2. As a production engineer, you are responsible for the manufacture of a certain product by a special process. Quality-control engineers have measured the process capabilities and have informed you that even when all controllable variations are within control, about 40 per cent of the output will not conform with specification requirements. Explain the alternative courses that are open to you.

DISCUSSION CASE

Echo, Inc., manufacturer of floor coverings, had been operating at a loss since the end of World War II. The owners, therefore, retained a management consultant to study operations and recommend improvements.

The consultant found most operating ratios to be in balance, but product quality was badly out of control. Defective floor covering amounted to 18 per cent of production, 2 per cent being scrap, and the remaining 16 per cent being seconds. Scrap, which was worthless, caused a loss of $4,000 monthly; seconds, which were sold at half price, brought a loss of $16,000. The consultant immediately concluded that the greatest chance for improvement lay in reduction of defectives.

Thirteen production machines were operating on 3 shifts. For a week the consultant prepared per cent defective charts for 5 machines on the day shift, securing the following data:

Machine Number	Per Cent Defective
1	18
2	8
3	13
4	15
5	6
Average	12

An analysis of the causes for defects showed that machine 1 was badly in need of repair. Machine 4 was in good condition, but its day-shift operator needed training.

During the second week the consultant maintained charts for 5 machines on the second shift. The results were:

Machine Number	Per Cent Defective
4	7
6	16
7	11
8	19
9	22
Average	15

The good performance of machine 4 confirmed the consultant's original findings, while an analysis of the causes for defectives produced by this machine on both shifts revealed the areas in which training was needed. Machines 6 and 9 were in bad order; 8 showed no real cause for its poor performance.

An 8-week study of all machines on all shifts produced the following figures:

Per Cent Defective

Machine Number	First Shift	Second Shift	Third Shift	Average
1 *	18	29	17	21.3
2	8	6	5	6.3
3	13	9	8	10.0
4	15	7	6	9.3
5	6	21	17	14.6
6 *	22	16	19	19.0
7	7	11	12	10.0
8	12	19	17	16.0
9 *	24	22	23	23.0
10	7	12	30	16.3
11	15	8	7	10.0
12 *	20	15	40	25.0
13	16	10	35	20.3
Average	14	14	18	15.4

* Machines requiring overhaul.

The consultant's recommendations included:

1. Completely overhaul machines 1, 6, 9, and 12.
2. Retrain the day-shift operators of machines 4 and 11, the second-shift operators of machines 5 and 8, and the third-shift operators of machines 10, 12, and 13.
3. Maintain control charts on all machines on all shifts.
4. Institute supervisory training for the three shift foremen.

Six months later, when the machines had been overhauled and the operators retrained, defective production declined to 11 per cent. The management neglected to provide supervisory training, and it refused to maintain control charts because the cost of rewinding inspection to classify the product and cull out seconds and scrap was already high.

Quality soon began to decline; 18 months after the consultant made his recommendations, defectives amounted to 17 per cent of production. Losses were proportionate to those suffered before the consultant was called in: $2,000 for each per cent of scrap and $1,000 for each per cent of seconds.

Tell what is wrong and why, and recommend corrective action.

22

Level Production
and Stable Employment

To plan production strictly from an engineering point of view is not too difficult, but to make production fit both the logic of engineering and the needs of human beings is a very different problem. It demands not merely technical skill but also a broad knowledge of causes and effects and an understanding of the need for balanced service to all segments of our socioeconomic world.

All too often, production planners have tried only to maintain inventories of finished goods within limits that are sound in terms of customer demand and working capital. In spite of this, the upper policy-making levels of management often are receptive to plans that involve short-term violations of economic rules but that are sound in their long-term benefits. For example, economic considerations may show a 6-week stock of finished goods as the maximum inventory. When it is reached, the economically obvious course is to announce an extended layoff for employees until the stock is reduced. But layoffs cause hardship and arouse popular resentment. The management group, concerned with public and employee relations as well as with inventory policy, therefore decides to exceed the stock limit by continuing production. If the upper stock limit cannot safely be exceeded, the employees may be paid to paint and refurbish equipment or buildings during slow periods.

Production and manufacturing planners must be constantly alert to situations that may cause temporary heavy employment followed by many layoffs or dismissals. When new products are introduced, for example, the sales department may demand that hand production be employed while automatic equipment is being designed and built. In one typical instance, the planning department found that 500 employees would be required to produce a new item by hand, but only 20 would be needed when automatic equipment arrived. Six months' time was required to design and construct the automatic machines. If the sales department had had its way, 500 people would have been hired to do hand work, and 480 of these would have been dismissed 6 months later. This would have meant widespread disappointment and hardship, would have lowered the company's reputation as an employer, and would have weakened it in the eyes of the community.

Management weighed the prospective results and decided against full-scale hand production. Instead, it directed the personnel office to hire 20 new workers who would turn out the new item by hand. When their production had accumulated for 3 months, the goods were released for a territorial trial that confirmed the need for the 20 machines then being constructed. As machines arrived, 20 new people were trained to operate them and so received permanent jobs. At the same time, the company avoided the difficulties that would have arisen had production been carried on by hand, for selling prices had been based on automatic production, and 6 months of full-scale hand production would have resulted in a substantial loss.

Production planners should question general policies from time to time. If it is found that the reasons for policies have ceased to exist, new ones may then be requested. During a period of tight working capital, for example, a company may be forced to establish a rigid rule that finished goods stocks of any item should never exceed 1 week's supply. In time the working capital situation improves so that a 3-week stock can be easily maintained. At the same time sales multiply so that prompt shipments no longer can be made from the rigidly limited stock. The planning department therefore compares losses from cancellation of orders with interest charges for an adequate finished goods inventory. If the former equals or exceeds the latter, the department urges an increase in inventory limits. The planning department also may show that an increased stock limit will simplify planning and help to stabilize employment.

The production planner should be equally alert to cooperate in maintaining small finished goods stocks where large ones would result in financial difficulties.

Many companies have never tried to achieve level production simply because no one has made an analysis to show its benefits and requirements. To discover what these actually are, let us consider a company whose sales show great seasonal fluctuations.

The first step is to prepare a schedule of working days in the year that are available for normal production planning. Assume that New Year's Day (celebrated on January 2), Memorial Day, Independence Day, a 2-week vacation period in July, Labor Day, Thanksgiving Day, and Christmas Day will be holidays during 1950. The schedule of working days will then be:

January	21	July	11
February	20	August	23
March	23	September	20
April	20	October	22
May	22	November	21
June	22	December	20
		Total	245

We may further assume a sales forecast of 36,000,000 units, with the following monthly variation:

January	1,000,000	July	6,000,000
February	1,500,000	August	5,000,000
March	2,000,000	September	3,000,000
April	3,000,000	October	2,000,000
May	4,000,000	November	1,500,000
June	6,000,000	December	1,000,000
		Total	36,000,000

With 245 working days normally available, the daily production rate is set at 146,939 units. Monthly production schedules, based on the normal working days available each month, are:

January	3,085,719	July	1,616,329
February	2,938,780	August	3,379,597
March	3,379,597	September	2,938,780
April	2,938,780	October	3,232,658
May	3,232,658	November	3,085,719
June	3,232,658	December	2,938,780
		Total	36,000,055

Assuming a finished goods stock of 5,000,000 units at the close of the preceding year, the estimated sales, production, and stock position will be as follows:

	Sales	Level Production @ 146,939 Units per Day	Finished Goods Stock 5,000,000 Dec. 31
January	1,000,000	3,085,719	7,085,719
February	1,500,000	2,938,780	8,524,499
March	2,000,000	3,379,597	9,904,096
April	3,000,000	2,938,780	9,842,876
May	4,000,000	3,232,658	9,075,534
June	6,000,000	3,232,658	6,308,192
July	6,000,000	1,616,329	1,924,521
August	5,000,000	3,379,597	304,118
September	3,000,000	2,938,780	242,898
October	2,000,000	3,232,658	1,475,556
November	1,500,000	3,085,719	3,061,275
December	1,000,000	2,938,780	5,000,055
Total	36,000,000	36,000,055	
Average inventory			5,229,111

These figures are shown graphically in Figure 103.

$$\text{Turnover} = \frac{36{,}000{,}000 \text{ annual sales}}{5{,}229{,}111 \text{ average inventory}} = 6.88$$

If a maximum stock limit of 1 month had been maintained, the turnover would have been 12.

The foregoing information has been based on units of products. To consider the financial aspects of the situation, assume that each unit has a cost value of $0.25. Then it becomes evident that to maintain level production, with a finished goods stock of about 10,000,000 units during the months of January to May, about $2,500,000 in working capital is required. In contrast, intermittent production with a stock of 3,000,000 units, the number indicated by stock control, will require $750,000. The difference, $1,750,000 in working capital, may be available or may not be; if it must be borrowed, the short-term interest will be about $30,000 or about 1.71 per cent of the cost value of the excess inventory. Whether capital is borrowed or ready for use, it will be subject to risk of loss through falling prices.

If a company is struggling for financial survival, these factors may

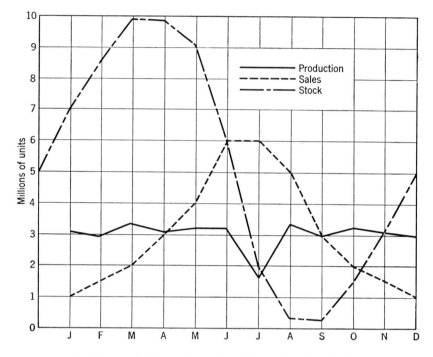

Fig. 103. Production, sales, and stock with level production.

compel it to defer the goal of level production. If it can afford to make the change, however, it will find compensatory benefits. Personnel losses will be greatly reduced, thus cutting down the cost of training new employees. Stable employment will encourage confidence and good will among employees and will promote good community relations. Finally, there will be a reduction of the manufacturing facilities that once were required to handle peak production requirements.

Companies that have achieved level production find that stable operation yields substantial benefits. These are evident in all divisions of these companies.

Operating divisions of these companies are the principal beneficiaries. The operating effectiveness that can be attained when a definite routine is followed day after day throughout the year is almost unbelievable. Tensions from rush work and interruptions, with the attendant lower quality and lower productivity, do not exist. Workmen and their leaders are freed from emotional doubts. Furthermore, they appreciate the freedom of turning out maximum production of top quality without the misgivings that next week or next month will bring cutbacks.

Sales divisions are challenged and thereby strengthened to study sales potential carefully, to plan for attractive and effective merchandising arrangements, and to direct actual sales forcibly. Perhaps the strongest incentive to sell is to have a planned inventory, produced well in advance of a sales season, and then to go out and sell. What may have seemed to be traditional sales seasons may develop into year-round sales if the merchandise is available and sales pressure is maintained. Any sales executive will admit that sales are greater when the merchandise is available for sale than when the supply is limited and subject to allocations and/or late deliveries.

Purchasing divisions actually benefit as much as operating divisions. To arrange for deliveries of raw materials in equal increments throughout the year greatly simplifies the purchasing function. Moreover, it permits the suppliers to share in the stability and often results in improved raw-material costs. Buyers who must wait until a few months before a season to procure raw-material requirements are often forced to take spot lots on the open market. Yearly contracts for raw materials can generally be effected at better prices. Of equal importance, quality assurance of the raw materials is generally much better with contracts than with spot purchases.

Treasury divisions meet the greatest challenge with level production. Schedules of income and expense must be carefully prepared. The capital requirements necessary to carry finished goods inventories through off-seasons certainly will have to be weighed against capital requirements for facilities capable of peak production. Cost improvements resulting from more effective stable operations may tip the balance in favor of level production. It must be appreciated that the treasurer of a company will insist on maintaining a safe net working capital. Great courage and foresight are required for him to agree to any arrangement that might delay the factory payroll for even a day.

Personnel and public relations divisions enjoy the greatest benefits from level production. Level production will not eliminate the need for all the other sound human relations practices, but it certainly solves the majority of those distasteful problems of layoffs, bumping, readjustments, and retraining. If short time has been resorted to instead of layoffs, level production eliminating it can also eliminate the primary cause of many personnel problems. The whole community looks with pride and respect on those companies in which production is stabilized.

Engineering and research can proceed in an orderly manner if production is leveled off. New and improved processes and products can be introduced after they have been carefully tested. With seasonal production peaks, engineering is often of the fire-engine type, putting out fires created by unusual demands. Research departments are often rushed to have a new process or product ready to catch a season. The results of such rushed developments are generally disappointing. The balancing of these benefits, challenges, and risks, and the development of plans to operate with level production or to control inventories to sales, requires careful consideration of all the contributory activities of management.

Other avenues may also lead to stabilized employment. Changing the date of the annual automobile show helped to level out sales. The development of new products with sales seasonally out of phase with those of old products frequently stabilizes production. Thus a small-arms manufacturer developed a line of refrigeration equipment, since hot months are out of phase with hunting seasons. Some food packers have introduced items to be produced between normal animal-killing periods.

The following is from an article by Russell W. Davenport,[1] in which he explains some of the accomplishments of leading industrial companies to assure full, year-round employment.

Richard R. Deupree of Procter & Gamble pointed out in 1945 that employment stabilization had accomplished many savings for his company, the biggest of which nobody had thought of before the annual wage was installed. This was the elimination of excess capacity, made possible by year-round production—a total saving over twenty-two years of $100,000,000 in plant investment, exclusive of depreciation, carrying charges, and interest on the money. Innumerable other examples could be cited. But perhaps the final word should be given to that august body, the Board of Directors of the Standard Oil Co. (N. J.) which declared in their annual statement for 1949: "as we see it, the basic interest of the stockholder—security for his investment and a fair return—is best served only if the corporation deserves and enjoys public confidence. Such confidence can be based only on recognition by people at large that their interest—the interest of society—is a factor in corporate action."

Mr. Davenport goes on to say that

If a hundred leading firms were to announce that from now on they intended to make themselves primarily responsible for [stable level employment] it would resound around the world like the crack of a gun. This light would reveal state socialism to be a great reactionary movement.

The foregoing, of course, has to do with companies manufacturing to stock. In job-order production, the production planner will exer-

[1] Russell W. Davenport, "The Greatest Opportunity on Earth," *Fortune Magazine*, October, 1949.

cise his skill in balancing the backlog of orders to assure steady employment. Many peaks and valleys in production loads can be eliminated by detailed study of delivery dates and by persuading customers to accept dates that fit into production schedules without inconvenience to the purchaser.

Load charts may show that equipment and skilled workmen will be idle unless salesmen put forth extra effort to sell products made on this equipment by these men. As an example, a machine shop may have only 1 week's backlog of orders for work produced on milling machines and shapers but a 20-week backlog of orders for work on automatic screw machines. Salesmen should be instructed to make the major portion of their calls on customers that normally use side frames and base plates. If sales efforts consistently fail to obtain enough orders to keep certain types of equipment busy, the production planner should suggest that some of these machines be sold and that operators be retrained for other work.

Among many other demands, organized labor has pressed for and received penalty or premium wages for overtime work. This has produced some plums for workmen in the form of extra compensation. The most important result of premium wages for overtime work, however, has been a strong incentive for engineers and managers to plan production carefully and thus avoid the cost of overtime premiums. Workmen do not generally contrive to create the need for overtime work, and where basic wages are high they are content to work regular hours and be free to plan their leisure time.

Industry is now confronted with demands for a guaranteed annual wage. For many companies, to give such guarantees would mean financial ruin. Other companies, however, will develop plans for stable employment and thus will be able to offer assurance of annual wages. The time probably will come when employers will view the now controversial guaranteed annual wage with no more alarm than that with which we now consider premium wages for overtime work, workman's compensation, and other factors that once seemed to threaten the foundations of industry.

This, of course, does not imply that all industrial companies will suddenly improve their production planning or that consumers will quickly abandon their traditional habits of seasonal buying. Both changes will come gradually—perhaps also slowly—and the guaranteed annual wage must keep pace with them. Still, if the problem is attacked with determination and enlightenment by both organized labor and industrial managers, the chance for satisfactory solution should be excellent.

The production planner should consider broad company policies, since they govern the overall job of planning. He should also assist operating foremen in planning their work arrangements. In this area alone, careful attention to changing levels of production can result in stabilized employment as well as realistic control of costs.

All healthy enterprises should show long-term increases in sales, increases that will require corresponding increases in production. All departments of a company should have plans in readiness at all times for increases in production up to 50 per cent. The factors and steps involved in such planning are indicated by the following example:

Assume that a manufacturing department operates 8 hours per day and 5 days per week with the following employees and wage costs:

60 direct workers	@ $1.50 per hour =	$ 90.00
1 foreman	@ 2.80 per hour =	2.80
2 material handlers	@ 1.25 per hour =	2.50
2 inspectors	@ 1.75 per hour =	3.50
1 cleaner	@ 1.20 per hour =	1.20

Total direct and indirect labor cost $100.00 per hour

Records show that each direct worker turns out 10 units of production per hour. The direct and indirect labor cost per unit, therefore, is:

$$\frac{\$100 \text{ per hour} \times 40 \text{ hours per week}}{60 \text{ men} \times 40 \text{ hours} \times 10 \text{ units per hour}} = \$0.1666 \text{ per unit}$$

If a 5 per cent increase in production is desired, it can be obtained by working 8 hours and 24 minutes per day for 5 days per week. Time and one-half is paid for all hours over 40. The direct and indirect labor cost per unit will then be:

$$\frac{(\$100 \text{ per hour} \times 40 \text{ hours}) + (2 \text{ hours} \times \$150 \text{ per hour})}{60 \text{ men} \times 42 \text{ hours per week} \times 10 \text{ units per hour}}$$

$$= \$0.1706 \text{ per unit}$$

A 5 per cent increase in production can also be obtained by adding a second shift of 3 direct workers and 1 foreman who also acts as an inspector and material handler. A 10 per cent shift premium is paid.

3 direct workers	@ $1.65 =	$4.95
1 group leader	@ 3.08 =	3.08

$8.03 per hour

If this course is chosen, the direct and indirect labor cost per unit will be:

$$\frac{(\$100 \text{ per hour} \times 40 \text{ hours}) + (\$8.03 \text{ per hour} \times 40 \text{ hours})}{63 \text{ men} \times 40 \text{ hours} \times 10 \text{ units per hour}}$$

$$= \$0.1715 \text{ per unit}$$

If a 10 per cent increase in production is desired, it can be obtained by working 4 hours overtime on Saturday forenoon. The direct and indirect labor cost per unit will be:

$$\frac{(40 \text{ hours} \times \$100 \text{ per hour}) + (4 \text{ hours} \times \$150 \text{ per hour})}{60 \text{ men} \times 44 \text{ hours per week} \times 10 \text{ units per hour}}$$

$$= \$0.1742 \text{ per unit}$$

The same increase can also be obtained by adding a second shift of 6 direct workers and 1 foreman who also acts as an inspector and material handler.

Again a 10 per cent shift premium is paid, giving the following figures:

$$
\begin{array}{lll}
6 \text{ direct workers} & @ \;\$1.65 \text{ per hour} = & \$\;9.90 \\
1 \text{ foreman} & @ \;\;3.08 \text{ per hour} = & \;\;3.08 \\
\hline
& & \$12.98 \text{ per hour}
\end{array}
$$

The direct and indirect labor cost per unit will be:

$$\frac{(\$100 \text{ per hour} \times 40 \text{ hours}) + (\$12.98 \text{ per hour} \times 40 \text{ hours})}{66 \text{ men} \times 40 \text{ hours} \times 10 \text{ units per hour}}$$

$$= \$0.1712 \text{ per unit}$$

If a 25 per cent increase in production is required, it can be obtained by working 1 shift 10 hours per day for 5 days per week. The direct and indirect labor cost per unit will be:

$$\frac{(\$100 \text{ per hour} \times 40 \text{ hours}) + (\$150 \text{ per hour} \times 10 \text{ hours})}{60 \text{ men} \times 50 \text{ hours per week} \times 10 \text{ units per hour}}$$

$$= \$0.1833 \text{ per unit}$$

The increase can also be obtained by adding an additional shift of 15 direct workers. A 10 per cent shift premium is paid. The direct and indirect labor cost for the extra shift will be:

15 direct workers	@ $1.65	per hour =	$24.75
1 foreman	@ 3.08	per hour =	3.08
1 material handler	@ 1.375	per hour =	1.375
1 inspector	@ 1.925	per hour =	1.925

$31.13   per hour

The direct and indirect labor cost per unit will be:

$$\frac{(\$100 \text{ per hour} \times 40 \text{ hours}) + (\$31.13 \text{ per hour} \times 40 \text{ hours})}{75 \text{ men} \times 40 \text{ hours} \times 10 \text{ units per hour}}$$

$$= \$0.1748 \text{ per unit}$$

A 50 per cent increase in production can be obtained by working 10 hours per day for 6 days per week. The direct and indirect labor cost per unit will be:

$$\frac{(\$100 \text{ per hour} \times 40 \text{ hours}) + (\$150 \text{ per hour} \times 20 \text{ hours})}{60 \text{ men} \times 60 \text{ hours per week} \times 10 \text{ units per hour}}$$

$$= \$0.1944 \text{ per unit}$$

A 50 per cent increase in production can also be obtained by working an additional shift with 30 direct workers. The direct and indirect labor cost per hour for the extra shift will be:

30 direct workers	@ $1.65	per hour =	$49.50
1 foreman	@ 3.08	per hour =	3.08
1 material handler	@ 1.375	per hour =	1.375
1 inspector	@ 1.825	per hour =	1.825

$55.78   per hour

The direct and indirect labor cost per unit will be:

$$\frac{(\$100 \text{ per hour} \times 40 \text{ hours}) + (\$55.78 \text{ per hour} \times 40 \text{ hours})}{90 \text{ men} \times 40 \text{ hours} \times 10 \text{ units per hour}}$$

$$= \$0.1731 \text{ per unit}$$

The graph (Figure 104) shows that it would be most economical to work overtime, in this particular department, until production is increased to 7 per cent. Since the cost differential between working overtime and starting another shift remains small until an increase of 15 per cent is reached, overtime may be desirable up to that point. Adding an extra shift involves training of personnel as well as in-

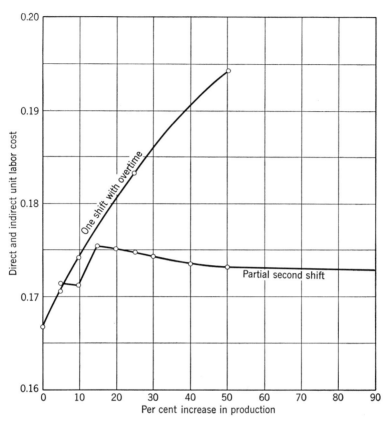

Fig. 104. A graphic analysis of overtime versus a partial second shift.

creased personnel turnover if the upswing in sales does not continue, but overtime can be eliminated without hardship to personnel if a cutback becomes necessary.

In addition to straightforward calculations, shop foremen and planners should have some estimate of actual operating effectiveness with overtime and with added shifts. This will vary with different situations. Generally employees will work 20 per cent over 40 hours per week for a few months without any appreciable drop in effectiveness. About a 5 per cent lower effectiveness is generally to be expected on the second shift. This is not always true. One experience showed that the second shift produced about 3 per cent more effectively than the first. The general foreman projected the theory that the machines ran faster at night because there was less load on the line. Machine speed studies disproved this. One workman who had worked on both shifts advanced the theory that there was less technical interference at night. His reasoning was correct. When experimental runs, engineering examinations of machines, etc., were subtracted from the input and output of the day shift, the two shifts were found to be about equal in operating effectiveness.

Each manufacturing department should have forward plans for as much as 50 per cent decrease as well as 50 per cent increase in production.

As has been said, this is a simplified example. It should be supplemented by planning for two- and three-shift operations at various production levels both with and without overtime. The reader may work out a full series of plans for such cutbacks, keeping in mind that it is poor employment policy to lay off one or more shifts yet work the remaining shifts or shift overtime.

The science of operations research and mathematical programming is being extended to include level production and stable employment as factors in the calculations. If a company's policy specifies level production and stable employment, production programming almost certainly is required. Without scientific programming studies it is doubtful that a company can achieve level production and stable employment without inordinately increasing the cost of doing business.

SUMMARY

Seasonal sales demand produces many problems, the most serious being unstable employment. Companies struggling for financial survival seldom can afford to level out seasonal fluctuations in production. Companies that have achieved financial stability should explore methods of stabilizing both production and employment. They may find that advantages outweigh the cost of carrying large finished goods inventories through the periods of low sales.

Companies with a limited array of seasonal products should consider the addition of other items that sell chiefly in other seasons. The timing of sales and advertising stimuli may also help to level production.

In job-order production there is no problem of maintaining finished goods stock. Production planners must seek to arrange delivery promises in uniform sequence and to maintain backlogs of orders as means of providing steady employment.

New products generally can be manufactured by the number of workmen eventually required, once equipment difficulties have been overcome and a learning period has increased operating effectiveness to a normal level. Withholding technological improvements temporarily until sales of old products show promise of increase, or until new ones have been introduced, can help to absorb workmen that would be eliminated by these technological improvements and can be an important factor in stabilizing employment.

Organized labor's demand for premium wages for overtime work, and recently for guaranteed annual wages, offers strong incentives for more careful production planning. The problem of overtime wages has been solved in a large measure by advanced planning that avoids sudden increases in production. The solution to the problem of annual wages will not only require much careful advance planning but it will also require consumer education to change traditional seasonal buying habits. A satisfactory solution to the problem of annual wages depends upon the cooperation of organized labor, managers, and consumers.

Production planners and supervisers should understand the economics of increasing production. They should know when and how long to obtain the added production by operating on overtime. They should understand when to eliminate overtime and add a shift. Plans should be in readiness for increases up to 50 per cent and for comparable decreases in production.

With a better understanding of production problems plans can be made that will result in more stable employment.

QUESTIONS TO CHECK COMPREHENSION

1. May the reasons for certain policies that affect production planning change over a period of years?

2. What are the unfavorable effects of full-scale production by hand while automatic equipment is under construction?

3. Can careful analysis of sales estimates, production scheduling, and inventory situations predict the problems and requirements of level production?

4. What are the advantages of level production?

5. What are some of its disadvantages?

6. How can the production planner help to reduce or level out a backlog of orders in job-order production?

7. Describe the steps in preparing an analysis that will indicate when an extra partial shift is more advisable than overtime operation.

8. Discuss the problems associated with the guaranteed annual wage.

PROBLEM

Assume that you are a production-planning engineer and that the principals of your company have asked you to make a detailed study of level production as it would apply to operations in your company's factories. Assume also that your union contract stipulates a 2-week vacation period any time between May and October, with dates to be decided by the employer and announced 3 months in advance. The contract also specifies that New Year's Day, Memorial Day, Independence Day, Labor Day, Thanksgiving Day, and Christmas Day shall be paid holidays.

The sales forecast for the coming year has been set at 6,000,000 units of production. Finished goods on hand at the beginning of the coming year are estimated to be 4,000,000 units and a minimum stock of 1,000,000 units is required to provide for unexpected sales demands. The traditional sales pattern has been:

Month	%	Month	%	Month	%
January	4	May	10	September	6
February	6	June	12	October	6
March	8	July	15	November	4
April	10	August	15	December	4
				Total	100%

Establish a level production schedule for the coming year and chart production, sales, and stock by months. Assume a cost of $0.50 per unit and compute the highest working capital requirement for finished goods with level production. Compare this with the working capital needed if production is controlled to a finished goods stock limit of 3,000,000 units.

DISCUSSION CASE

The Hansome Company had become so large that its organization was decentralized into five operating units. These were based upon kindred products since geographic separation was not practical. All manufacturing units were on the same lot, and three were in a single building. Employees of all five units were represented by the same union. Policies such as for seniority, wage rates, and conditions of work were uniform throughout all operating units. Employees as well as operating executives of all units maintained social relationships in intercompany bowling leagues, softball, etc.

The production planner in unit 4 had developed considerable skill in maintaining level employment by careful attention to sales forecasts and production schedules. He also solicited work from other units on a subcontract basis to fill in his own production schedules.

Unit 3 had a bad reputation for erratic schedules, since its employees often were laid off for weeks at a time. Units 2 and 5 generally ran behind in production two or three times a year, and their whole operating force had to work several Saturdays and Sundays. All hours over 40 per week were paid for at the rate of time and one-half. Unit 1 had been free from erratic production, but its finished goods inventory was known to be excessive.

At a meeting of unit executives, the manager of unit 4 complained that because of the plant seniority policy (which was a part of the union contract) his employees were being bumped when there were layoffs in other units. This, he said, was unfair and produced resentment. The works manager reported that the union president had complained about layoffs in unit 3 and about overtime in units 2 and 5.

A few months later a new contract was negotiated. The union, thereupon, demanded:

1. Termination pay of 1 month's wages for each year of employment. If an employee was reinstated within a week, no termination pay would be required provided that the employee had not been previously laid off during the year. If the employee was reinstated after 1 week but within 1 month, only half the termination pay was to be paid. All terminations were to continue on a strict plant seniority basis.

2. Overtime pay at the rate of time and one-half for overtime of 1 hour per day or less during the 5-day week. Double time for overtime in excess of 1 hour per day, during the 5-day week. Double time for work on Saturdays, Sundays, and holidays.

During the 6 weeks just before the contract-renewal date, the works manager had made the following analysis of the preceding 12 months' operations:

Unit Number	1	2	3	4	5
Finished goods turnover	3	11	6	10	10
Labor turnover *	5%	8%	23%	4%	6%
Labor cost variance	+1%	+16%	+12%	−2%	+18%
Overtime hours	2%	6%	1%	0.2%	7%
Grievances	3	23	46	2	15

* This calculation was based on the unit causing the release. It does not show the actual terminations in each unit as a result of bumping.

Assume that a meeting has been called to discuss union contract negotiations and that you have been invited to attend. List the causes for what is wrong and determine what must be done to correct each fault.

23

Solving Forecasting, Planning, and Control Problems

We have found that forecasting, planning, and control are not simple, clear-cut operations to be carried out by one or a few persons within a single department. They demand ramifying yet close cooperation among members of several departments; their success depends upon attitudes and ways of thinking as much as upon the exercise of this or that particular skill. They may be likened to a symphony—a symphony performed not by musicians but by operating personnel, industrial engineers, production-planning engineers, quality-control engineers, and purchasing and accounting executives. In an orchestral symphony one mistake may spoil the whole recital. In this industrial symphony an error is not too serious if the interrelations are close, and if others recognize the fault and counsel the errant section or member. As in an orchestra, however, there is no place for the lone performer.

As we have seen, planning and control have grown from rule-of-thumb and art to science. Beyond formal organization, however, cooperative relationships among individuals have been reduced neither to rule-of-thumb nor to science. Cooperation remains an art, a complex, flexible, and warmly human art that unites different and even antagonistic persons into a smoothly functioning team. Experience has proved that these persons can form a team only when their numbers are few, for large groups inevitably mean division, formality, and lack of personal contacts. Teams must be small to be well integrated and to permit the uninhibited, friendly relationships on which true cooperation depends.

This fact indicates the first step to be taken in building up an organization that can solve the problems of production forecasting, planning, and control. *Break the large and complex down into com-*

ponents that are small and simple. This rule may be applied to factories in the form of physical decentralization; it may be applied with equal success to problems of management, production, planning, and control. Any problems that involve more than a few hundred workers and several hundred products are bound to defy solution by one man or by any group small enough to work together in effective cooperation. True, the man or the group may *decide*, but that decision will not and cannot be based on intimate knowledge, understanding, and appraisal of all the significant details.

This is a rule, a disembodied and perhaps as yet unconvincing generalization. Let us illustrate it by the example of a company with 2,000 production employees who manufacture about 1,000 different textile items. In the past, a single production manager has attempted to make all decisions, basing them upon data supplied by a large group of assistants. The manager's span of control, however, has been too broad; lack of intimate knowledge about important details has confused his decisions.

Using the foregoing facts for an assumed situation, what can be done about it? Let us explore the possibilities for simplification.

The first step is to classify the line of products. As has been said, these number about 1,000, but they fall into the 4 categories of industrial fabrics, fancy dress goods, wash goods, and sheetings. Raw materials also number 4: cotton, rayon, nylon, and silk. Processes, however, are 5: spinning, weaving, bleaching, dyeing, and tentering. Analysis shows the following relationships among these various categories:

Product	Spinning	Weaving	Bleaching	Dyeing	Tentering
Industrial fabrics	Cotton	Cotton	Cotton	Cotton	Cotton
		Nylon		Nylon	Nylon
Fancy dress goods		Nylon		Nylon	Nylon
		Silk		Silk	Silk
Wash goods	Cotton	Cotton	Cotton	Cotton	Cotton
	Rayon	Rayon		Rayon	Rayon
Sheetings	Cotton	Cotton	Cotton	Cotton	Cotton

Breakdown or decentralization may be based upon the magnitude and relationship of elements in this table. If the 4 product categories are of approximately equal magnitude, planning and control may be broken down accordingly. One small group will then forecast, plan, and control industrial fabrics; if work is on a job-order basis, all orders will clear through this group. Comparable forces will perform the same functions for fancy dress goods, wash goods, and sheetings.

On the other hand, figures may show that some product categories are too small to justify separate groups but should be combined. Thus, forecasting, planning, and control of both wash goods and sheetings may be carried on by a single group, whereas industrial fabrics and fancy dress goods have separate organizations.

This basis for breakdown may be the right one, but others must be considered. Four raw materials are used, and they may determine machines, processes, and sales. If they do, forecasting, planning, and control may be divided according to materials rather than products. This will have the added advantage of simple planning and control with raw materials at the beginning of operations.

If identical machines and processes are employed for different raw materials and for different products, a breakdown by process may be in order. One group then will plan and control the production of yarn, another will do the same for weaving, and so on. This plan is advantageous for scheduling and control of production but does not provide for separate sales estimates or preparation of master schedules. These will be assigned to one centralized office.

These plans assume no physical separation of equipment and operation. That, however, must also be considered, for physical decentralization improves both operation and forecasting, planning, and control. Even though the decentralized units remain in one building, they become separate entities. Each one plans, operates, and controls independently of the other; each makes its own claim upon the loyalty of employees and builds up its own *esprit de corps.* Yet each unit enjoys the benefits of broad, basic company policies.

Once the team has been set at a practical size or reduced to it, the members may prepare themselves to make its work effective. This means that each member sets out to *know the others and be known by them.* Each member also develops a working knowledge of what his associates do.

Knowing one's associates may seem to be a simple matter, but it really is not. Human beings are exceedingly complex creatures in whom a variety of abilities, traits, and patterns of action are inextricably combined. Some men are more able than others, of course, and some are much easier to work with. But even the best have faults and limitations, imposed by illness or past experiences over which they have no control. One great problem in group collaboration is to bring out and utilize the most desirable qualities of each member while undesirable traits are kept in the background. This demands both understanding knowledge and realistic appraisal. It also demands tolerance and skill in dealing with people.

Knowledge is not too hard to gain; when men work together they soon learn each other's traits and abilities. Understanding is much more difficult. Is A really a slow thinker, or is he wisely cautious— the sort of fellow who takes things apart and weighs every element before saying that he understands them? Is B actually cold and remote, or does he merely have that manner as a consequence of early training? Is C prone to take unpredictable offense, or has some experience—never mind what—set up a reaction that he cannot curb? Is D a helpless creature of habit, or does he wisely let habit take care of routine, leaving his mind free for matters requiring analysis and decision? Such questions require correct answers, for without them one is almost sure to make frequent and serious errors.

After understanding come appraisal and tolerance. Which is the more desirable: a quick, perhaps sparkling, answer to questions, or the carefully prepared replies that come with annoying slowness from A? One may dislike the formality of B, but is it a real obstacle to cooperation? And is C's occasional anger serious, especially in a man who is a whiz at putting together sales forecasts or laying out operations? Again, such questions demand the right answers, without which a potential team is likely to be riven by discord.

Finally, there is the need to know, understand, and appraise oneself—though not to be self-tolerant. Businessmen, on the whole, are not introspective, yet their relations with other men will profit by some self-analysis. Can I do this sort of thing well, or can't I? Did I judge C or misjudge him—and why? Is my decision in this matter reasonable, or am I yielding to wishful thinking, habit, or prejudice? For a third time, such questions must be answered—and *only the right answers will prevent serious mistakes.*

Knowing what people do is easier than knowing and understanding men. The reasons also are more obvious. Many an executive who would question the need for understanding will readily agree that each member of a team should know what his associates do, what records they keep, what reports they utilize or prepare, and what problems they have to solve. Production planning rests in part on procurement; the production planner therefore consults buyers in the purchasing department, who show him what must be done to translate a purchase requisition into raw material delivered to stores. In the course of their talk, the engineer may find that he can use some of the buyer's records or that some of his records duplicate needlessly those of the purchasing department. He may also find that he can simplify the buyer's work by simple, added information on purchase requisitions.

This process, begun with buyers, should be repeated with industrial engineers, cost accountants, operating executives, and other persons on whom the planning engineer depends and with whom he must cooperate. Office visits should lead to discussions at lunch, in which problems, solutions, and experiences will be freely pooled. That pooling, not formal organization, will make these men a *team*.

Our first two steps apply to any group that works in cooperation; the third applies directly to groups concerned with forecasting, planning, and control. In it, members of the group *develop an understanding of sound, profitable inventory control.*

A pamphlet titled *How to Get Profits from Inventories*, copyrighted and published by Remington Rand, division of Sperry Rand Corporation, 315 Park Ave. South, New York 10, N. Y., presents the clearest explanation of these basic concepts. The following discussion is included in this pamphlet and is reprinted by permission of Remington Rand. This pamphlet, which has also been published in a revised edition entitled *Inventory Control for Manufacturers*, should be obtained and studied.

Turnover of stock affects the entire operation of a business because profits come from goods that move and not those that lie in the stock bins. Skill in controlling inventory is one of the most important tests of business management. Without effective inventory control a thriving business can quickly become unprofitable—as a result of losses suffered on excessive or unbalanced stocks. Government statistics show that this is one of the most common causes of business failure.

The burden of slow inventories is graphically illustrated in the chart in Figure 105.[1] Not only is capital tied up in inventory-capital which might be profitably employed elsewhere—but ever-mounting carrying costs eat into profit. The interest on money invested in stock, the shipping and handling costs, the costs of storage and insurance, the wages of people required to handle excess stock, the losses due to obsolescence and markdown—these carrying costs amount to at least 12% of the value of the goods each year. Some companies keeping careful cost records have found annual carrying costs running as high as 18% to 20% of inventory value. This inventory eats up over 1% of its value every month!

For example, on an annual sale of goods costing $100,000—if only one turnover is secured—$100,000 of capital must be invested and cost of carrying the inventory amounts to at least $12,000 per year. See what happens when the turnover rate is increased from one to two—$50,000 in capital is released for another profitable use and an annual saving of $6,000 is effected in carrying costs. Each successive increase in turnover releases more

[1] Figures are renumbered by permission of Remington Rand to fit the sequence of this book.

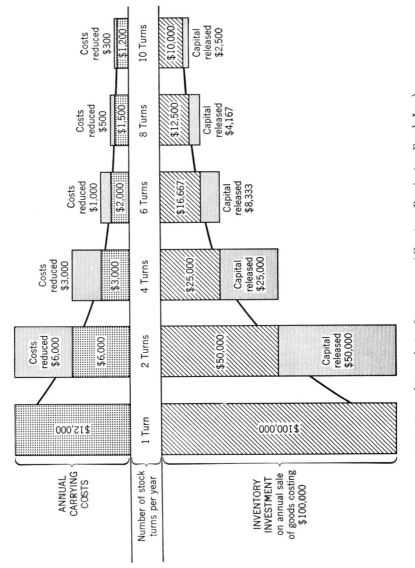

Fig. 105. A graphic analysis of turnover. (Courtesy Remington Rand, Inc.)

capital and further reduces carrying costs. With a turnover of six—a possible achievement in most lines of business—capital investment is reduced from $100,000 to $16,667 and annual carrying costs are cut from $12,000 to $2,000.

The greatest costs and most serious business losses occur from overstocks and slow turnover. The temptation to overbuy for the purpose of securing discounts—of the attempt to reduce costs by producing more than can be sold in a reasonable period of time—leads directly to slow turnover and high cost of possession. On the other hand, there is often a danger in too fast turnover on popular items. This results from carrying skimpy stocks and ordering so frequently, in such small amounts, that the cost of acquisition on these items goes up. Carrying skimpy stocks of fast movers means low cost of possession but it leads to out-of-stock conditions which hamper production or cause loss of sales and customer good-will.

The ideal turnover rate varies in different businesses. Some, such as coal and grocery concerns, make their greatest profit on 10 to 24 turnovers, but for a majority of companies, the most profitable turnover is around six or eight. As Figure 106 shows, the ideal turnover rate, the smallest costs and greatest profit are achieved when the cost of possession has been reduced to a moderate amount and yet ordering is not on such a hand-to-mouth basis that cost of acquisition becomes excessive.

It is an easy matter to compute average turnover for the stock as a whole. Simply divide the total cost of goods moved by the total value of the inventory. But there is a danger in accepting such average turnover figures, because they conceal instead of revealing unbalanced stock conditions.

Frequently the situation develops in which a company does 80% of its business on relatively few items while the rest of the stock moves slowly. If the truth were known, it would be found that overstocks in slow movers are tying up capital, while stocks of fast movers are starved and many "rush" orders must be placed. Profits are sacrificed at both ends, yet the average turnover figure may seem satisfactory.

For example, suppose that goods costing $100,000 are moved in one year from a stock with an inventory value of $37,000. $100,000 divided by $37,000 equals 2.7, the yearly turnover for the stock as a whole. Does it mean that the company is enjoying a normal profit advantage? Not at all! For analysis of individual items, illustrated in the chart, Figure 107, shows that stocks are badly out of balance.

Items 1, 2, and 8 are making one turn or less. As shown in the chart in Figure 107, the Cost of Possession on these items is extremely high, and profit is reduced to a low figure. Items 3, 5, and 7 are moving moderately well—but notice what is happening to Items 4 and 6. These popular items are turning nearly 12 times a year. Cost of Possession on these items is small, but cost of acquisition is so high that profits are less than they should be!

A fourth step to the solution of problems in forecasting, planning, and control is to *provide management with accurate, clear, and well-organized summaries of facts as a basis for its decisions.*

Young engineers often complain that management will not accept or even seriously consider suggestions involving new ideas. To young

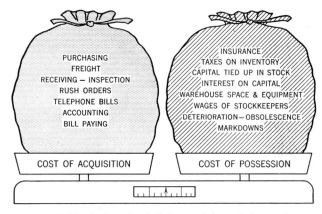

To determine the most profitable turnover rate for your business, it is necessary to weigh carefully your Costs of Acquisition against your Costs of Possession. The turnover rate giving you the lowest total cost is the ideal rate, as shown in the chart below.

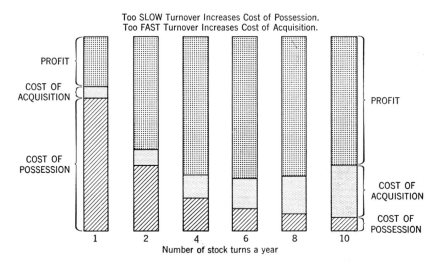

Fig. 106. Graphic illustration of cost of acquisition and cost of possession. (Courtesy Remington Rand, Inc.)

men, this is evidence that executives have become old fogies, unwilling to experiment or change established ways. As a rule, the reverse is true. Any man sufficiently experienced to be a high executive has seen his industry change. He knows that competitors are searching for new products, new methods, new machines, new markets. He knows that he must do so too, and for years he has been seeking im-

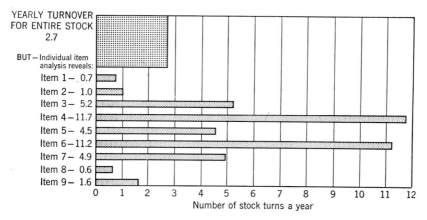

Fig. 107. Unbalanced stocks revealed by item control. (Courtesy Remington Rand, Inc.)

provements as actively as his rivals. During these years he has made some excellent strikes and has developed the ability to grasp good ideas and visualize them in operation. He also has accepted many ideas that were supported by the vast enthusiasm of their authors rather than by detailed evidence. Most of those ideas failed, with losses in time, effort, and money. Such failures have taught the executive that it paid to consider only suggestions based upon well-marshaled facts.

It is here that many a young engineer gets into difficulty. In his enthusiasm he presents his ideas briefly and sketchily. He gives only part of the pertinent facts and does not show how they support his thesis. Since executives demand such support, the document is rejected.

Though rejection is inevitable, its results are unfortunate. First, it may deprive the company of a really good idea whose value was obscured by faulty presentation. Second, it may discourage the young engineer, who becomes unwilling to submit ideas after repeated rejection. Third, it lowers the young man in the estimation of management. Executives begin to doubt his judgment, his thoroughness, his ability to learn from experience. When promotions are made they are likely to go to men with a better record.

The remedy for all this is careful supervision and training. The young engineer's superior should show him how to prepare suggestions or recommendations, at the same time explaining why thoroughness is essential. If documents still remain deficient, management may return them with a request for critical revision. If further help and guidance are needed, the training department may provide it through formal or informal instruction. Though such instruction is likely to be expensive, its benefits will greatly outweigh its cost. Engineers must be trained to speak as well as write clearly and effectively.

Sometimes instruction comes from other and surprising sources. One young man had a wife who, though deeply interested in his work, was slow of comprehension. When he told her his problems and new ideas, he had to do so simply, coherently, and clearly, with digests of the supporting evidence. If she understood his argument, he felt sure that his boss would do so, and so would the men higher up. In a few years, this home training prepared the man for an important executive position. Though he did not realize it, his wife also proved herself to be an excellent teacher who made her one pupil want to do what was most necessary for his success.

This does not mean that technical men must indulge in "fine"—really artful—writing, nor need they burden their suggestion with the mass of indigested data that keeps bookkeepers busy. When an executive reads a recommendation or report, he wants it to be clear, simple, and well organized, with a compact summary of facts needed for decision. Artful writing is likely to arouse suspicion, and an excess of detail will suggest that the author himself is not sure of its significance.

A fifth step toward solving the problems of forecasting, planning, and control is to secure *clear-cut statements of objectives and policies from top management.* These statements should begin with fundamentals and progress as far as necessary into detailed standard practices. The fundamentals, however, are of basic importance and should be made available to everyone from messenger or sweeper to president and chairman of the board.

By fundamentals we mean the objectives and understandings that govern a company's conduct. If a company's prime objective is the accumulation of money as a means to survival, that objective should be stated clearly. Moreover, it should be accepted by every executive and employee, and both should use all honorable means of achieving that goal.

After financial survival has been won, a company may and should add other objectives. Perhaps the first is superior quality and customer service. Another is stable employment. These, therefore, must be added to the statement of fundamentals.

When a company matures to the point that its management can serve as trustees for consumers, employees, and investors, and can act for the welfare of their community, their state, and their nation, the declaration of fundamental policy must be revised and expanded

again. Though this task will be difficult, the statement will tell everyone in the company where it is going. Standard procedures based on
fundamental policy will show how it intends to get there.

Once objectives have been defined, policies can be formulated. A
policy is a definition of a general path to be followed within a specific
framework to accomplish a given objective. A policy cannot be too
general or it will fall of its own weight. "Our policy is to do good"
would be entirely too general. On the other hand, policies should not
be too specific lest they become so numerous that no one will bother
to learn and follow them. In a foregoing chapter we found that to
establish an upper and a lower stock limit on each item of finished
goods would be ridiculously unwieldy. On the other hand, management can establish a general policy that stocks of one class of finished
goods shall not exceed 10 weeks' normal sales nor be less than 3 weeks'
of normal sales. Such a rule is neither unwieldy nor confusing, since
it does not go into excessive detail.

The production planner should not only ask for basic policies and
standard procedures—he may even be able to help formulate them.
Assume, for example, that he is alternately criticized for inadequate
and then excessive inventories of finished goods. If there is no overall
policy to govern inventories, he must show the need for one and at
least suggest its limits. A sixth step toward the solution of these
problems is to *keep planning separate from, and well ahead of, performance.*

To prepare a production schedule today for use tomorrow is only a
little better than futile. It gives the planning engineer no chance to
analyze items that should be scheduled for production in combinations, nor does it enable him to avoid excessive and costly setups.
Operating supervisors are sensitive to such poor planning, and workmen are severely critical of it. They know when their schedules go
awry and their time is wasted, and they do not respect the planner
who makes tardy, inadequate plans. On the other hand, when a
planner who has won their respect does make a mistake, workers rally
to his side and help him out of his difficulty.

All planners should have long-range as well as short-term plans
and schedules. From a good overall plan for a quarter year, a planner
can generally arrange a definite schedule for one week. Knowing that
the current week is provided for, he can spend part of it making certain of his schedule for the next week. Some planners prefer to use
a year for long-term planning and a month for definite schedules
covering short-term operation.

It also is well to have alternative plans of action. Except in unusual emergencies, such as machine failure, these alternative plans

ond, each man must know the other members of the team and their activities. Third, everyone in the organization should understand the basic factors of inventory control. Fourth, facts should be carefully prepared and presented for decisions by management. Fifth, management must provide clear-cut statements of objectives and policies. Sixth, planning should be kept separate from, and well ahead of, performance. Seventh, production planners must keep themselves progressive and well informed. Eighth, all members of the team and their associates should be well trained, including understudies of the planning engineer.

Those associated with production forecasting, planning, and control are rewarded in the personal satisfaction that comes from the realization of service to all segments of our social structure.

QUESTIONS TO CHECK COMPREHENSION

1. How can large and complex problems be most effectively solved?

2. Why should planners know production, engineering, and accounting executives and understand their work?

3. Why should others understand both the practical and the theoretical factors involved in inventory control if the planner already has mastered them?

4. What does management require as a basis for its decisions?

5. Is it advisable for everyone in an industrial organization to maintain wide freedom of action, or should comprehensive policies be established as guides?

6. What happens when planning is not completed more than a day or two before performance?

7. Why should engineers know anything about economics and the social impact of industry?

8. As a planning engineer, could you confidently expect promotion if you had never taken the trouble to train an understudy?

PROBLEM

A company manufactures gas ranges, electric refrigerators, sewing machines, bicycles, lawn mowers, and kitchen cabinets. Manufacturing operations are performed in 4 buildings—a foundry, a sheet-metal shop, a machining shop, and an assembly shop.

Gas ranges, refrigerators, kitchen cabinets, and sewing machines are sold in household supply stores. Bicycles and lawn mowers are sold in hardware and sporting goods stores. Assume that sales of all these product groups are of equal value.

The organization consists essentially of 6 key men. The sheet-metal shop manager is young and has excellent management potential. The foundry manager is a 62-year-old operating executive with good ability. The machine shop manager is technically competent but lacks managerial skills. The assembly manager is technically well qualified and is a good manager. A production-planning engineer is responsible for the planning and scheduling of all operations. He is capable, but serving four masters makes his work inordinately difficult. He has one assistant who has been well trained and is capable.

Operations must be expanded about 100 per cent. The company's president realizes that planning and control have become almost unmanageable. He and the directors decide to decentralize both operations and organization. Funds are available for new equipment and buildings or additions to existing buildings. There is ample room for expansion except on the foundry property.

Analyze this company's operations by products, by classes of work, and by sales outlets. Prepare a recommendation for splitting operations and re-forming the organization into two divisions. Include arguments to support your recommendation.

DISCUSSION CASE

Before World War II, the Main Company had been a one-man enterprise in the sense that George Main, owner and president, had handled purchasing, sales, planning, and engineering. Except for one accountant, he did almost everything except operate the machines. His product was good but was produced only to meet local orders.

Soon after World War II began, the armed services of supply became interested in his product and asked him to expand his operations. Main was reluctant but recognized the urgent need and agreed to expand production. The 25-man shop soon became a new building employing 600 men.

The original 25 men became executives almost overnight. Main carefully explained to each man what was expected of him in his new position. As an example, the new chief engineer was told to hew to the line of engineering and not to bother himself with anything else.

The man appointed as purchasing agent was told to get the material in and not worry about production or engineering. The operating executive was told to get the production out as it was scheduled by the planning executive.

Company policies had never been clear except in Main's mind. The only rule given each executive was to handle his own functions and let other people take care of theirs.

When the enthusiasm of promotion had worn off, production began to lag far behind schedules. The services of supply became alarmed, and a War Production Board consultant was sent to the plant to recommend improvements. He studied the work of each executive and found an exceptional eagerness to do a good job. Technical knowledge was excellent. His major recommendation was the appointment of a personnel manager.

One of the original workmen was appointed to this position. In explaining his duties, Mr. Main made it clear that the new personnel manager was to forget all about production and to get to know the workmen and their problems.

Despite many improvements in equipment, production continued to be about 20 per cent less per man-hour than it had been before the war. All executives were greatly disturbed, and each one asked himself what he could do to improve the situation. There was no evasion or faultfinding. When deliveries of raw materials were delayed, the planning engineer and the operating executive felt that the purchasing agent had done his best and that nothing more was possible. The purchasing agent did not complain when he received late notice telling what raw materials were wanted. As old associates, it never occurred to either of these men to be critical of each other's work. Moreover, they had been told to attend to their own knitting.

Although production was essential, certain draft deferments were not extended. One of the men drafted for military service was the production-planning engineer. Between the time of notification and that of reporting for induction, he tried to train a man who was to replace him. This training consisted of instructions to tour the plant every morning. If raw materials seemed to be running short the new man was to send a note to that effect to the purchasing agent. He was instructed to base the schedule for the following day on what materials were available. If there were shortages he was instructed to consult with the operating executive and find some suitable work for the men.

Mr. Main wished that he could return to the former small-shop situation where he could run everything in an orderly manner and serve his many local customers.

You are serving on a board of inquiry for the armed services to discuss Mr. Main's problems. List the causes for what is wrong and suggest remedies.

24

A Practical Problem

To test the effectiveness of the study of production forecasting, planning, and control, let us make certain basic assumptions that will cover a small but complete enterprise. Upon this assumed basis we then may plan the operation of the business. In this no venture capital will be risked since all will be done on paper. Nevertheless, general principles and rules will be applied to what might well be a real situation. Besides gaining skill in application we shall learn an important lesson. This lesson is that it is generally possible to learn in advance, and within reasonably good working limits, whether an enterprise has a chance to become profitable. If there is such a chance, capital may be invested; if there is not, the only cost will be that of the preliminary study.

To keep the example within reasonable limits, certain factors, for instance, are simplified or condensed. None, however, is distorted or made improbable. To guide the reader through the problem, assumptions are identified by letters. Determinations of fact or policy, in cluding diagrams, are deductions identified by numbers.

A. THE INCENTIVE TO START A BUSINESS

Three men want to go into business together, in industry rather than commerce. They have a combined capital of $500,000. Smith has had considerable experience in the manufacture of paint. He is a trained chemist, holds patents for certain solvents and their use, and has $100,000 available for investment. He wants to manage the company. Brown and Jones each have $200,000 available for investment. They want to invest this money in an industry that will give them a greater return than their present average of 6 per cent. They do not want active parts in management.

B. MARKET ANALYSIS

Smith has made a market analysis and has found a *definite* demand for 6,000 gallons of paint per day in local building developments. The analysis also indicates a *potential* demand for 10,000 gallons per day if white, green, gray, and brown paint are manufactured. If all other considerations prove favorable, production will be started at 8,000 gallons per day, in white and these 3 colors.

C. PROPOSED FACTORY BUILDING

A suitable factory can be bought for $100,000 cash or rented for $1,000 per month with a 3-year option to purchase at the same price. The building is a concrete flat-slab structure with three stories, measures 150 by 70 feet, is situated between two streets, and has a railroad siding parallel to one long side. The local property tax is $2,000 per year. The owner will permit leasehold improvements but will make no repairs or replacements. The building is equipped with a 10 by 10 foot freight elevator, an adequate power panel, toilets, an oil-fired boiler, and space heaters. A 20 by 30 foot enclosure on the first floor can be used as an office. The original owner manufactured food products. Adjacent to the railroad siding are two 20,000-gallon buried tanks that are in good condition. The whole facility is adequate for the purpose of manufacturing paint.

DETERMINATION 1

Without considering the need for working capital, find out whether it will be more economical to buy or rent. Then consider the need to safeguard investment and the risks involved in starting a new enterprise. Should the building be leased or rented at first?

D. THE BILL OF MATERIAL

Smith has developed the following basic formula for the paints, to be produced in batches of 2,000 gallons:

	Pounds	Gallons	Price
Lithopone	7,200		$0.07 per pound
Pigment	600		0.25 per pound
Extender	8,000		0.013 per pound
Linseed oil	9,500	1,230	0.176 per pound
VMP naphtha	1,800	255	0.15 per gallon
Per batch		2,000	

For simplicity, assume that the three color pigments have the same price. Assume an equal value for titanium dioxide, substituted when white paint is made. Also assume that all paint will be sold in gallon cans. These, with covers and labels, will cost $0.20 for each gallon of paint.

DETERMINATION 2

Compute the basic material cost of paint per gallon. Compute the total direct material cost per gallon in gallon cans.

E. FACTORY PLANNING

In his factory planning, Smith has decided that linseed oil will be received in tank cars and stored in the 20,000-gallon buried tanks. A 10,000-gallon tank will be bought for the storage of VMP naphtha. Metering pumps and recording and controlling meters will be used. Valves and meters will be set, a pump started, and the pumping continued until it is stopped automatically when the desired amount will have been delivered into a tank or mill.

Pigments, lithopone, and extenders will be stored on the third floor and dumped through ducts in the floor into ball mills on the second floor.

Ball mills, which are large rotating cylindrical tanks in horizontal position containing steel balls or pebbles, will be used to thoroughly grind and mix the pigments and extenders with linseed oil and naphtha. Each ball mill will handle a 2,000-gallon charge of paint. See Figure 108.

The pigment and extender mixed in the oil will be dumped through the floor of the second story into 2,000-gallon cylindrical, vertical mixing tanks on the first floor, where, after an hour's mixing, the paint will

Fig. 108. A typical ball mill. (Courtesy Paul O. Abbe, Inc., Little Falls, N. J.)

be ready to be filled into cans. Cans will be placed upon conveyors and filled, and will be automatically labeled. Figure 109 shows an isometric diagram of the building and rough sketches of the equipment.

DETERMINATION 3

Roughly sketch in (on Figure 109) four mixers on the first floor and four ball mills on the second floor. Sketch in a conveyor arrangement passing the mixers and running to both street entrances and the rail siding.

F. FACTORY PLANNING (CONTINUED)

Four 2,000-gallon mixing tanks and four 2,000-gallon ball mills, used but in good condition, are available at prices substantially less than

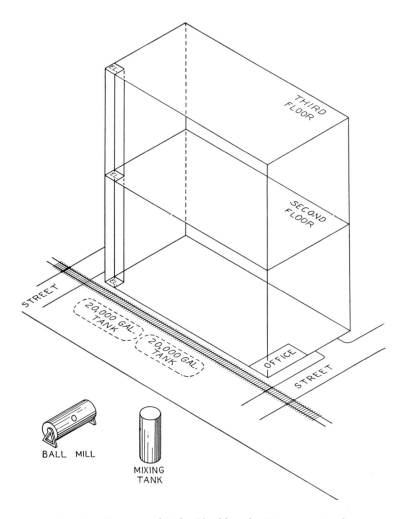

Fig. 109. Isometric sketch of building for Determination 3.

those for new equipment. New motors and switch gear will have to be purchased, as will conveyors and pumps. Two hand-lift trucks and 1,000 pallets will be required to handle and store pigment and finished paint. Office and laboratory equipment will be purchased new.

The equipment estimate is as follows:

One 10,000-gallon storage tank	$ 500
Four 2,000-gallon used mixing tanks @ $1,000 each	4,000
Four 10-hp electric motors @ $100 each	400
Four switches @ $30 each	120
Four 2,000-gallon used ball mills @ $2,000 each	8,000
Four 20-hp electric motors @ $150 each	600
Four switches @ $40 each	160
Installation of mixers and mills	1,500
Electrical wiring and labor	2,000
Conveyor, installed	4,000
Two hand-lift trucks @ $400 each	800
1,000 5' by 5' wood pallets @ $6.00 each	6,000
Four fillers and labelers @ $500 each	2,000
Two pumps complete with automatic metering devices @ $800 each	1,600
Piping to buried tanks, including labor	1,500
Office furniture and equipment	2,000
Laboratory equipment and installation	3,000
Tools	500
Miscellaneous repairs to building	2,000
	$40,680

Though repairs are not properly termed equipment, they are included in this estimate as a mater of convenience.

G. LABOR ANALYSIS

Smith has consulted the local paintmakers' union to learn wage scales and work loads and has found them to be as follows:

Master paintmakers	$2.00 per hour
Paintmaker's helper	1.75 per hour
Paint fillers	1.80 per hour
Shipping and receiving handlers	1.75 per hour

The master paintmaker is responsible for the operation of the ball mills. He sets the pumps to transfer oils and solvents. His helper assists in dumping pigments into the ball mills, cleans up, and disposes of empty bags.

Paint fillers are not permitted to work above the first floor. They may, however, assist in the work of shipping and receiving.

The work day is not to exceed 8 hours. Five days constitute a work week. Time and one-half is to be paid for all overtime.

H. MANUFACTURING PLANNING

The paint will be made in two operations. The oil, solvent, pigment, and extenders are thoroughly ground together in ball mills, where steel balls or pebbles are rotated with the paint mixture. After this operation, the paint is dumped into stationary cylindrical mixing tanks equipped with agitators. These tanks, however, are set in vertical position.

1. Ball-Mill Operation. The master paintmaker sets the pumps to meter the correct quantities of oil and solvent into a ball mill. He and his helper load the pigment into the mill, bolt the cover on, and start the motor that turns the mill. These operations require 3 hours by both men for each 2,000-gallon charge.

The ball mill continues rotating unattended for not less than 19 hours. At the end of that time the cover is removed from the ball mill, the agitator on the mixing tank on the first floor is started, and the contents of the ball mill are dumped into it. These operations require an hour's work and attention by both the master paintmaker and his helper.

2. Mixing and Filling. The paint is allowed to mix in the mixing tank for 1 hour unattended before it is filled into gallon cans. One man, a paint filler, takes 4 hours to fill and label 2,000 one-gallon cans. The filled cans are taken away by conveyor, and material handlers stack them on pallets or load them directly into motor trucks for shipment.

DETERMINATION 4

Using the chart in Figure 110, lay out the work of each man and each piece of equipment. Some men may start work as early as 7

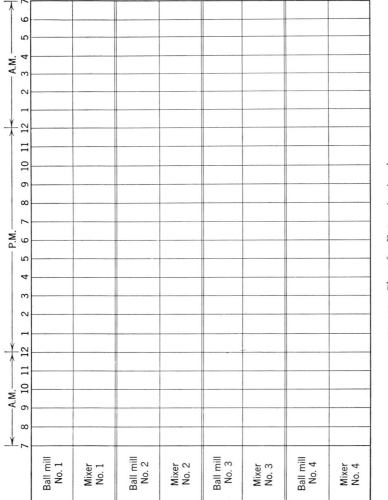

Fig. 110. Chart for Determination 4.

PRODUCTION ROUTING

Code 1528   Sheet 1
House Paint in Gallon Cans   of 1 Sheets

Operation	Description	Hours per Batch	Labor Rate per Hour	Number of Men	Direct Labor Cost per Batch

Fig. 111.   Production-routing form.

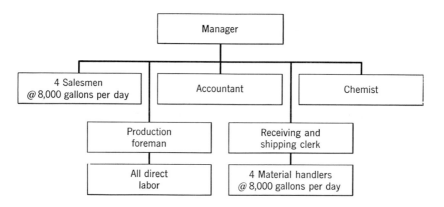

Fig. 112.   Organization chart.

A.M. and others as late as 9 A.M. if that will help operations. All men stop work at 12 noon for a 30-minute lunch period.

DETERMINATION 5 PRODUCTION ROUTING AND DIRECT LABOR COST

List the operations on the production-routing form shown in Figure 111. Using the labor rates shown in assumption G, calculate the direct labor cost per batch and per gallon complete in gallon cans.

J. ORGANIZATION AND EXPENSE

The organization plan is simple, as Figure 112 reveals.

The manager at $800 per month, the chemist at $300, the foreman at $450, the receiving and shipping clerk at $300, and the accountant at $400 are considered as fixed expense. In addition, 8 per cent of the sum of these salaries will be expended for payroll taxes, insurance, and vacations. The other items that are considered as fixed expense are rent at $1,000 per month and a power stand-by charge of $200 per month for connected load.

DETERMINATION 6 FIXED EXPENSE

Calculate the fixed expense per month. The variable expense items per month are as follows, when production averages 8,000 gallons per day:

Eight per cent of the direct labor cost per gallon (as worked out in determination 5) × 21.5 days per month × 8,000 gallons per day. Four material handlers × $1.75 per hour × 172 hours per month. Power (kilowatt-hours used), $600 per month. Heat, $100 per month. Factory supplies, $200 per month. Office supplies, $50 per month. Four salesmen at $400 per month each, at 8,000 gallons per day.

DETERMINATION 7 VARIABLE EXPENSE PER MONTH

Calculate the variable expense per month.

DETERMINATION 8   VARIABLE EXPENSE PER GALLON

Calculate the variable expense per gallon when production is 172,000 gallons per month.

DETERMINATION 9   TOTAL VARIABLE COST PER GALLON

Using the direct material cost per gallon calculated in determination 2, the direct labor cost per gallon calculated in determination 5, and the variable expense per gallon calculated in determination 8, compute the total variable cost per gallon.

K. PRODUCTION AND PROFITABILITY ANALYSIS

Success of the whole project depends upon high-volume local sales, to be secured by offering good paint at low prices. Assume that the selling price is set at $1.53 per gallon F.O.B. the factory.

DETERMINATION 10

Using the selling price of $1.53, the variable cost per gallon from determination 9, and the fixed expense per month from determination 6, compute the number of gallons that must be sold per month for the business to break even.

DETERMINATION 11

If a profit is indicated at 8,000 gallons per day, compute the estimated annual profit on sales of 2,000,000 gallons per year.

L. PROCUREMENT AND RAW-MATERIAL STOCKS

Linseed oil will be received in 20,000-gallon railroad tank cars. VMP naphtha will be received in 5,000-gallon tank trucks. Lithopone and extender will be received in 50-ton carloads. Titanium dioxide and pigments will be received in less than carload lots. Suppliers of these materials are near by and dependable. Cans and covers will be received from a local can company in daily deliveries.

DETERMINATION 12 PROCUREMENT AND RAW-MATERIAL STOCKS

Calculate the frequency of delivery of each raw material. Also estimate the stock limits for each one.

DETERMINATION 13

Calculate the value of raw-material stocks, assuming that they are kept at their upper limits.

M. FINISHED GOODS STOCK

As much as possible, the company will produce to customers' orders. A 2-week stock of finished goods will be carried if sales occasionally lag.

DETERMINATION 14 FINISHED GOODS INVENTORY

Calculate the cost value of the finished goods inventory at a maximum of 2 weeks' supply.

P. WAGES, SALARY, AND OTHER EXPENSES

Plans call for cash on hand to meet the wage and salary payroll as well as power, heat, and rent bills for 2 months in advance.

DETERMINATION 15

Using figures computed in determinations 5, 6, and 7, calculate the amount of cash needed to conform to plan.

DETERMINATION 16   CAPITAL REQUIRED

Referring to assumption F for equipment capital expenditures, determination 13 for raw-material inventory value, determination 14 for finished goods inventory value, and determination 15 for wage, salary, and other expenses, calculate the total capital required and add 10 per cent for contingencies.

Q. SALES FORECAST

Smith has discussed the quantities of each color with the contractors and dealers who will buy the paint. They report that the current color preference is 50 per cent white, 25 per cent gray, 12½ per cent green and 12½ per cent brown. Smith has also estimated sales of 2,000,000 gallons per year in the following monthly percentages:

January	7%	July	10%
February	7%	August	10%
March	8%	September	8%
April	8%	October	8%
May	10%	November	7%
June	10%	December	7%
			100%

DETERMINATION 17

Prepare the sales forecast, using the form in Figure 113.

R. MASTER PRODUCTION SCHEDULE

To obtain some practice in developing a master production schedule from a sales forecast, assume the following finished goods stock on hand at the first of the year:

White	−40,000 gallons (back order)
Gray	+10,000 gallons
Brown	+5,000 gallons
Green	+5,000 gallons

SALES FORECAST					
	White	*Gray*	*Brown*	*Green*	*Total*
January					
February					
March					
April					
May					
June					
July					
August					
September					
October					
November					
December					

Fig. 113. Chart for Determination 17.

DETERMINATION 18

Establish a master production schedule for the first quarter, keeping in mind that the back orders must be filled promptly and that finished goods at the end of the quarter should not exceed 20,000 gallons.

S. PROCUREMENT TAKE-OFF

Smith wishes to place orders for all raw materials required in January production.

DETERMINATION 19   PROCUREMENT TAKE-OFF

Using the January schedule established in determination 18, make a raw-material take-off showing the total quantity of each required. Make sure that the take-off is in quantities adequate for full batches.

T. PERSONNEL SCHEDULES

Smith realizes that there will be neither storage space nor working capital to schedule level production throughout the year. He also realizes the advantages of steady employment. In a discussion with the employees it was agreed that each employee would receive 10 working days' vacation with pay and 4 paid holidays, New Year's Day, Labor Day, Christmas Day, and a day in January instead of Independence Day. It was further agreed that the employees would take one or more days of vacation at times of reduced work, as indicated by the production schedule. The employees further agreed to work any Saturday during the summer at pay rates of time and one-half. Assume the following days per month available on the basis of a 5-day work week:

Jan.	21	April	20	July	21	Oct.	20
Feb.	20	May	23	Aug.	23	Nov.	22
Mar.	23	June	22	Sept.	20	Dec.	20

DETERMINATION 20   PERSONNEL SCHEDULES

Assuming production of 8,000 gallons per day, prepare a schedule showing the number of days that must be worked in each month. Show what days will be taken off as vacation and instead of Independence Day. Show the number of Saturdays that will be worked during various months.

25

Solution to the Problem

The reader may now compare his solution to the problem in the preceding chapter with the solution that follows. Even if his results are not in full agreement with it, he will have had the opportunity to exercise his skill and judgment in the application of techniques described in the text. In spite of any differences, he will, in all probability, have arrived at a correct decision as to whether or not the enterprise should be undertaken.

DETERMINATION 1 PURCHASE OR RENTAL OF BUILDING

Under assumption A it was stated that there is an average return of 6 per cent on the capital as now invested. This means that $100,000, the purchase price of the building, is now earning $6,000. This sum plus $2,000 in property taxes equals $8,000, which is only two-thirds of the $12,000 annual rent. On a long-term basis, therefore, the building should be purchased.

Considering the risks involved in starting a new business, however, the additional $4,000 per year spent for rent will be good insurance. The final decision, therefore, is to rent and take an option. Subsequent steps in the problem will be based upon renting for at least one year.

DETERMINATION 2   DIRECT MATERIAL COST
PER BATCH OF 2,000 GALLONS

	Pounds	Gallons	Price	Cost per Batch
Lithopone	7,200		$0.07 per pound	$ 504.00
Pigment	600		0.25 per pound	150.00
Extender	8,000		0.013 per pound	104.00
Linseed oil	9,500	1,230	0.176 per pound	1,672.00
VMP naphtha	1,800	255	0.15 per gallon	38.25
Per batch	27,100	2,000		$2,468.25

$$\frac{\$2,468.25 \text{ per batch}}{2,000 \text{ gallons}} = \$1.23413 \text{ per gallon}$$

Cans, covers, and labels   =   0.20   each

Direct material cost per gallon in gallon cans = $1,43413

DETERMINATION 3

Figure 114 shows the arrangement of equipment.

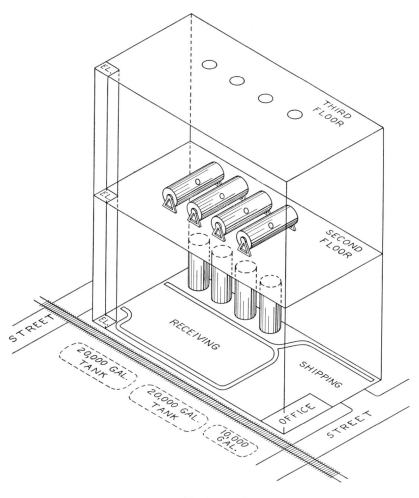

Fig. 114. Equipment layout.

DETERMINATION 4

Figure 115 shows the basic operating cycle for equipment and personnel.

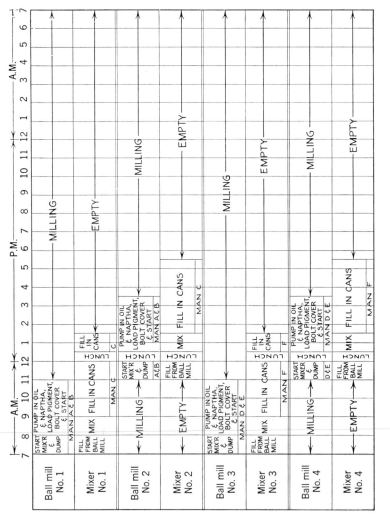

Fig. 115. The operating cycle.

DETERMINATION 5

Figure 116 shows the calculation of total direct labor cost.

		PRODUCTION ROUTING			
Code 1528					Sheet 1
House Paint in Gallon Cans		2,000 Gallons per Batch			of 1 Sheets
Opera-tion	*Description*	*Hours per Batch*	*Labor Rate per Hour*	*Number of Men*	*Direct Labor Cost per Batch*
1	Set pumps to pump 1,230 gallons linseed oil and 255 gallons VMP naphtha into ball mill.		Paintmaker $2.00		
2	Load 7,200 pounds lithopone, 600 pounds color and 8,000 pounds extender in ball mill.	3	Helper $1.75	2	$11.25
3	Bolt on cover and start.				
4	Mix in ball mill.	No labor required			
5	Start mixer and dump paint from ball mill into mixer.	1	$2.00 $1.75	2	3.75
6	Mix in mixer.	No labor required			
7	Fill into gallon cans, label, and close.	4	$1.80	1	7.20
		Total direct labor cost per batch			$22.20
		Total direct labor cost per gallon			$ 0.0111

Fig. 116. Completed production-routing form.

DETERMINATION 6   FIXED EXPENSE

1 manager	$800.00
1 chemist	300.00
1 foreman	450.00
1 receiving and shipping clerk	300.00
1 accountant	400.00
	$2,250.00
Plus 8% for payroll taxes, insurance, and vacations	180.00
	2,430.00
Rent	1,000.00
Power (stand-by for connected load)	200.00
Estimated monthly fixed expense	$3,630.00

DETERMINATION 7   VARIABLE EXPENSE PER MONTH

8% of direct labor cost per month for payroll taxes, insurance, and vacations = 8% of direct labor cost per gallon (determination 5) or $0.0111 × 21.5 days per month × 8,000 gallons per day	$ 152.74
4 material handlers × $1.75 per hr. × 172 hr. per month	1,204.00
Power (kilowatt-hours used)	600.00
Heat	100.00
Supplies, factory	200.00
Supplies, office	50.00
4 salesmen @ $400 per month each	1,600.00
Estimated variable expense per month at 8,000 gallons per day	$3,906.74

DETERMINATION 8   VARIABLE EXPENSE PER GALLON

$$\frac{\text{Estimated variable expense per month } \$3,906.74}{172,000 \text{ gallons per month}}$$

$$= \$0.022714 \text{ Estimated variable expense per gallon}$$

DETERMINATION 9   COST PER GALLON

Direct material cost per gallon	(2)	$1.43413
Direct labor cost per gallon	(5)	0.01110
Variable expense per gallon	(8)	0.022714
Estimated variable cost per gallon		$1.467944

$$\frac{\$3{,}630 \text{ fixed expense per month}}{172{,}000 \text{ gallons per month}} = \text{Fixed cost per gallon} \quad 0.02110$$

Total estimated cost per gallon	$1.489044

DETERMINATION 10   BREAK-EVEN POINT

$$\frac{\text{Estimated fixed expense } \$3{,}630}{\text{Selling price } \$1.53 - \text{Variable cost } \$1.47}$$

$$= 60{,}500 \text{ gallons per month to break even}$$

Since monthly sales are estimated at 172,000 gallons and the break-even point is 60,500 gallons per month, the project promises to be profitable.

DETERMINATION 11   ESTIMATED ANNUAL PROFIT

Gross income from sale of 2,000,000 gallons @ $1.53 per gallon		$3,060,000
Variable cost (2,000,000 gallons @ $1.47)	$2,940,000	
Fixed expense ($3,630 × 12 months)	43,560	
Less annual cost of sales		$2,983,560
Estimated annual net profit before taxes		76,440
Less estimated federal tax 45% *		34,398
Estimated net profit		$ 42,042

* This percentage will change from time to time.

DETERMINATION 12   PROCUREMENT

1. Lithopone

7,200 pounds per batch $\times$ 4 batches per day = 28,800 pounds per day

$$\frac{100,000 \text{ pounds per carload}}{28,800 \text{ pounds per day}} = 3.47 \text{ days per carload}$$

A 2-week stock, or 288,000 pounds, should be carried as reserve. A carload, therefore, should be ordered every fourth day and an extra carload every fifth week.   The stock limits should be not less than 2 weeks' supply and not more than 3 weeks' supply.

2. Pigment and Titanium Dioxide

600 pounds per batch $\times$ 4 batches per day = 2,400 pounds per day

A 2-week stock, or about 24,000 pounds, should be carried as reserve.   An order should be placed each week for 12,000 pounds.   The stock limits should be the same as for lithopone: minimum 2 weeks, maximum 3 weeks.

3. Extender

8,000 pounds per batch $\times$ 4 batches per day = 32,000 pounds per day

$$\frac{100,000 \text{ pounds per carload}}{32,000 \text{ pounds per day}} = 3.125 \text{ days per carload}$$

A 2-week stock, or 320,000 pounds, should be carried as reserve. A carload should be ordered every third working day, and 1 additional carload every twenty-fourth working day.   The stock limits should be the same as for lithopone, a minimum of 2 weeks and a maximum of 3 weeks.

4. Linseed Oil

1,230 gallons per batch $\times$ 4 batches per day = 4,920 gallons per day

The two 20,000-gallon tanks will be used for oil, one tankful being held as reserve.   A tank car of 20,000 gallons will be ordered approximately every fourth working day.   The stock limits will be not less than 1 week and not more than 2 weeks.   In emergencies a tank car can be held on the railroad siding by paying demurrage charges.

5. VMP Naphtha

225 gallons per batch $\times$ 4 batches per day = 900 gallons per day

A full tank of 10,000 gallons will be on hand at the start. A tank truck of 5,000 gallons will be ordered in about once per week. The stock limit will be not less than 1 week and not more than 2.25 weeks.

6. Cans and Covers. Per day, 8,000. Since the can supplier is not far from the factory, only 40,000 cans will be stocked as reserve. Orders will be placed for delivery of 8,000 cans and covers every working day. The stock limit will, therefore, be 6 days maximum and 5 days minimum.

DETERMINATION 13 RAW-MATERIAL INVENTORY VALUE

Lithopone, 3-week supply (432,000 pounds @ $0.07)	$ 30,240
Pigment and titanium dioxide, 3-week supply (36,000 pounds @ $0.25)	10,000
Extender, 3-week supply (480,000 pounds @ $0.013)	6,240
Linseed oil, 2-week supply (49,200 gallons or 380,000 pounds @ $0.176)	66,880
VMP naphtha, 2$\frac{1}{4}$-week supply (10,000 gallons @ $0.15)	1,500
Cans and covers, 6-day supply (48,000 @ $0.20)	9,600
Total raw-material inventory value at maximum limits	$124,460

DETERMINATION 14 FINISHED-GOODS STOCK

2 weeks' stock or 80,000 gallons @ $1.49 per gallon $119,200

DETERMINATION 15 RESERVE FOR WAGES, SALARIES AND OTHER EXPENSES

Direct labor cost per gallon ($0.0111 $\times$ 172,000 gallons per month) (5)	$ 1,909.20
Estimated monthly fixed expense (6)	3,630.00
Estimated monthly variable expense (7)	3,906.74
	$ 9,445.94
2 months	2
Cash needed for wages, salaries, and other expenses	$18,891.88

DETERMINATION 16   CAPITAL REQUIRED

Capital expenditures for equipment	(F)	$ 40,680
Raw-material inventory	(13)	124,460
Finished goods stock	(14)	119,200
Wages, salaries, and other expenses	(15)	18,892
		$303,232
Plus 10 per cent for contingencies		30,323
Total capital required		$333,555

DETERMINATION 17   SALES FORECAST

Sales Forecast

	White	Gray	Brown	Green	Total
January	70,000	35,000	17,500	17,500	140,000
February	70,000	35,000	17,500	17,500	140,000
March	80,000	40,000	20,000	20,000	160,000
April	80,000	40,000	20,000	20,000	160,000
May	100,000	50,000	25,000	25,000	200,000
June	100,000	50,000	25,000	25,000	200,000
July	100,000	50,000	25,000	25,000	200,000
August	100,000	50,000	25,000	25,000	200,000
September	80,000	40,000	20,000	20,000	160,000
October	80,000	40,000	20,000	20,000	160,000
November	70,000	35,000	17,500	17,500	140,000
December	70,000	35,000	17,500	17,500	140,000
	1,000,000	500,000	250,000	250,000	2,000,000

DETERMINATION 18   MASTER PRODUCTION SCHEDULE

Since the finished goods stock does not exceed 20,000 gallons and there is a back order of 40,000 gallons of white paint, 160,000 gallons should be produced during each month of the first quarter. January's schedule then will be:

	White	Gray	Brown	Green	Total
January sales forecast	70,000	35,000	17,500	17,500	140,000
±Production for stock	+ 40,000	− 10,000	− 5,000	− 5,000	+ 20,000
January schedule	110,000	25,000	12,500	12,500	160,000

With this schedule, back orders will be cleared and the entire stock of finished goods will be exhausted. A 20,000-gallon stock can be built up in February as follows:

	White	Gray	Brown	Green	Total
February sales forecast	70,000	35,000	17,500	17,500	140,000
+Production for stock	10,000	5,000	2,500	2,500	20,000
February schedule	80,000	40,000	20,000	20,000	160,000

The March schedule can be the same as the March sales forecast.

DETERMINATION 19 PROCUREMENT TAKE-OFF

	Gallons Scheduled	Full Batches Scheduled
White	110,000	55
Gray	25,000	13
Brown	12,500	7
Green	12,500	7
Total	160,000	82

Cans, covers and labels (2,000 per batch × 82 batches)	164,000 sets
Lithopone (7,200 pounds per batch × 82 batches)	590,400 pounds
Titanium dioxide (600 pounds per batch × 55 batches)	33,000 pounds
Gray pigment (600 pounds per batch × 13 batches)	7,800 pounds
Brown pigment (600 pounds per batch × 7 batches)	4,200 pounds
Green pigment (600 pounds per batch × 7 batches)	4,200 pounds
Extender (8,000 pounds per batch × 82 batches)	656,000 pounds
Linseed oil (1,230 gallons per batch × 82 batches)	100,860 gallons
VMP naphtha (255 gallons per batch × 82 batches)	20,910 gallons

coupled with enlightened ideas of an expanding economy based upon competitive enterprise free of restrictive trade practices.

In the long run, productivity for better living may be more important as well as more satisfying than productivity for defense. There is no sharp distinction between the two. They use the same skills, principles, and practices. In today's changing and hostile world, however, production for defense is the more urgent. For that reason we shall discuss forecasting, planning, and control for war production.

A. WAR PRODUCTION FORECASTING, PLANNING, AND CONTROL

We have seen that forecasting, planning, and control are essential tools of effective peacetime production. Their importance grows during periods of preparation for or to forestall war, when military demands are added to normal civilian requirements. They become still more vital during war itself, when high productivity under adverse conditions becomes the price of victory and survival.

Many otherwise well-informed people believe that democracies—especially our own—drift fatuously during periods of peace and then take tardy and essentially unplanned measures when war actually arrives. Others go further, maintaining that competitive industry, privately owned, can never willingly accept the regimentation that modern, or "total" warfare demands.

There is truth behind these generalizations, for peace-loving and independent people neither like to plan for conflict nor willingly surrender all liberties when conflict is thrust upon them. Moreover, there are always a few rugged ultra-individualists who demand the right to go their own way regardless of the national welfare. On the whole, however, both the American people and American industry realize that war is an element of the future—an element that must be considered in forecasting and planning. If war comes, it requires almost total planning and control. To make both effective, our foremost industrial executives volunteer their services. This has been true despite the fact that total planning and control are highly distasteful to these same men under a peacetime economy.

B. FORECASTING FOR WAR PRODUCTION

During times of peace the armed forces forecast the possible demands of war and pass those forecasts on to industry. Every large manufacturing company has a list of military items that it will probably be called upon to make in the event of mobilization. This type of forecasting is not done on the spur of the moment when this or that aggressive power makes some threatening move. War forecasting is a continuous process, which looks as far as possible into the future, yet constantly modifies its lists of requirements to fit new discoveries, new methods, and the changing world situation. Forecasts provide for civilian health and welfare as well as for military operations.

Inevitably, these peacetime forecasts of requirements for war are less accurate and more fluid than industrial sales forecasts. Sales forecasts are based upon recent sales records as well as analyses of demand, but forecasts for war production have only estimates as their basis. They must also provide for rapid and often untested developments in methods, materials, machines, and transportation. New planes, new explosives, new missiles, new guns, new combinations of aggressors—these and a hundred other factors complicate military forecasting during periods of peace and reduce its accuracy.

Once hostilities begin, the situation is clarified. Aggressors and neutrals are defined; methods and weapons can be appraised; demand becomes sufficiently clear to permit quantitative forecasts. As in peacetime industrial work, these forecasts can then be adjusted to fit actual requirements at home and in the field of conflict. Inevitably, however, military estimates include a much greater plus margin for error than do those of peacetime industrial forecasts. When the penalty for shortages is defeat, planners must strive to provide more than is likely to be needed.[1]

Since World War II, military production forecasting, planning, and control have changed so much that only one major factor remains—the factor of uncertainty. New weapons, new raw materials, new processes, new stratagems create a constant shifting of emphasis and a need for replanning of new systems and combinations of systems. Plans for mobilization are maintained, but totally new plans are required for defense against hostilities that can be sudden, of short duration, and inordinately devastating.

In another war there will be no time to conduct training courses for production specialists or to send out orders for billions of tons of hardware and support items. The initial attack will be swift, brief, and violent. It may also be decisive—but since no one can be sure of this, plans must be made to replenish stockpiles of war implements.

[1] This applies to *needed* materials, and especially to those required in actual combat. It does not excuse excessive orders for any and all things used or desired by the military.

It is both fortunate and wise that the military services have trained men who can cope with the complex problems of production and who can manage all the factors needed for quick retaliation followed by prolonged hostilities. No expense has been spared to avoid delays and errors in keeping track of materials, facilities, and resources. Electronic computer systems assure the effectiveness of this function.

Too little is generally known about the excellent scientific and technical training in the military services. The Joint Staff, Industrial College of the Armed Forces, Fort McNair, Washington, D. C., the Army Logistics Management Center, Fort Lee, Virginia, the Naval Postgraduate School, Monterey, California, the Air Force Institute of Technology, Wright-Patterson Air Force Base, Ohio, and many other schools are developing officers and civilians to plan, organize, and direct industrial production and procurement as effectively as do their counterparts in private industry.

C. PLANNING FOR WAR PRODUCTION

Once forecasts for war production are prepared, industries can develop plans to fill prospective requirements. Some items are so important that they must be produced during peace and stockpiled; others demand that special equipment and trained personnel be maintained in readiness for an emergency. For less critical items, it is sufficient to prepare drawings of equipment and complete operating instructions, as well as lists of materials needed for production in various volumes. Companies also prepare plans for converting their factories from peacetime to wartime production. These are revised periodically to keep up with changes in products, methods, and machines.

In general, manufacturers plan to convert to production of war materials that resemble their peacetime products. A telephone manufacturer, for example, can quickly convert to production of radar, and a maker of hearing aids can produce the electronic instruments needed for guided missiles. An automobile maker, on the other hand, makes military cars, tanks, or airplanes; a fabricator of structural steel produces prefabricated units for ships. Large companies that turn out complex products avoid delay by making advance arrangements with smaller organizations that can act as subcontractors.

Military planning requires foreknowledge of how much capacity there is or will be available for many critically needed items that will start to be drawn from stockpiles and will need scheduled production for replacement. This foreknowledge must also include facts and figures showing how much of their capacities manufacturers must reserve for civilian production, as well as lead times or intervals required to expand production and to change over from civilian to military items. All these facts can be portrayed graphically for a company, for the class of work performed by a company, or for one of its products.

Assume, for example, that Calories Inc. has the capacity to produce 1,000 tons of dehydrated foods per day. It now produces only 500 tons. In the event of war, it will wish to retain 300 tons of its capacity for civilian needs. If called upon to produce military dehydrated ration packs it will require one month to procure packaging materials and an additional month to get 20 per cent of its capacity of military items on stream. It will require a second month to increase its military production to an additional 25 per cent of its capacity and a third month to increase its military production to 30 per cent civilian and 70 per cent military production, which is its total capacity. All these facts can be graphically represented as shown in Figure 117. It may also be desirable to show quantities available for military demands. These, based upon 25 days of production per month, are tabulated below the chart in Figure 117.

So far only availability of production capacity has been considered except for civilian production which has been shown as loaded and not available for military planning. At this stage the charts might well be called capacity profile charts. Now suppose we assume that M day has come. Assume also that 35,000 tons of ration packs will be needed 5 months hence, and that a contract for this amount, authorized by the Navy Department, has been awarded to Calories Inc. This information is graphically represented on the load chart by writing in the contract number and cross hatching or otherwise designating the part of the capacity that has been loaded and is not available for military planning. This is done in Figure 118.

Assume further that the Army awards another contract for 40,000 tons of ration packs to Calories Inc. It becomes immediately clear that this contract cannot be filled before $M + 7$ but that 17,500 tons per month can be provided. This contract is also loaded on the chart which now shows that 31,250 tons of productive capacity are available in $M + 8$ and $M + 9$.

Thus, by a glance at several charts for companies producing the same categories of items, the cognizant Armed Services Procurement Planning Officer can know where capacities for various items are available at present or will be available for procurement planning.

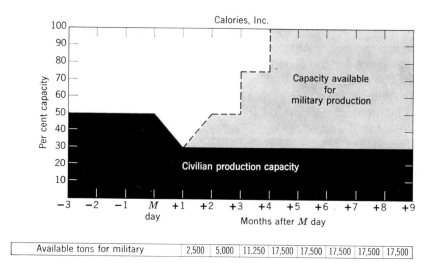

| Available tons for military | 2,500 | 5,000 | 11,250 | 17,500 | 17,500 | 17,500 | 17,500 | 17,500 |

Fig. 117. Calories, Inc., capacity data.

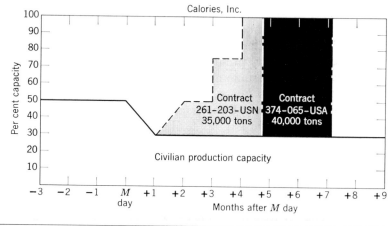

Available tons for military	2,500	5,000	11,250	17,500	17,500	17,500	17,500	17,500
Cumulative tons available	2,500	7,500	18,750	36,250	53,750	71,250	88,750	106,250
Contracts loaded		35,000			40,000			
Cumulative contracts loaded		35,000			75,000			

Fig. 118. Calories, Inc., loading chart.

Machine Hours Available	M Day	+1	Months After M Day +2	+3	+4
Coil winding	30,000	60,000	80,000	80,000	
Printed circuits	12,000	18,000	20,000	20,000	
Transistors	60,000	120,000	150,000	150,000	
Condensers	90,000	170,000	200,000	200,000	
Assembly	20,000	25,000	40,000	40,000	
Test	20,000	25,000	40,000	40,000	

Fig. 119. EMF Electronics Company capacity data.

The example given is made so simple that the principles involved are obvious. In actual practice, a company may produce several critical products and there will be interaction between them. In such cases separate charts may be needed for different products or for different classes of work. It may even be necessary to show capacities in terms of machine hours.

Assume again that a company produces electrical equipment. It tells its Armed Services Procurement Planning Officer that on M day it will have the available capacities shown in Figure 119. Charts

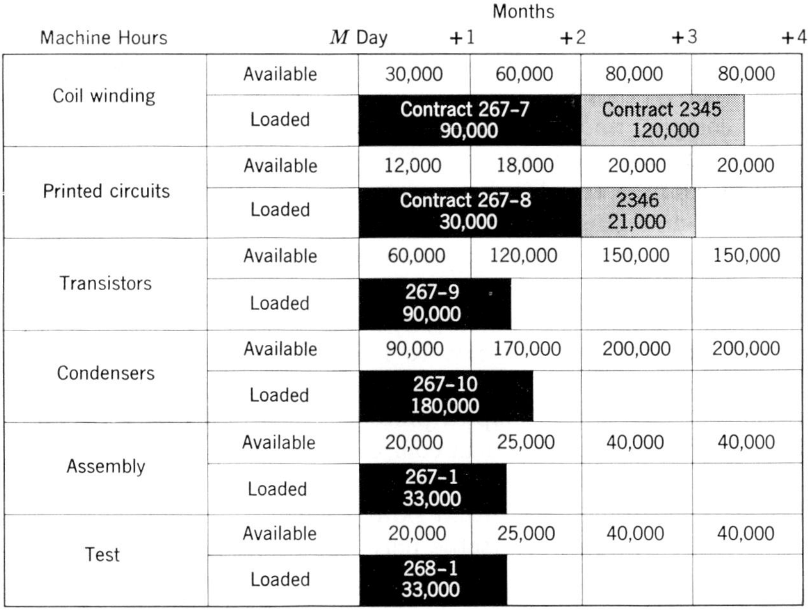

Machine Hours		M Day	+1	Months +2	+3	+4
Coil winding	Available	30,000	60,000	80,000	80,000	
	Loaded	Contract 267-7 90,000		Contract 2345 120,000		
Printed circuits	Available	12,000	18,000	20,000	20,000	
	Loaded	Contract 267-8 30,000		2346 21,000		
Transistors	Available	60,000	120,000	150,000	150,000	
	Loaded	267-9 90,000				
Condensers	Available	90,000	170,000	200,000	200,000	
	Loaded	267-10 180,000				
Assembly	Available	20,000	25,000	40,000	40,000	
	Loaded	267-1 33,000				
Test	Available	20,000	25,000	40,000	40,000	
	Loaded	268-1 33,000				

Fig. 120. EMF Electronics Company loading chart.

then can be prepared to show the summary figures that are given in Figure 120.

Any production constrictions shown in these charts can be overcome by subcontracting. For example, it may develop that a company may lack some of the printed-circuit capacity to produce completed electronic assemblies. It may be desirable to have as many of the components as possible made and the assembly and testing done under this company's control so some printed circuits are subcontracted. The use of *machine hours* in such complex situations permits the planning of large, medium, and small coils, variations in printed circuits, and the major variations in different assembly items.

War's demands are too great, however, to be met simply by conversion from one product to another allied to it. As a result, many companies volunteer to plan, build, and operate plants producing military items with which they are completely unfamiliar. During World War II, for example, a manufacturer of surgical dressings built and operated a shell-loading plant, a maker of concrete blocks built small ships, and a business machines company made ammunition. Despite their unfamiliarity with products, methods, and equipment, such companies delivered war materials with speed and economy that surpassed all expectations. Their success also proved that managerial skills can be transferred from one manufacturing field to another with little or no loss of effectiveness. This transfer has become an important factor in current war planning.

Another type of planning developed during World War II separated complex undertakings into component portions, carried each part to its conclusion, and then integrated all parts to produce the desired result. The Manhattan project was one example of such planning—an example in which teams of scientists, engineers, production planners, and military experts worked effectively without necessarily knowing that their final objective was the atom bomb. Production of the tiny radio receiving sets contained in projectiles was a second example, and there were many others. They proved the soundness of the management principle discussed in Chapter 23—that of breaking the large, complex problem down into simple ones that fall within the limits of human comprehension.

The effectiveness of this subdivision of production and the increasing need for highly specialized skills has led to the organization of complex but extremely versatile networks of prime contractors, subcontractors and sub-subcontractors. These teams can produce military hardware, under a system of accelerated production, in a fraction of the time required in the past. They can also switch production almost instantly from items that suddenly become obsolete to others that replace them.

Subdivided accelerated production, stockpiles of war materiel, and the ability to shift quickly from one weapon system to another assure our ability to retaliate effectively after a sudden attack. In tomorrow's war there will only be time to quickly replace the weapons consumed in the initial act of retaliation.

Some manufacturing and factory planning has been amazing in its detail and effectiveness. In 1917, for example, the du Pont Engineering Company began work on 40 acres of drawings for a radically new type of powder plant. Three months and nine days after the construction contract was signed, the first 100,000-pound powder unit at Old Hickory, Tennessee, was completed and began production. In 10 months, both the powder factory and a city fully organized for 30,000 inhabitants, including railroads, streets, and utility services, was erected upon what had been vacant fields.[1] Even greater feats of planning and engineering were achieved by du Pont and other companies during World War II.

War production planning follows the same basic procedures as peacetime industrial planning. When designs for war items are completed and tested, blueprints and models are studied by the manufacturing-planning engineers. Detailed production routings and bills of material are prepared. Factory planning then designs and constructs new buildings or selects and remodels existing buildings and plans the arrangement of equipment in them. Even before manufacturing facilities are ready for operation, production-planning engineers prepare to meet material and personnel requirements. They also schedule the various operations so that parts will be ready for subassemblies and subassemblies ready for final assemblies when each is needed. Planning may also include schedules for subcontractors who supply parts or subassemblies.

Conversion to war production also brings new duties and objectives. During periods of peace, industry tries to satisfy both the needs and the wishes of civilian customers, for military orders consume a small fraction of the total output. In wartime the first duty of industry is to meet military demands as a means of preserving the nation. Its second duty is to provide for the actual needs of civilians. Only after this is done can attention be given to satisfying civilian wishes.

[1] William S. Dutton, *DuPont, One Hundred and Forty Years*, Charles Scribner's Sons, New York, 1949.

In words this seems simple; in practice it is most difficult. Military needs must first be determined; as we have seen, that cannot be done within narrow limits of precision. Then someone must distinguish between the things civilians *need* and those they merely *want*. Finally, materials and labor must be divided equitably among producers, dealers, and customers.

Equitable division means allocations, both by government and by industry. Dealers and customers are allotted available goods in proportion to quantities normally ordered during times of peace. If, for example, a dealer has normally purchased 3 per cent of a producer's output, he is allowed 3 per cent of the goods available under wartime conditions. Exceptions are made only for dealers in regions where population—and civilian need—is increased by an influx of war workers and their families. To maintain rigid percentage quotas for dealers in such areas would be unjust to them and to civilians in need of essential goods.[1]

It sometimes happens that no supplies of certain materials remain after military requirements are met. When that occurs, the companies affected must discontinue all civilian production. Since such material shortages generally are industry-wide, the companies affected are placed at little or no competitive disadvantage.

D. QUALITY ASSURANCE

The right quantity of material at the right time is only part of the defense problem. Commodities purchased by the Armed Services must be of the right quality or plans can be worthless and defense can fail.

Some military requirements such as those for missile components are critically precise. These components must be tested carefully and subjected to rigid provisional trials. Other requirements like those for ammunition must depend upon scientific statistical sampling. A definitive test for a shell or a torpedo requires firing it. Once this is done, only test results remain.

Scientific acceptance sampling assured the reliability of armament for the Allies' invasion of Europe in 1944 even before it started. This success encouraged the Armed Services to continue their pioneering application of scientific quality control to procurement and produc-

---

[1] This statement does not imply that any system of allocations can be perfect, or that manufacturers always follow their own rules. It does indicate the method that has given best results and that represents the goal of conscientious companies.

tion. Industry at first objected to the requirement of Military Standard 105, Acceptance Sampling Tables, and comprehensive military procedures for the control of quality. These procedures and standards proved to be so effective, however, that progressive industrial companies have adopted them for their commercial operations.

Military quality assurance is not simply the use of sampling acceptance plans. The complete military quality plan includes several elements which we may summarize as follows:

1. Specifications. Thousands of military specifications, in addition to thousands of Federal nonmilitary specifications, enable contracting officers to purchase commodities on the basis of specifically described requirements in terms of numerical values. These specifications are complete even to the sampling plans and the acceptable quality limits required.

2. Qualification. Special skills and equipment are required to make many commodities. Some of their critical requirements need special equipment and time-consuming tests for their evaluation. Obviously, no company should be given a contract for such commodities unless it has first proved its ability to produce them within specification limits. The Armed Services, therefore, require that prospective producers of these commodities submit samples to an official testing laboratory. Its tests can provide assurance of a supplier's process capability or show the shortcomings of his product. In other words, they prove that a company made the tested commodity properly at least once. They cannot, however, guarantee that all future products of this kind will conform to specifications.

3. MIL-Q-9858. This document specifies that quality shall be controlled in all manufacturing operations. There must be inspection and testing during manufacture and before shipment; quality control shall also be maintained over all incoming materials and components. The document further specifies procedures for isolating nonconforming products and materials and demands dynamic correction of causes for substandard quality. Thus MIL-Q-9858 assures the Armed Services that companies producing for them have satisfactory quality-control facilities and adhere to acceptable practices.

Objective Evidence and Verification of Conformance. This part of quality-control checks a producer's past records of both variables and attribute inspection and testing of products to determine in advance whether the producer has the process capability, the quality control facility, and the quality control capability to produce within specification limits. The responsibility for testing and inspecting his products is placed squarely upon the supplier. He must also report the results of his tests and inspections.

The degree of verification required by an independent agency is based upon statistical analysis of a supplier's performance. These relatively inexpensive verification tests assure that a supplier's control system and capabilities are in satisfactory continuum.

Specification, qualification, quality control procedures, objective evidence and verification of conformance with specification requirements, have provided economical and reliable practices that can be used for civilian as well as military production.

It is comforting to know that our military services have well conceived plans for:

1. Retaliation against sudden attack
2. Mobilization support for prolonged hostilities
3. Shifting emphasis and stratagems as conditions, opponents and war technology change
4. Supplies for essential civilian needs
5. Quality reliability assurance

One important fact must be understood and always remembered. Any capabilities for war production that we and the free nations of the world have or may develop are the results of the accumulation and extension of peacetime industrial skills. That is why this book is primarily intended to stimulate thinking that will lead to greater refinement and broader use of better techniques for forecasting, planning, and control of peacetime production. When war comes it is too late to develop such skills for productivity. In the words of the late Wendell Willkie, "Only the productive can be strong, and only the strong can be free."

Bibliography

MANAGEMENT CONCEPTS

Davis, Ralph C., *The Fundamentals of Top Management*, Harper & Brothers, New York, 1951.

Drucker, Peter F., *The Practice of Management*, Harper & Brothers, New York, 1954.

Fayol, Henri, *Industrial and General Administration* (an English translation from the French), Sir Isaac Pitman & Sons, London, 1949.

Owens, Richard N., *Management of Industrial Enterprises*, Richard D. Irwin, Homewood, Ill., 1953.

Spriegel, William R., and Richard H. Lansburgh, *Industrial Management*, John Wiley & Sons, New York, 1955.

Taylor, Frederick W., *Scientific Management*, Harper & Brothers, New York, 1947.

Trundle, George T., Jr., and S. A. Peck, *Managerial Control of Business*, John Wiley & Sons, New York, 1948.

ORGANIZATION

Anderson, E. H., and G. T. Schwenning, *The Science of Production Organization*, John Wiley & Sons, New York, 1938.

Gillmor, R. E., *A Practical Manual of Organization*, Funk & Wagnalls, New York, 1948.

Holden, P. E., L. S. Fish, and H. L. Smith, *Top Management Organization and Control*, McGraw-Hill Book Company, New York, 1951.

Roscoe, E. S., *Organization for Production*, revised edition, Richard D. Irwin, Homewood, Ill., 1959.

FORECASTING

Brown, Robert G., *Statistical Forecasting for Inventory Control*, McGraw-Hill Book Company, New York, 1959.

Hood, William C., and Tjalling C. Koopmans, *Studies in Econometric Method*, Cowles Commission Monograph 14, John Wiley & Sons, New York, 1953.

Maisel, Sherman J., *Fluctuations, Growth, and Forecasting*, John Wiley & Sons, New York, 1957.

Tintner, Gerhard, *Econometrics*, John Wiley & Sons, New York, 1952.

Wright, Wilson, *Forecasting for Profit*, John Wiley & Sons, New York, 1947.

PRODUCTION CONTROL

Bethel, Lawrence L., et al., *Production Control*, McGraw-Hill Book Company, New York, second edition, 1948.

Koepke, Charles A., *Plant Production Control*, John Wiley & Sons, New York, 1949.

Landy, Thomas M., *Production Planning and Control*, McGraw-Hill Book Company, New York, 1950.

Moore, Franklin G., *Production Control*, second edition, McGraw-Hill Book Company, New York, 1959.

Ritchie, William E., *Production and Inventory Control*, The Ronald Press Company, New York, 1951.

Waffenschmidt, Walter, *Produktion*, Verlag Anton Hain, K.C., Meisenheim/Glan, Germany, 1955.

WORK MEASUREMENT

Barnes, Ralph M., *Motion and Time Study*, John Wiley & Sons, New York, third edition, 1949.

Barnes, Ralph M., *Motion and Time Study Applications*, John Wiley & Sons, New York, second edition, 1953.

Carroll, Phil, *How to Chart Timestudy Data*, McGraw-Hill Book Company, New York, 1950.

Geppinger, H. C., *Dimensional Motion Times*, John Wiley & Sons, New York, 1955.

Maynard, H. B., G. J. Stegemerten, and J. L. Schwab, *Methods-Time Measurement*, McGraw-Hill Book Company, New York, 1948.

Mundel, Marvin E., *Motion and Time Study*, Prentice-Hall, New York, second edition, 1955.

Nadler, Gerald, *Motion and Time Study*, McGraw-Hill Book Company, New York, 1955.

Niebel, Benjamin W., *Motion and Time Study*, Richard D. Irwin, Homewood, Ill., 1955.

PLANT LAYOUT

Immer, John R., *Layout Planning Techniques*, McGraw-Hill Book Company, New York, 1950.

Ireson, W. Grant, *Factory Planning and Plant Layout*, Prentice-Hall, New York, 1952.

Mallick, Randolph W., and Armand T. Gaudreau, *Plant Layout: Planning and Practice*, John Wiley & Sons, New York, 1951.

AUTOMATION

Canning, Richard G., *Electronic Data Processing for Business and Industry*, John Wiley & Sons, New York, 1956.

Charnes, A., W. W. Cooper, and A. Henderson, *An Introduction to Linear Programming*, John Wiley & Sons, New York, 1953.

Diebold, John, *Automation*, D. Van Nostrand Company, New York, 1952.

Farrington, G. H., *Fundamentals of Automatic Control*, John Wiley & Sons, New York, 1951.

Grabbe, E. S., ed., *Automation in Business and Industry*, John Wiley & Sons, New York, 1957.

OPERATIONS RESEARCH

Churchman, C. W., R. Ackoff, and E. L. Arnoff, *An Introduction to Operations Research*, John Wiley & Sons, New York, 1957.

Morse, P. M., and G. E. Kimball, *Methods of Operations Research*, published jointly by The Technology Press of Massachusetts Institute of Technology and John Wiley & Sons, New York, 1951.

COST AND BUDGETARY CONTROL

Carroll, Phil, *How to Control Production Costs*, McGraw-Hill Book Company, New York, 1953.

National Industrial Conference Board, *Budgetary Control in Manufacturing Industry*, 1931.

PURCHASING

Heinritz, Stuart F., *Purchasing*, Prentice-Hall, New York, 1951.

Westing, J. H., and I. V. Fine, *Industrial Purchasing*, John Wiley & Sons, New York, 1955.

STATISTICS

Barnes, Ralph M., *Work Sampling*, Wm. C. Brown Company, Dubuque, Iowa, 1956.

Bowker, Albert H., and Gerald J. Lieberman, *Handbook of Engineering Statistics*, Prentice-Hall, New York, 1955.

Burr, Irving W., *Statistics and Quality Control*, McGraw-Hill Book Company, New York, 1953.

Freeman, Harold A., *Industrial Statistics*, John Wiley & Sons, New York, 1942.

Hald, A., *Statistical Theory with Engineering Applications*, John Wiley & Sons, New York, 1952.

Metzger, Robert W., *Elementary Mathematical Programming*, John Wiley & Sons, New York, 1958.

Simon, Leslie E., *An Engineers' Manual of Statistical Methods*, John Wiley & Sons, New York, 1941.

Tippett, L. H. C., *Technological Applications of Statistics*, John Wiley & Sons, New York, 1950.

Tippett, L. H. C., *The Methods of Statistics*, John Wiley & Sons, New York, 1952.

Vaijda, S., *Readings in Linear Programming*, John Wiley & Sons, New York, 1958.

Yule, George U., and M. C. Kendall, *An Introduction to the Theory of Statistics*, C. Griffin & Company, London, 1937.

QUALITY CONTROL

Dodge, Harold F., and Harry G. Romig, *Sampling Inspection Tables*, John Wiley & Sons, New York, 1944.

Grant, Eugene L., *Statistical Quality Control*, McGraw-Hill Book Company, New York, 1952.

Juran, J. M., *Quality Control Handbook*, McGraw-Hill Book Company, New York, 1951.

Rice, William B., *Control Charts in Factory Management*, John Wiley & Sons, New York, 1947.

Index